TRANSISTOR CIRCUIT
ANALYSIS AND DESIGN

Fused-junction transistor without cover. (*Courtesy Raytheon Company, Semiconductor Division*)

Edited by

HERBERT J. REICH

Dunham Laboratory, Yale School of Engineering

SHEINGOLD, ABRAHAM — Fundamentals of Radio Communications

KING, DONALD D. — Measurements at Centimeter Wavelength

REICH, H. J., ORDUNG, P. F., KRAUSS, H. L., SKALNIK, J. G. — Microwave Theory and Techniques

REICH, H. J., SKALNIK, J. G., ORDUNG, P. F., KRAUSS, H. L. — Microwave Principles

MURPHY, GORDON J. — Basic Automatic Control Theory

MURPHY, GORDON J. — Control Engineering

HUTTER, RUDOLF G. E. — Beam and Wave Electronics in Microwave Tubes

FITCHEN, FRANKLIN C. — Transistor Circuit Analysis and Design

MOON, PARRY, and SPENCER, DOMINA E. — Foundations of Electrodynamics

MOON, PARRY, and SPENCER, DOMINA E. — Field Theory for Engineers

GÄRTNER, WOLFGANG W. — Transistors: Principles, Design, and Applications

REICH, H. J. — Functional Circuits and Oscillators

KU, Y. H. — Transient Circuit Analysis

PESKIN, EDWARD — Transient and Steady-State Analysis of Electric Networks

A series of text and reference books in electronics and communications. Additional titles will be listed and announced as published.

TRANSISTOR CIRCUIT ANALYSIS AND DESIGN

by

FRANKLIN C. FITCHEN

Associate Professor of Electrical Engineering
University of Rhode Island

D. VAN NOSTRAND COMPANY, INC.

PRINCETON, NEW JERSEY

TORONTO   LONDON

NEW YORK

D. VAN NOSTRAND COMPANY, INC.

120 Alexander St., Princeton, New Jersey (*Principal office*)
24 West 40 Street, New York 18, New York

D. VAN NOSTRAND COMPANY, LTD.
358, Kensington High Street, London, W.14, England

D. VAN NOSTRAND COMPANY (Canada), LTD.
25 Hollinger Road, Toronto 16, Canada

Published simultaneously in Canada by
D. VAN NOSTRAND COMPANY (Canada), LTD.

Library of Congress Catalogue Card No.: 60–15151

First Published June 1960

*Reprinted January 1961,
July 1961, July 1962, January 1963
August 1963, December 1963*

PRINTED IN THE UNITED STATES OF AMERICA

PREFACE

Although the scope and content of this textbook is designed for a one-semester transistor circuits course for electrical engineering students at the junior or senior level, by selective screening of the text material and assigned problems it may well apply to the advanced technical institute student. The advanced course that assumes little prior knowledge of the subject material may also find food for thought and study in the text and in the problems and references included. It is felt that the practising engineer, encountering transistors for the first time, will find the analysis and design examples helpful as background for the solution of his specific problems.

It is assumed that the reader has had an introduction to vacuum-tube electronics, and has a working knowledge of the fundamentals of both a-c and d-c circuit theory. This book is introductory and requires no prior knowledge of transistors or of semiconductor physics.

The length of the text has been limited for two reasons: it seems appropriate for a one-semester course; and it is realized that the user may wish to inject additional material considered to be of importance. Especial effort has been made to extract from the vast quantity of semiconductor literature, and from unpublished work and practical experience, only that which appears necessary in order to analyze and design the simpler semiconductor circuits. Only the three most important of the many transistor equivalent circuits are considered, and no detailed explanations are made of topics such as solid-state physics, pulse circuits or video amplifiers, as it is expected that this book may be used at a lower academic level than others in the same field. The problems and discussion questions included at the end of each chapter are used to introduce more advanced material as well as to enable the reader to gain self-confidence in his abilities.

Chapter 1, while including only introductory material, has purposely been written as the most important few pages of the entire book. Indeed, a solid grounding in the subjects of bias current directions, characteristics curves, leakage currents and amplification factors is necessary, and, it is believed that if useable material is presented early in the text, interest will be stimulated in the subject matter to follow. The Physics of Semiconductors, the subject of Chapter 2, is treated in great detail elsewhere. For this reason, only a very brief and simplified treatment is given here. Additional material on this subject would not be in keeping with the title of this text. The material of Chapter 3 may be compressed if a more general treatment of the biasing problem is used. Derivation of expressions for circuit gains and impedances accounts for much of Chapter 4; I believe, however, that we cannot pass over these applications of circuit theory too lightly, and in latter chapters good use can be made from the experience gained in Chapter 4.

Portions of Chapters 5, 6, 7 and 9 reflect an "industrial approach," to electronics. Because so many of our graduates step directly from the campus into jobs that require creative circuit design, it seems desirable that they be prepared to take on this responsibility as rapidly as is feasible.

This book is an outgrowth of work and associations with the General Electric Company, West Lynn, Massachusetts, and the General Dynamics Corporation, Electric Boat Division, Groton, Connecticut, as well as the University of Rhode Island. My thanks are extended to these organizations, to the other assisting industrial concerns and to the many reviewers and typists for their cooperation.

FRANKLIN C. FITCHEN

Kingston, Rhode Island
April, 1960

CONTENTS

Chapter 1

INTRODUCTION TO THE TRANSISTOR

The main application of the transistor as an electrical signal amplifier places it in a class with such well-known devices as the vacuum tube, magnetic amplifier, relay, and transformer. Its history dates back to 1948, when it was invented by Drs. W. H. Brattain and J. Bardeen of the Bell Telephone Laboratories. In the brief span of years since its inception, the transistor has made fantastic inroads into applications formerly reserved for other active circuit elements.

The transistor has been successfully employed for uses other than signal amplification. Transistor oscillators, modulators, demodulators, shapers, inverters, and gates are highly successful; new designs of electronic circuitry are very predominantly transistorized. Since the vacuum tube has been a faithful servant for five decades, it is natural to wonder what manner of device this transistor is, and how it can nudge vacuum-tube circuitry into obsolescence so easily. Some of the basic advantages of the transistor that have enabled it to replace the vacuum tube in many applications follow:

1. Long operating lifetime
2. No heating (cathode) power required
3. Operation at low voltages
4. Small physical size
5. Extreme ruggedness

Because the transistor does not require a heating element to raise its temperature well above ambient, as is the case with the familiar vacuum tube where a hot cathode is mandatory, transistor circuits are relatively cool. Since heat is a main contributor to circuit-component breakdown, transistor circuits are exceedingly reliable. Coupling this advantage with the long operating life of the transistor itself (estimates up to forty years as compared to 2,000 to 10,000 hours for tubes), and with the possible miniaturization and shock and vibration resistance also afforded, it is not difficult to comprehend the widespread application of the transistor wherever feasible.

1

The transistor is not a perfect active device; indeed we should be astonished if it were. Among the limitations presently being minimized by industrial research are:

1. Variations in characteristics among units of the same type
2. Sensitivity to ambient temperature
3. Inefficient high-frequency operation

Early transistors were limited in their power-handling capacity, and were electrically noisy. The power limitations have been essentially overcome; at present a single power transistor may be used to control a load of several kilowatts, and this frontier is being extended almost daily, with the upper limit virtually nowhere in sight. Reductions in noise have resulted in transistors with typical noise factors of two decibels, compared to the 50- to 60-decibel factors of early production types. Improved manufacturing techniques are reducing the variations in operating characteristics among units of the same type, and it is believed that soon this will no longer constitute a major problem confronting the circuit designer. Research directed toward improved high-frequency performance has greatly extended the operating frequency range and, if some of the transistor types now in the developmental stage prove feasible, high-frequency limitations will be nullified. Although low-voltage operation is generally a distinct advantage, in certain applications operation at higher voltages is a requirement, and the electronic engineer has been provided with a family of transistors that will operate at all practical voltage levels.

The introduction of the *junction transistor* in 1951 and its subsequent development was a major factor in the rapid growth of transistor electronics. Prior to 1951 transistors were of the *point-contact* variety; the junction type is the mainstay of today's manufacture because it can handle larger amounts of power, is more easily fabricated, and generates less noise. *This text is devoted to the analysis and design of junction transistor circuits.*

1–1. Semiconductors. The transistor is a solid structure formed from *semiconductors.* Semiconductors are materials whose electrical resistivity is lower than that of insulators and higher than that of conductors. By way of comparison, the resistivities of conductors are of the order of 10^{-6} ohm-cm; of insulators, 10^6 ohm-cm and greater; and of semiconductors 10^1 ohm-cm. But electrical resistance is not the only defining characteristic of a semiconductor. The resistivity of semiconductors decreases with temperature, rather than increasing, as is common with metallic conductors. Another characteristic of a semiconductor is the type and degree of the binding force between atoms, and a fourth characteristic of such materials is the extent to which electrical properties depend upon impurity content. Two members of the carbon family, the elements *germanium* and *silicon*, in their crystalline form are classified as semiconductors, and have widespread use in solid-state devices. The addition of small amounts of impurities to the pure elements alter their conductional properties and the composite is termed either *n-type* material, which has an excess of free electrons compared to a crystal of the pure element, or *p-type* material, which has a deficiency of electrons in its crystalline structure when so compared. By sandwiching *n*-type and *p*-type materials together, various conduction characteristics may be achieved. Fig. 1–1 symbolizes the construction of the two common forms of the junction transistor. Both *n-p-n* and *p-n-p* structures can be manufactured and are in common use. Designation of the terminals as shown in Fig. 1–1 is discussed in Sec. 1–3.

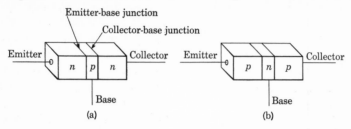

Fig. 1–1. Symbolic construction of the junction transistor; (a) *n-p-n;* (b) *p-n-p*.

The physical principle of operation of the transistor, and also the semiconductor diode, bears no similarity to that of the familiar vacuum tube. Vacuum-tube operation relies upon the control of the movement of free electrons through a vacuum, or in certain tube types, through a gas. In semiconductor devices, charge movement occurs *within* solid materials, and a high temperature is not required for electrons to escape from a surface, because operation is not dependent upon surface emission. A more detailed treatment of semiconductor physics and a discussion of the interesting process by which amplification is achieved is reserved for Chapter 2.

1–2. Diodes. Before proceeding with the discussion of the junction transistor, let us briefly consider the semiconductor diode, a two-element device useful for rectification and detection in electronic circuits. The *junction diode*, which consists of a single *p-n junction*, is similar to its vacuum-tube counterpart in that it is incapable of amplification (except in special circuits [2]) and is characterized by the property of allowing current to pass easily in but one direction. Vacuum-tube nomenclature is applicable to all semiconductor diodes; they are said to pass current easily from anode (plate) to cathode.

Circuitwise and constructionwise, the semiconductor diode may be symbolized as shown in Fig. 1–2. The arrowhead (which is an integral part of the symbol) serves to indicate the direction of "forward" conventional current. If a positive potential is applied to the anode, the diode is said to be *forward-biased*, and will exhibit a fairly low value of forward resistance. On the other hand, a direct-voltage supply of the opposite polarity provides a *reverse bias*,

[2] Superior numbers refer to references cited at the end of each chapter.

very little current flows, and the diode exhibits a high reverse or back resistance. Should this reverse voltage exceed a certain value, called the rated *peak-inverse-voltage* (P.I.V.) of the diode, normal operation ceases, and a large back current is evident. These characteristics of a junction diode are graphed in Fig. 1–2b.

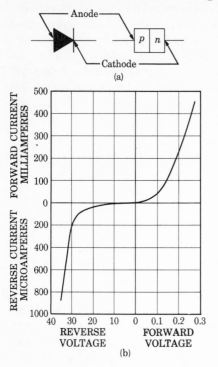

It is interesting to note that semiconductor diodes are widely accepted because they provide the circuit designer with an efficient, rugged component with a long operational life. Units are available to cover all operating voltage and current ranges.

Diodes will be further discussed in Chapter 2 and in other passages throughout the text where their use is complementary to transistor circuitry. For a discussion of rectifying circuits, power supplies, and filtering, the reader is referred to a standard vacuum-tube text.[7]

1-3. Transistors. The common transistor is a three-terminal device and is referred to as a triode. The terminals are denoted as the *emitter*, the *base*, and the *collector* (refer again to Fig. 1–1). Fig. 1–3 shows various symbols used in circuit diagrams to

Fig. 1–2. Semiconductor diode: (a) circuit symbol and symbolic construction; (b) typical characteristic.

represent junction transistors. In this text symbols (a) and (b) of that figure will be used exclusively. Since the *p-n-p* device is the predominant of the two forms it will be considered the more frequently here. The differences between *p-n-p* and *n-p-n* devices will be described later.

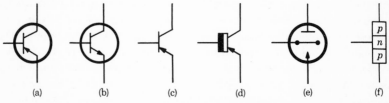

Fig. 1–3. Common transistor symbols: (b) is an *n-p-n* unit, all others are *p-n-p*. In all cases the left-hand terminal is the base, the uppermost terminal is the collector, and the lower terminal is the emitter.

One terminal of the transistor may be designated as the input terminal, one as the output terminal and the third as the common. Thus there are six possible configurations that could be utilized, only three of which have proved useful and will be seriously considered here: the *common-emitter* configuration (also called grounded-emitter), in which the input signal is applied between base and common; the *common-collector* configuration (also called grounded-collector), with the base again the input terminal; and the *common-base* configuration (also called grounded-base), in which the emitter terminal is supplied by the signal source. Since power gain is desired in application, the

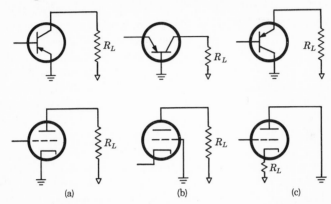

Fig. 1–4. Transistor and vacuum-tube configurations: (a) common-emitter and grounded-cathode; (b) common-base and grounded-grid; (c) common-collector (emitter-follower) and grounded-plate (cathode-follower).

base terminal must always be one of the two input terminals and the collector must always be one of the two output terminals. The three useful amplifying configurations and their vacuum-tube analogs are shown in Fig. 1–4. From performance studies such as those of Chapter 4, it can be concluded that the common-emitter transistor connection corresponds most closely to the grounded-cathode circuit, the common-collector transistor connection (also called *emitter-follower*) corresponds most closely to the cathode-follower circuit, and the common-base transistor connection is similar to the grounded-grid vacuum-tube orientation.

It has previously been noted that no filament or heater is required with semiconductor devices. *Another important difference between the transistor and the vacuum tube is the finite and relatively small-valued input impedance of the former.* When a potential is applied to the input terminals of a transistor in any configuration, an input current is evident. Because the circuit load is supplied with an amplified version of this input voltage and current, the transistor is considered to be a *power amplifier*. Since the device provides power amplification, we need not expect voltage gain from all circuitry nor should we expect current gain from all usable connections, but in almost all practical circuits a transistor will raise the power level of a signal supplied to its input.

The existence of transistors of opposite conductivity types (*p-n-p* and *n-p-n*) permits *complementary-symmetry* circuits impossible with vacuum tubes. For push-pull amplifiers no phase inverter is necessary, and in direct-coupled amplifiers, the need for numerous supply voltages is reduced. As applications for complementary circuits arise they will be treated.

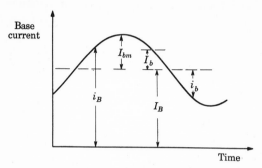

Fig. 1–5.   Example of transistor notation.

1–4. Symbols. A system of symbols to be used to designate circuit quantities in this book is both desirable and necessary, for a great many abbreviations will be encountered by the reader. In general, transistor circuit notation follows several general rules—they are listed here and will be used in the pages that follow. Symbols have been chosen to conform with current practice.[3]

1. D-c values of quantities are indicated by capital letters with capital subscripts (I_B, V_{CE}). Direct supply voltages have repeated subscripts (E_{BB}, E_{EE}).
2. Rms values of quantities are indicated by capital letters with lower-case subscripts (I_c, V_{cb}).
3. The time-varying components of currents and voltages are designated by lower-case letters with lower-case subscripts (i_x, v_{cb}).
4. Instantaneous total values are represented by lower-case letters with upper-case subscripts (i_C, v_{BE}).
5. Maximum or peak values are designated like rms values but bear an additional final subscript m (E_{cm}, V_{bem}).
6. Circuit elements are given capital letters (R_1, C_P); transistor parameters have lower-case symbols (r_e, h_{11}).

Fig. 1–5 may help in understanding this notation system. In the diagram i_B is the instantaneous total value of the wave, and i_b is the instantaneous value of the time-varying component of i_B. I_B designates the average or d-c value, I_{bm} represents the peak and I_b the effective value of the alternating component.

To designate a constant-current source or generator on circuit diagrams, the two symbols of Fig. 1–6a are employed. The arrowhead serves to show the direction of current being supplied, and the "cycle" ($\sim$) specifies an alternating quantity.

Constant-voltage sources are symbolized as shown in (b) of Fig. 1–6. The conventional battery symbol designates a direct voltage source, and the circle with the "cycle" represents a source of alternating potential, with polarity marks representing the instantaneous condition.

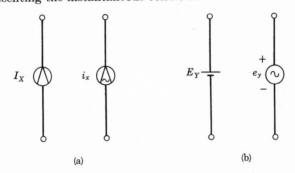

(a)   (b)

Fig. 1–6. Symbols for sources.

1–5. Graphical Characteristics. A graphical representation of the operating properties of the transistor is desirable because it is a nonlinear active circuit element. It has been stated that the input impedance is finite; therefore an input characteristics curve is required, as well as a curve to represent output-circuit properties. Indeed, *two sets of curves are necessary to completely specify transistor operation.*

For *each* of the three practical circuit configurations, both an input curve and an output curve are applicable. Consider first the common-emitter oriented transistor shown in Fig. 1–7a, with supply potentials and appropriate indicating devices. Intentional variations in the supply potentials yield data for the curves of Figs. 1–7b and 1–7c, commonly known, respectively, as the static *collector characteristics* and the static *base characteristics* for a common-emitter connected transistor. A family of curves is necessary in each instance because

$$I_C = f(I_B, V_{CE}) \tag{1–1}$$

and

$$I_B = f(V_{BE}, V_{CE}). \tag{1–2}$$

From study of these curves some generalizations can be made. The output characteristics are similar to those of a pentode tube, since both the transistor

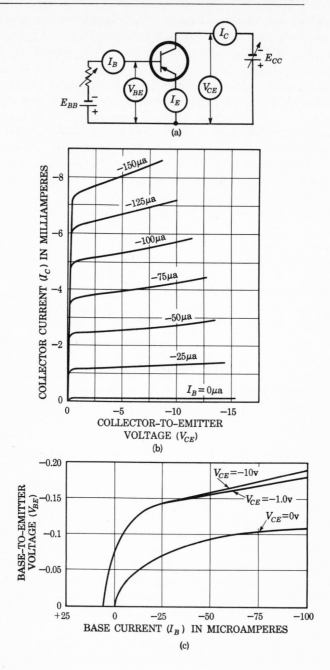

Fig. 1–7.　Common-emitter configuration: (a) circuit for determination of characteristics; (b) typical output family; (c) typical input family.

and the pentode are "current sources," to the extent that their output currents are nearly independent of supply voltage (as evidenced in the figure by the nearly horizontal nature of the lines of constant base current). Depicted here are the characteristics of a low-power transistor, but from this and other information we shall eventually reach a general conclusion, that *the transistor is a low-voltage, high-current device* whereas *the vacuum tube is a high-voltage, low-current device.* With the transistor any base-current variation dictates a corresponding collector-current excursion, while vacuum-tube operation may be described by grid-voltage swings controlling plate-current magnitude.

Negative signs preceding current and voltage values on the curves are the results of the conventions of general network theory; currents flowing *into* a device or circuit node are considered *positive*, and when potentials are designated by double subscripts, the first subscript indicates the point imagined to be the more positive. The use of negative signs preceding base current and collector current values in Fig. 1–7b suggests that for normal operation the static portions of these currents must be leaving their respective terminals (*p-n-p*). Emitter current, although not used in the curves, must enter the transistor and therefore would be considered positive. V_{CE} is shown as negative because the collector (first subscript) is *not* more positive than the emitter (second subscript).

Often the information contained in the curves may be displayed in other ways for special purposes. *Transfer characteristics*, a plot of collector current versus base current for specific collector-to-emitter voltages, is sometimes employed. Occasionally the transfer characteristics relating base-emitter voltage to collector current may be utilized. Information for these presentations may be obtained from the regular characteristics (see Problem 1–11).

A complete set of data taken of all currents and potentials in the circuit of Fig. 1–7a would enable us to plot not only the common-emitter curves, but the common-base and common-collector characteristics as well. For the common-base configuration, interest is centered about the collector-to-base voltage (V_{CB}) and collector current (I_C) as output quantities, and emitter-to-base voltage (V_{EB}) and emitter current (I_E) as input quantities. The static input and output characteristics for this configuration are displayed in Fig. 1–8.

The common-base collector curves are extremely flat, indicating a high output resistance, and the spacing between curves of constant input current is extremely uniform, denoting little contribution to output waveform distortion. Distortion, however, is also dependent upon the shape of the input characteristics.

Common-collector circuits exhibit output characteristics similar to those of the common-emitter, for output quantities are nearly the same ($V_{EC} = -V_{CE}$ and $I_E \cong I_C$). Some of the problems at the end of the chapter may be used to investigate this connection further.

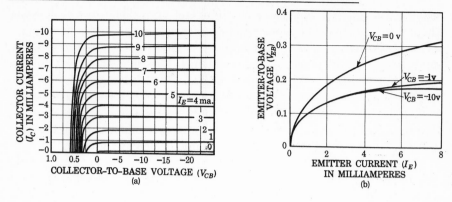

Fig. 1-8. Common-base connection: (a) typical output family; (b) typical input family.

1-6. The Operating Point. Establishing a proper operating point for a transistor stage is necessary in order for the input signal to be transferred to the load faithfully and to be amplified successfully. A proper operating point is achieved by providing appropriate direct potentials to both the input and the output terminal pairs. *For biasing purposes only,* a junction transistor can be thought of as two junction diodes, one associated with the *p-n* junction of the emitter-base circuit, and the other associated with the *n-p* junction of the base-collector circuit. For transistor operation it will be shown that *the emitter-base diode is always forward-biased* and *the collector-base diode is always reverse-biased.*

A helpful rule for *p-n* junctions follows: "for forward-biasing connect supply positive to *p*-material." Naturally, the converse is true for reverse biasing. This rule is applied to the *p-n-p* transistor in the three practical configurations shown in Fig. 1-9. For each connection, the emitter terminal is made more positive than the base, and the collector terminal is made more negative than the base.

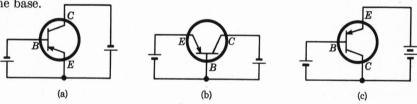

Fig. 1-9. Supply potential connections for normal transistor operation (*p-n-p*): (a) common-emitter; (b) common-base; (c) common-collector.

Although the transistor can be visualized as two junction diodes to assist in the establishment of an operating point at some desired point in the active region of the collector characteristics, transistor operation, as we shall see in Chapter 2, is *not* that of two back-to-back diodes.

Circuitwise, the major difference between *p-n-p* and *n-p-n* units can be appreciated from the practical circuit of Fig. 1–10. Base current for a *p-n-p* transistor flows away from the base terminal; for an *n-p-n* unit it must flow into the base. Collector-voltage polarities are also opposite: the *p-n-p* type requires a negative collector potential; the *n-p-n*, a positive.

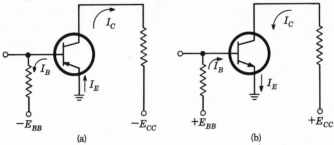

Fig. 1–10. Biasing for transistors: (a) *p-n-p* unit; (b) *n-p-n* unit.

A summation of currents entering the transistor yields a very important relationship describing the magnitudes of the terminal currents:

$$I_E = I_C + I_B. \tag{1-3}$$

Eq. (1–3) applies to either conductivity type and will play an important role in the discussions to follow. The actual directions of these currents are as shown in Fig. 1–10. The arrowhead in the transistor symbol is useful in describing the direction of emitter current. A knowledge of the magnitude of the various currents of Eq. (1–3) is indispensable; such information may be gained from the curve of Fig. 1–7b. At a specific collector potential, -5 volts for example, it is obvious that when base current is -25 μa, collector current is -1 ma. Therefore emitter current, which is the sum of the other two, must be 1.025 ma. A general rule for junction triodes is valuable: *emitter current is the largest of the three currents, and is approximately equal in magnitude to collector current.*

1-7. Amplification. "Current-amplification factor" is a term frequently used to describe transistor quality and is symbolized by the Greek letters α (alpha) and β (beta). It is the ratio of the variation in output current to the variation in the input current that caused it, with constant collector potential.

For the common-base configuration, α is used most extensively to represent "current gain," and is defined as

$$\alpha = \frac{\partial i_C}{\partial i_E}\bigg|_{v_{CB}=\text{const.}} \tag{1-4}$$

Here we are making use of symbols that denote total quantities. When the amplification of an alternating signal is being considered, Eq. (1–4) requires that the transistor load be an a-c short circuit in order for the current amplification to be α.

A pictorial definition of α is shown in Fig. 1–11. A vertical line satisfies the requirement that total collector voltage be constant. Along that line, if a sample variation in i_E is assumed and the resulting excursion in i_C measured, the value of α may be calculated. For junction transistors α never exceeds unity and generally lies between 0.9 and 1.0. Graphically it is difficult to

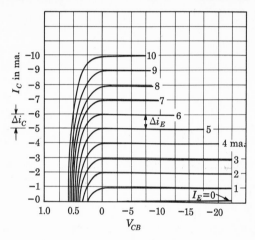

Fig. 1–11. Pictorial definition of α.

perform a precise measurement of the two current quantities, because of their near equality.

Beta represents the "current gain" of a transistor in the common-emitter configuration

$$\beta = \frac{\partial i_C}{\partial i_B}\bigg|_{v_{CE}=\text{const.}} \tag{1–5}$$

β is very large in comparison with α. Practically, β takes on values up to 300 and higher, although most commercial units have a β of perhaps 25 to 100. Since Eq. (1–3) related the three transistor currents, the amplification factors are also related:

$$\beta = \frac{\alpha}{1 - \alpha}. \tag{1–6a}$$

Also of importance is the complementary relationship:

$$\alpha = \frac{\beta}{\beta + 1}. \tag{1–6b}$$

Other names and symbols exist in the literature [5] as a means of describing amplification quantities, some of which will be developed later in the text. For common-collector circuits the current-amplification factor may be approximated by β/α or by β alone.

Although α does not exceed unity and thus load current is smaller than input current in the common-base configuration, power gain is nevertheless possible because of different impedance levels. The input resistance, R_i, generally is very low, of the order of 50 ohms, when the device is connected to a load, R_L, of 50,000 ohms. Since power gain, G, is the ratio of signal power delivered to the load to signal power supplied to the input terminals,

$$G = \frac{P_o}{P_i} = \frac{I_c^2 R_L}{I_e^2 R_i} \cong \frac{\alpha^2 R_L}{R_i} \cong 1000$$

with the quoted values.

The common-emitter configuration exhibits an input resistance that is higher than that of the common-base connection, and an output resistance that is lower, but because of the greater value of current gain ($\beta \cong 50$) considerable power gain can result. If R_i is assumed to be 1000 ohms, and, a sample stage is feeding a 2000-ohm load, the resulting power gain is

$$G = \frac{I_c^2 R_L}{I_b^2 R_i} \cong \frac{\beta^2 R_L}{R_i} \cong 5000.$$

For a transistor used as a common-collector amplifier, the current gain is approximately β/α but the input resistance is higher; 100,000 ohms would be a realistic value. Thus, for a load of 2000 ohms,

$$G = \frac{I_e^2 R_L}{I_b^2 R_i} \cong \left(\frac{\beta}{\alpha}\right)^2 \frac{R_L}{R_i} \cong 50.$$

The quantities α and β were previously defined as short-circuit current-amplification factors. Since, in the examples cited above, the load resistance was not zero, and consequently v_C was not constant, the preceding power gain calculations were approximations. More exact expressions for circuit gains are presented in Chapter 4.

The amplification properties of a device or circuit can be specified by the numerical ratio of the magnitudes of output to input quantities or by the *decibel*, a logarithmic unit of power ratio. By definition, power gain in decibels is

$$\text{Gain in db} = 10 \log \frac{P_o}{P_i}, \tag{1-7}$$

where the subscript o again represents an output or load quantity and the subscript i, the quantity supplied to the circuit by a signal source. Should we wish to extend this definition to voltage and current quantities, then Eq. (1–7) becomes

$$\text{Gain} = 10 \log \frac{V_o^2/R_o}{V_i^2/R_i} \qquad \text{db},$$

or

$$\text{Gain} = 10 \log \frac{I_o^2 R_o}{I_i^2 R_i} \qquad \text{db}.$$

If $R_o = R_i$,

$$\text{Gain} = 10 \log \left(\frac{V_o}{V_i}\right)^2 = 20 \log \frac{V_o}{V_i} \qquad \text{db}, \qquad (1\text{–}8a)$$

and

$$\text{Gain} = 20 \log \frac{I_o}{I_i} \qquad \text{db}. \qquad (1\text{–}8b)$$

Eqs. (1–8a) and (1–8b) are correctly employed only for identical resistance levels. In transistor circuits the levels may be vastly different. Nevertheless it is customary to use the voltage and current equations in practice regardless of resistance levels.

As an example of the use of the decibel, the results of the three preceding gain calculations may be expressed in this unit. A power gain ratio of 1000 is 30 db, 5000 is 37 db, and 50 is equivalent to 17 db.

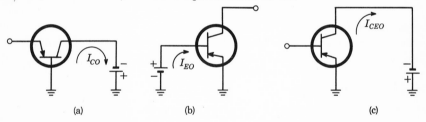

Fig. 1–12. (a) I_{CO} is collector-base current with emitter open; (b) I_{EO} is emitter-base current with collector open; (c) I_{CEO} is collector-emitter current with base open.

1–8. Leakage Currents. Refer now to Fig. 1–8a and note that when the emitter is open, i.e., no emitter current is permitted; a small collector current does exist. This current, termed I_{CO} (I_{CBO} by some), is the reverse or leakage current of the reverse-biased collector-to-base junction, and in germanium units is generally of the order of several microamperes. I_{CO} may vary considerably among otherwise similar units, and is extremely temperature-sensitive. A slight increase is noted in I_{CO} with collector voltage, but generally it is considered a constant for a particular transistor at a specified temperature. The circuit of interest is that of Fig. 1–12a. The importance of the leakage current lies in the effect of its variations upon the operating point, a thorough discussion of which is reserved for Chapter 3.

We may now describe the common-base collector characteristics mathematically with a knowledge of α and I_{CO}. At any particular collector potential,

$$I_C \cong \alpha I_E + I_{CO}. \tag{1-9}$$

If the collector of a transistor is unconnected as in Fig. 1–12b and a voltage applied from emitter to base to reverse-bias that junction, the resultant current is termed I_{EO} (also I_{EBO}). I_{EO} is, of course, temperature-dependent, and is the reverse or leakage current of the emitter-to-base p-n junction. This junction is forward-biased in normal operation.

Leaving the base terminal unconnected, and applying a potential from collector to emitter that serves to provide a reverse bias for the collector-to-base junction, as shown in Fig. 1–12c, results in a small current termed I_{CEO}. The relative magnitude of I_{CEO} may be studied by substituting Eq. (1–3) into Eq. (1–9):

$$I_C \cong \alpha(I_C + I_B) + I_{CO}. \tag{1-10}$$

Rearranging,

$$I_C \cong \frac{\alpha I_B}{1 - \alpha} + \frac{I_{CO}}{1 - \alpha}. \tag{1-11}$$

If Eq. (1–6a) is substituted into Eq. (1–11),

$$I_C \cong \beta I_B + (\beta + 1)I_{CO}. \tag{1-12}$$

From the common-emitter collector characteristics, when $I_B = 0$ the resulting collector current is I_{CEO}. Therefore, for any particular collector potential,

$$I_{CEO} = (\beta + 1)I_{CO}. \tag{1-13}$$

Then Eq. (1–12) becomes

$$I_C \cong \beta I_B + I_{CEO}. \tag{1-14}$$

Eq. (1–14) provides a mathematical description of the common-emitter characteristics.

To summarize the above discussion, I_{CO} is the collector-base leakage current, when a normal collector potential is applied and the input circuit (emitter) is open for the common-base configuration. For the common-emitter connection, the collector current when the input (base) is open is I_{CEO}, and is many times greater than I_{CO}.

1–9. Saturation and Cutoff Regions. The common-emitter configuration has become the favorite of circuit designers primarily because of the high degree of power amplification it provides. It therefore seems appropriate that a thorough study be made of this connection. In doing so, we find that the collector characteristics can provide more information concerning operation than is immediately apparent from examining a typical curve such as Fig. 1–7b.

Suppose that we investigate the low-voltage region of the collector characteristics. The region of the curve from zero to several hundred millivolts has been called the *saturation region* because incremental changes in base current do not cause the correspondingly large collector-current changes that are found at higher collector voltages. (This region is also referred to as the *bottomed* region.) Although Fig. 1–7 seems to indicate superimposed lines of constant base current, they are not actually superimposed when an expanded

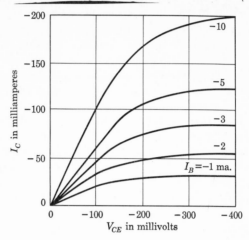

Fig. 1–13. Saturation region of a medium-power transistor, common-emitter configuration.

scale is used to depict the low-voltage region of the characteristics, as in Fig. 1–13.

Both *p-n* junctions are forward-biased in the saturation region. The existence of this region is commonly specified by a *saturation resistance*, symbolized by R_{CS}, which may be determined from the slope of the constant base current lines in Fig. 1–13. For germanium transistors, R_{CS} is generally less than 20 ohms, and in the majority of applications can be neglected; low-power silicon transistors, however, exhibit a saturation resistance of several hundred ohms, which seriously limits the allowable operating portion of the characteristics. It is evident from the figure that the magnitude of the saturation resistance is dependent upon base current and therefore a value ascribed to R_{CS} pertains at the specified I_C and I_B.

Let us turn our attention to the low-current region of the collector characteristics. The symbol I_{CEO} has been introduced to designate collector current when I_B is zero, and our curves indicate the relations between I_C and V_{CE} when base current is leaving the base terminal of a *p-n-p* transistor. The question now arises "can the transistor be operated with reverse base current?" If, to answer this question, we were to view a few typical collector characteristics, we should find no indication that operation is possible below I_{CEO}, because lines of constant base current are not drawn for that region. However, if a little thought is given to the common-base configuration, the answer to this question is available, for the leakage current I_{CO} flows *into* the base of a *p-n-p* transistor, and, consequently, operation is possible as low as I_{CO} in the common-emitter connection.

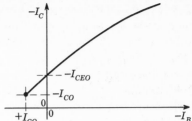

Fig. 1-14 is intended to clarify the relationships among the quantities of interest in the *cutoff* region. Base current cannot take on values more

Fig. 1-14. Portion of the transfer characteristic depicting leakage currents, common-emitter configuration.

positive than I_{CO} because I_{CO} represents a leakage current that is generally independent of applied potential.

1-10. Summary. Transistor operation has been described by the various curves, definitions, and equations contained within this chapter. This material, while mainly descriptive, is the most important portion of the text and, as the reader progresses, he will notice that the succeeding chapters serve mainly to clarify and extend the concepts introduced here, in order to gain a usable understanding of the transistor and transistor circuitry.

It is possible for the reader with a solid grounding in vacuum-tube circuit techniques to employ the material thus far discussed for the design of workable transistor circuits. However, without a knowledge of the pitfalls inherent in semiconductor circuits, namely biasing stability, thermal runaway, and parameter variations, good circuit design is not probable.

Chapter 2 is an introduction to the physics of semiconductors. Every engineer who would work with transistors should have a knowledge of their physical operation in order to appreciate their limitations. Familiarity with the physical processes will enable the reader to cope more easily with the advances in the science of solid-state physics and the art of semiconductor device design that are to be expected in the coming decade.

PROBLEMS

1-1. Explain how the term "signal amplification" applies to the vacuum tube, magnetic amplifier, transformer, and relay.

1-2. Calculate β from Fig. 1-7b for $V_{CE} = -10$ volts. Does β vary with collector voltage? Does β vary with collector current?

1-3. Explain the convention used in Fig. 1-7b that results in V_{CE}, I_C, and I_B having negative signs. What signs would be used for the currents of an *n-p-n* device? Would you expect all manufacturers and engineers to follow this convention?

1–4. Design a circuit to obtain the static characteristics curves for a common-base connected low-power transistor.

1–5. By using the information contained in Fig. 1–9, draw diagrams similar to Fig. 1–10a and 1–10b for both *p-n-p* and *n-p-n* transistor types in the common-base and common-collector configurations.

1–6. Explain why the input characteristics of a common-base connected transistor are similar to the forward characteristics of a semiconductor diode.

1–7. Use Fig. 1–7c and the definition of the dynamic input resistance of the transistor as the slope of that characteristic to plot dynamic input resistance against base-to-emitter voltage for a constant collector voltage of -10 volts.

1–8. Explain why I_B in Fig. 1–7c can take on positive values up to I_{CO}. Draw the circuit to provide $V_{BE} = 0$ to assist your explanation.

1–9. A given transistor exhibits a short-circuit current amplification of 0.995 when used in a common-base circuit. Calculate its short-circuit current gain as a common-emitter amplifier and also as a common-collector amplifier.

1–10. Discuss the similarities and differences between common-emitter operation of the 2N475 transistor (Appendix I) and a pentode such as the 6AU6 (see tube manual).

1–11. Using the information contained in Fig. 1–7, plot static transfer characteristics

(a) With collector current as abscissa and base voltage as ordinate for values of collector voltage of 0, 5, and 10 volts.

(b) With collector current as abscissa and base current as ordinate for values of collector voltage of 0, 5, and 10 volts.

1–12. Express the ratio β/α solely as a function of β and solely as a function of α.

1–13. Derive Eqs. (1–6a) and (1–6b).

1–14. Calculate the approximate voltage gain for each configuration using the same numbers for α, β, R_i and R_L as used in the text examples of Sec. 1–7.

1–15. Using Eqs. (1–3) and (1–9), derive an expression for I_E in terms of I_B and I_{CEO}, and from your derived expression predict and sketch the output characteristics for a transistor in the common-collector configuration. Discuss the spacing between lines of constant I_B and also discuss the $I_B = 0$ line.

1–16. A transistor known to have $\beta = 100$ and $I_{CO} = 5$ μa is connected in a circuit as a common-emitter stage and a measurement of the collector current yields $I_C = 1$ ma with zero load resistance. Calculate I_E, I_B, α, and I_{CEO} under these conditions.

1–17. Calculate the d-c collector saturation resistance R_{CS} from Fig. 1–13 for each displayed value of base current at $V_{CE} = 100$ millivolts.

1–18. A sound-amplifying system supplies a loudspeaker with 4 watts of

2–1.   PORTION OF THE PERIODIC TABLE INCLUDING ELEMENTS OF INTEREST TO SEMICONDUCTOR WORK

Group 3	Group 4	Group 5
Boron 5 10.8	Carbon 6 12	Nitrogen 7 14
Aluminum 13 27	Silicon 14 28.1	Phosphorus 15 31
Gallium 31 69.7	Germanium 32 72.6	Arsenic 33 75
Indium 49 114.8	Tin 50 118.7	Antimony 51 121.8

en a small number of arsenic atoms, for example, are added to a crystal manium, the lattice remains intact; that is, covalent bonding exists n all adjacent atoms. But since each arsenic atom has five electrons outermost orbit, it is apparent that an electron is left over from each f the impurity; one electron does not enter into the covalent bonding. ectron can be termed a free electron because it is easily detached from enic atom. Fig. 2–2 depicts the situation. As would be expected, the ity of the crystal is decreased because of the presence of free electrons. is the term most often applied to elements that, when added to pure ium, serve to donate free electrons to the lattice. The composite l thus formed is *n-type* germanium, the *n* being an abbreviation for e, the sign of charge on the electron. In *n*-type material electrical tion is primarily an electron movement.

addition of an impurity with three electrons in its outer orbit has an e effect upon the lattice. As shown in Fig. 2–3 there now are too few s to satisfy all the covalent bonds. Between each atom of the im- and the surrounding atoms there will be a void of one electron; this of an electron is called a *hole*. *Acceptor* is used to specify elements when added to an intrinsic semiconductor can result in holes in the acceptor meaning that the element will accept an electron, if one is e, to fill its commitments in the lattice. *p-type* material, then, has an f holes; *p* is an abbreviation for positive, the sign of a hole (since the

audio power when the system, which has an input resistance of 10,000 ohms, is supplied with a 0.2-volt signal. The speaker is of the common 4-ohm variety and is assumed to be noninductive.

(a) Express the power gain in db.

(b) Express the voltage gain in db.

(c) Express the current gain in db.

(d) Express the resistance-level ratio in db by extension of Eq. (1–7), and subtract from the answer of part b in order to arrive at the answer to part a.

1–19. By using the expression, Eq. (1–12), that predicts the idealized collector characteristics show that, for a common-emitter oriented transistor, a base current of $-I_{CO}$ causes a collector current of equal magnitude.

1–20. On a single sheet of graph paper, approximate the common-base and common-emitter collector characteristics for a transistor with $\alpha = 0.975$, $I_{CO} = 10$ μa, and $R_{CS} = 200$ ohms. Let collector currents range to 5 ma and collector-junction potentials to 20 volts.

1–21. I_{CBO}, I_{CEO}, and I_{EBO} have been used to symbolize transistor leakage currents.

(a) Suggest the system being used that results in this three-subscript notation.

(b) Sketch circuits to independently measure each of these currents for an *n-p-n* transistor.

REFERENCES

1. Bevitt, W. D., *Transistors Handbook*, Prentice-Hall, Inc., Englewood Cliffs, New Jersey, 1956.
2. "Diode Amplifier," *National Bureau of Standards Technical News Bulletin*, vol. 38 (Oct., 1954).
3. "IRE Standards on Letter Symbols for Semiconductor Devices, 1956," *Proc.* IRE, vol. 44 (July, 1956).
4. Kiver, M. S., *Transistors in Radio and Television*, McGraw-Hill Book Co., Inc., New York, 1956.
5. Lo, A. W., *et al.*, *Transistor Electronics*, Prentice-Hall, Inc., Englewood Cliffs, New Jersey, 1955.
6. Riddle, R. L., and Ristenbatt, M. P., *Transistor Physics and Circuits*, Prentice-Hall, Inc., Englewood Cliffs, New Jersey, 1958.
7. Ryder, J. D., *Electronic Fundamentals and Applications*, 2nd Ed., Prentice-Hall, Inc., Englewood Cliffs, New Jersey, 1959.
8. Shea, R. F., *Principles of Transistor Circuits*, John Wiley & Sons, Inc., New York, 1953.
9. Shea, R. F., *Transistor Circuit Engineering*, John Wiley & Sons, Inc., New York, 1957.

Chapter 2

SEMICONDUCTOR PHYSICS

Semiconductor devices have been used in electrical circuits since the *galena crystal* or "cat's whisker" of pre-vacuum-tube days. Dry rectifiers using *copper oxide* and *selenium* were widely accepted for battery charging and electronic rectification during the two decades prior to the introduction of the transistor and the junction diode; and thermistors and photoelectric devices of semiconducting materials were useful circuit components. Understanding of the operation of these earlier semiconductor devices is now more complete because of the vast research in solid-state physical phenomena that commenced in the late 1940's.

The elements germanium and silicon constitute the semiconductors of paramount importance today. Investigations of other materials are under way and it seems reasonable to speculate that new materials, possibly bimetallic compounds such as gallium-arsenide, indium-phosphide, or aluminum-antimonide, will play a major role in electronics of the not-too-distant future.

At this point in the study of transistors it seems appropriate that some attention be given to the principles of semiconductor physics, the applications of those principles, and the methods of transistor manufacture. Although it is theoretically unnecessary for a circuit designer to be aware of the physical processes involved, such knowledge is of very great assistance in appreciating transistor limitations, fully understanding circuit operation, and keeping abreast with developments in the field.

2–1. Structure. The fourth column of the periodic table includes silicon and germanium—they have four electrons in their outermost *orbit* or *shell*, and tend to form a crystal when in the pure elemental state. A crystal is a solid in which atoms are arranged in a definite order or pattern that is regularly repeated throughout the solid. Crystals may consist of different geometrical arrangements of atoms; the three-dimensional pattern repeated throughout the crystals of interest here is known as the *face-centered diamond cubic lattice*, a structure identical with that of the diamond form of carbon.

The distribution of the four valence electrons in the germanium or silicon atom is such that one electron is shared with each of the four neighboring

atoms in the crystal. This condition, known as *covale* filled outer shell for each atom, for in addition to its atom is sharing four other electrons with its neighbor its outer ring contains eight electrons, the atom is no free electrons exist in the ideal structure at 0° the crystal has insulating properties, since it is the that is characteristic of conducting materials.

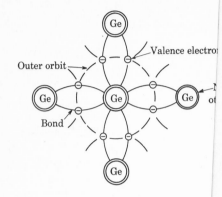

Fig. 2–1. Portion of the crystal structure of

Pure germanium (or silicon) is referred to as Electrical conduction is possible because some co thermal energy even at room temperature. An el can also supply enough energy to break covalent to serve as charge carriers.

It is of course possible to measure and also calc bonds due to the addition of energy to an intrinsic which is about normal room temperature, the re is about 50 ohm-cm, with more than 10^{13} charge of material. The resistivity of silicon at that sa mately 240,000 ohm-cm, with some 10^{10} carriers

2–2. Impurities. A perfect crystal is not used facture; the characteristics of such devices depen crystal to alter its intrinsic conducting propertie tor results from imperfections in the lattice stru due to foreign materials remaining after the refir addition of known impurities, a process called purposely added to elements in the fourth colu manium and silicon) are elements from the thi 2–1 provides the portion of the periodic table major importance to semiconductor work.

charge on an electron is negative, the absence of an electron would seemingly be equivalent to a positively charged particle). In *p*-type materials electrical conduction is primarily a hole movement. The resistivity of pure germanium

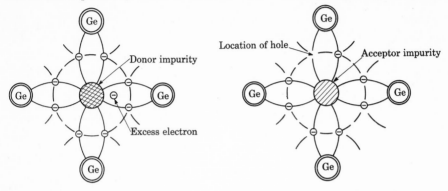

Fig. 2–2. The addition of a donor to the germanium crystal of Fig. 2–1 results in a free electron.

Fig. 2–3. The addition of an acceptor to the germanium crystal of Fig. 2–1 results in a hole.

is decreased by the addition of acceptor impurities; thus the hole serves as an electrical carrier and is comparable in effectiveness to the free electron.

The movement of a free electron is random in a specimen of *n*-type material; the electron is free to wander. So it is with a hole in *p*-material, for electrons in neighboring bonds find it easy to fill the void, and the hole ap-

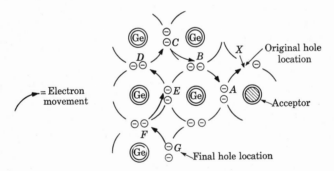

Fig. 2–4. The movement of electrons to fill holes in the lattice results in hole movement.

pears to move randomly through the material. When under the influence of an electric field, holes naturally behave oppositely to electrons—they are attracted to negative charges.

The *diffusion* or movement of holes from regions of high concentration to regions of low concentration without an applied field is illustrated in Fig. 2–4.

If a hole is initially located in the outer orbit of the acceptor atom, as at X in the diagram, it is possible for an electron at A to move from its position to fill the hole, since it is in the same orbit and no additional energy is required. After this movement, there is a hole at A. The electron at B can fill the new hole at A, so that the void is then located at B. In a like manner we may conceive of the hole reaching location G and beyond. We may conclude that hole movement is possible, that it is in the opposite direction to electron flow, and, significantly, it takes place within the valence shells of atoms. It is interesting to note that the rate of this random movement of holes is about one-half that for electrons.

In securing a clear picture of semiconductor phenomena, it must be understood that the *impurities are immobile;* it is the free electrons and holes that are the carriers, for their movement dictates the movement of charge and hence what are called *electrical currents.* Electrons in *n*-type material and holes in *p*-type material are *majority* carriers, while any electrons in *p*-type material or any holes in *n*-type material are termed *minority* carriers. The net charge of a specimen of *p*-type or *n*-type material is normally zero, for neither electrons nor holes have been added to or removed from the atoms that constitute the crystal, and the atoms themselves are electrically neutral. The lattice may have an excess of electrons or holes because of the type of impurity added, but this excess is only relative to a perfect lattice structure.

2–3. Energy-Level Diagrams. Modern atomic theory stresses that for an atom of any element there is an integral number of orbits or levels to which electrons can belong, and each level represents a particular value of energy ascribed to the electrons "residing" there. To move an electron from one level to a higher energy level, the system must be furnished with an amount of energy equal to the energy difference between levels; this can be supplied from any convenient energy source. Electrons closest to the nucleus are in the lowest energy levels; those farthest from the nucleus have the highest energies. The higher the energy of a given electron, the less is its attraction to its nucleus.

Thus far in this discussion only a single atom has been considered. When a tremendously large number of atoms are congregated to form a solid, the energy-level picture of the individual atom is no longer valid, because of interactions between it and its neighboring atoms. The number of energy levels for a solid is very great, but they are generally very close. A number of close levels is termed an energy *band;* and each band, in a solid, is separated from other bands by a *forbidden gap*, a series of energies that electrons in that solid cannot possess. Not all solids have gaps in their energy band picture, but semiconductors do.

From an energy-level standpoint the differences between insulators, conductors, and semiconductors can be appreciated. The width of the forbidden gap between the *valence band* of allowable energy levels and the *conduction band* of allowable energy levels is a key to that understanding. If a great deal of energy (in the form of heat or otherwise) must be added to a material to increase its conductivity to a reasonable value, then the forbidden gap of that material must be large, and consequently the material under normal conditions is an insulator. On the other hand if a negligible amount of added energy is needed to establish good electrical conductivity, a given specimen is classified as a conductor. A gap of intermediate width connotes a semicon-

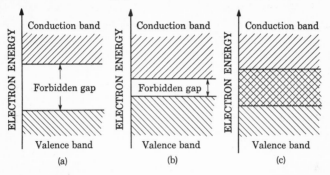

Fig. 2–5. Representation of solids by energy-level diagrams: (a) insulator; (b) semiconductor; (c) conductor.

ductor. A pictorial representation of energy levels for different materials is Fig. 2–5. It must be borne in mind that whereas other gaps exist in a given atomic structure, it is the forbidden gap between the valence band (also called the filled band) and the conduction band (also referred to as the empty band) that is the important one.

In germanium or silicon, the gap is small enough so that, at room temperature, an appreciable number of interatomic bonds are broken by thermal energy, and a number of electrons will acquire sufficient energy to move from the valence band to the conduction band of the crystal. The forbidden gap for germanium is 0.72 electron volt, while for silicon a generally recognized figure is 1.1 electron volts. (The electron volt, eV, a unit of energy, is equivalent to 1.6×10^{-19} watt-sec.)

Let us consider the other elements of column four of the periodic table (Table 2–1). Carbon, in the diamond form, has a gap of 7 eV, and is therefore nonconductive up to very high temperatures. The crystalline form of tin, called gray tin, has a gap of only 0.1 eV and consequently is a stable crystal at very low temperatures only. Neither material may be used for transistor manufacture.

The presence of electrons with conduction band energies because of broken interatomic bonds results in holes in the valence band. A *pentavalent impurity*, that is a donor, when added to germanium, will add electrons to the crystal *without* adding any new holes. However, it is interesting to note that the energy-level system is further complicated by this donor; this impurity introduces new energy levels into the energy-band picture. The location of these new levels is slightly below the bottom of the conduction band for pure germanium (the gap was forbidden to electrons of the pure crystal only). The total width of the gap was previously stated as 0.72 eV; the energy required to move an electron from a donor impurity into the conduction band is of the order of 0.01 eV, and since at normal ambient temperature thermal energy is considered to be about 0.02 eV, it is concluded that almost all electrons are detached from donor atoms and have conduction band energies.

The introduction of a *trivalent impurity* can also be investigated. As before, the presence of the impurity creates new energy levels. For acceptors, however, these levels are in the gap in the neighborhood of the top of the valence band of energies. Ambient temperature results in ionization of most acceptor atoms and thus an apparent movement of holes from the acceptor levels to the valence band. (Energy-level diagrams are plots of electron energies; energies for holes are highest near the valence band and decrease vertically upward.) Alternatively, one might say that electrons are accepted by the acceptors; these electrons are supplied from the valence band, leaving a preponderance of holes in the valence band.

Summarizing, then, under ambient conditions n-type material has a surplus of electrons, and electrical conduction is primarily a conduction-band electron drift; in a p-type material there is a hole surplus and electrical conduction is primarily a valence-band hole drift.

2–4. p-n Junctions. A p-n junction is created when p-type and n-type material are bonded to form a single crystal. The methods of junction manufacture are discussed in Sec. 2–6 and in other texts. Immediately after formation, carrier diffusion results in some electrons from the n-region crossing the boundary while some holes from the p-region are migrating to the other side. After crossing the junction, an electron from the n-region finds itself in an area of high hole concentration. Recombination is probable and the electron as a carrier is therefore annihilated. A similar process can be visualized for holes from the p-region crossing the junction. Since each region was originally electrically neutral, electron-hole recombinations on both sides and in the vicinity of the junction result in layers of ionized acceptors in the p-region and ionized donors in the n-region. Therefore the p-region has experienced a net accumulation of negative charge, the n-region a net accumulation of positive charge. This charge buildup continues until an equilibrium condition prevails and further carrier diffusion across the junction is discouraged by the repelling force between the carrier and the charge concentration across the boundary. The p-n junction in equilibrium is symbolized in Fig. 2–6a.

Because of the accumulated charges in the vicinity of the p-n junction, a potential difference is evident. Figs. 2–6b and 2–6c are concerned with the distribution of charge and the potential picture. During the equilibrium process carriers in the neighborhood of the junction have been "swept out," and the area is referred to as the *depletion* or *transition* or *space-charge* region.

An energy-level diagram for the *p-n* junction is shown in Fig. 2–7. Because the *p*-region has lost some high-energy holes and gained some high-energy

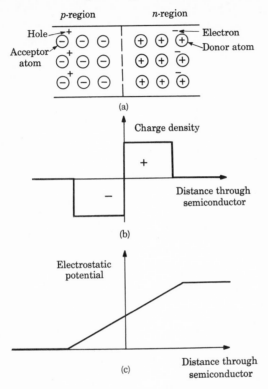

(a)

(b)

(c)

Fig. 2–6. The *p-n* junction: (a) after diffusion and recombinations; (b) charge distribution; (c) potential hill.

electrons, and therefore is no longer electrically neutral, its electron energy diagram will be relatively displaced above that of the *n*-region by an amount of energy equal to eV_J, where e is the charge on the electron and V_J is the electrostatic potential difference across the junction.

In order for an electron to move from the *n*-region to the *p*-region it would be necessary for it to have sufficient energy to climb the *potential hill* (the electron would have to invade the *p*-region which has more of a negative charge than the *n*-region). Likewise, when we consider holes in the *p*-region, they would need to be supplied with external energy in order to climb the potential hill confronting them. Thermal agitation accounts for some carrier flow across the junction at ambient temperatures but any net movement of majority carriers is balanced by minority carriers. Minority carriers, although relatively few in number, find it easy to slide down the potential hills.

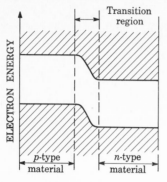

Fig. 2-7.   *p-n* junction energy-level diagram.

If a reverse bias is applied to the *p-n* junction as shown in Fig. 2–8a, the potential hill for electrons in the *n*-region becomes more difficult to climb. The only current possible results from the few minority carriers on each side of the junction. This leakage or reverse current is controlled by the constitution of the *p* and *n* materials; if highly *n*-type material is joined to lightly *p*-type material, reverse current will be mainly an electron flow. On the other hand, a reverse current consisting primarily of holes can be achieved by an opposite process.

Leakage current is generally constant and almost independent of the magnitude of the reverse biasing voltage until the *avalanche* voltage or *Zener*

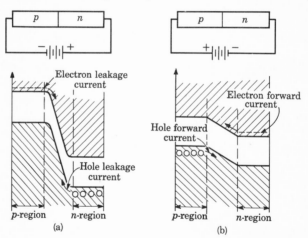

Fig. 2–8.   *p-n* junction with applied voltage: (a) reverse bias; (b) forward bias.

voltage is exceeded. Reverse current then increases very rapidly. Avalanche breakdown occurs when the electric field across the junction produces ionization because resulting high-energy carriers collide with valence electrons. Zener breakdown appears to be a "field emission" phenomena, the strong electric field in the junction region pulling carriers from their atoms.

With forward bias applied to a *p-n* structure the movement of majority carriers across the junction is increased. Fig. 2–8b indicates that the height of the potential hill has been reduced so that less energy must be expended in climbing it. Although the reverse current still exists, it is negligible compared with the current associated with the movements of the majority carriers.

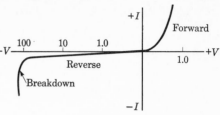

The volt-ampere characteristic of the junction diode, shown in Fig. 2–9, can be described theoretically by the following relationship:

Fig. 2-9. Characteristic curve for a *p-n* junction (diode).

$$I = I_R(\epsilon^{eV/kT} - 1) \tag{2-1}$$

where I = junction current in amperes,
$\quad I_R$ = saturated value of reverse current in amperes,
$\quad e$ = charge on an electron, 1.602×10^{-19} coulomb,
$\quad V$ = potential difference in volts,
$\quad T$ = absolute temperature in degrees Kelvin,
$\quad k$ = Boltzmann's constant, 1.380×10^{-23} joule per °K.

This equation holds for both polarities of voltage, and agrees with experimental data.

The effect of ambient temperature upon diode leakage or reverse current is important. Higher temperatures cause more electron-hole pairs to be thermally generated, the resulting additional carriers cause larger diode leakage currents. In Chapter 1, I_{CO} and I_{EO} were introduced as leakage currents of *p-n* structures within the transistor. These currents are extremely temperature-sensitive; the degree of that sensitivity will be further discussed in Chapter 3.

In summary of the operation of a *p-n* junction diode, the following points are of interest. Joining *p*-type material to *n*-type material establishes a contact-potential hill which consequently limits random movement of majority carriers across the junction. Minority carriers, generated by thermal energy or otherwise, can easily cross a reverse-biased junction, their flow being essentially independent of the magnitude of the bias, unless breakdown conditions are exceeded. With forward biasing, the height of the potential hill is reduced and majority carriers cross the junction in great number.

2–5. Transistor Operation. With understanding of *p-n* junction operation comes insight into transistor operation, for the common junction transistor is merely two rectifying junctions. The basic structure can take on either of the forms shown in Fig. 1–1, a *p-n-p* *sandwich*, or an *n-p-n* *sandwich*. The emitter and collector regions form the two outside portions of the structure; between them is the thin base region. External circuitry is connected by relatively large metal contacts to each of the elements to insure nonrectifying terminations. It was noted in Chapter 1 that under normal biasing conditions, the emitter-base junction is biased in the forward or high-conduction direction, while the collector-base junction is biased in the reverse direction.

Now consider Fig. 2–10a, which shows a *p-n-p* transistor and its energy-level diagram in the absence of biasing. The potential hills are apparent in

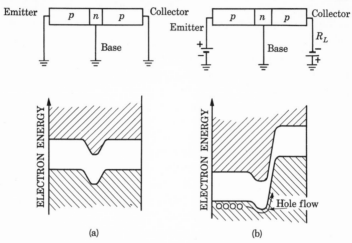

Fig. 2–10. The junction transistor with energy-level diagrams: (a) no bias voltages; (b) normal bias voltages.

the electron-energy diagram, and, as would be expected, there is no net flow of charges. The emitter junction can now be forward-biased, the collector junction reverse-biased with a negative potential through a load resistor for normal operation.

Majority carriers, namely holes in the emitter *p*-region, will move toward the base region because forward biasing has been applied to the emitter-base junction. When they arrive in the base area they see a large potential hill to slide down, the hill created by the collector-base voltage, and thus carriers from the emitter will readily travel to the collector. This is transistor amplification as discussed in Chapter 1, namely the passage of current from a low-resistance to a high-resistance circuit. When a time-varying signal is applied between base and emitter terminals, that signal just serves to modulate the emitter-base potential, or, in other words, it alters the potential hill between emitter and base to allow a greater or lesser number of emitted charges to reach the collector.

The number of holes reaching the collector from the emitter in the *p-n-p* transistor is less than the number injected by the emitter because of recombinations of electrons and holes in the base region. The number of recombinations must be kept low in order for the amplification efficiency to be high. Consequently the base region is made exceedingly thin, and the impurity density of the base wafer is controlled during manufacture; these measures reduce the time spent by holes while diffusing through the base region and limit the number of electrons with which recombination can take place. The value of alpha, the fraction of emitted charges which are collected, depends directly upon such recombinations.

High-frequency performance also depends upon base thickness. Since an absence of strong electric fields is to be expected in that region, diffusion of carriers across the base is a relatively slow process and the distance traveled by a charge is an important factor in the ability of a transistor to follow high-frequency commands.

The junction regions are essentially devoid of carriers, and therefore are regions of high resistivity; almost the entire bias voltage drop occurs there resulting in strong electric fields in the junction regions and weak fields in the remainder of the transistor.

Because a higher reverse bias causes more majority carriers to leave the vicinity of a junction, thus leaving behind more immobile ions, the thickness of the space-charge region widens with increasing reverse bias. This is a capacitive effect for $C = dq/dv$, and the phenomenon is referred to as *transition, depletion, barrier,* or *space-charge capacitance.*

The temperature limitation on transistor operation is clear when one considers that the normal concentrations of free carriers attributable to impurities are supplemented by thermally generated hole-electron pairs. At sufficiently high temperatures these thermally derived carriers can be in such great numbers as to numerically "overpower" the impurity-derived carriers and transistor action is therefore impossible.

Other currents exist in the sample p-n-p transistor. I_{CO}, the collector-to-base current with the emitter unconnected, is composed of minority carriers from the collector (electrons) moving toward the base. Electrons flowing from base to emitter constitute another carrier flow; this however is purposely kept as low as possible, compared with the hole flow from the emitter, by control of base electron concentration.

Now if the conventional current leaving the base terminal is symbolized by I_B (actually an electron movement toward the base), and the holes from the emitter that are collected is termed I_C, then we have the relationship that

$$I_C = I_E - I_B. \tag{2-2}$$

Naturally electron flow is the negative of hole flow.

Eq. (2-1) which indicates a nonlinear relationship between voltage and current, applies to the transistor, for, as we have seen, the transistor uses junction diodes for its building blocks. Nonlinearities in the volt-ampere curves have resulted in the popular statement that the transistor is a current-amplifying device, for although voltage, current, and power gain can be achieved, the device tends to amplify input current linearly. Therefore most transistor characteristics are plotted using currents; one who is versed in vacuum-tube amplification may find this approach quite different, but the results analogous.

2–6. Transistor Fabrication. The quality level of commercial transistors is presently high, largely because of improvements in manufacturing techniques. Several different methods of fabrication are of importance, and it is reasonable to assume that new methods will develop from the trend toward complete automatization of transistor manufacture.

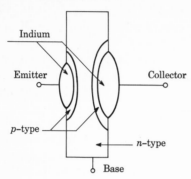

Fig. 2–11.   Alloy-junction transistor construction.

The method of manufacture is seldom a basis for selection of a particular transistor for a given circuit application.   Although the manufacturing method does account for important operational differences, it is a study of characteristics and not of fabrication that eventually determines the transistors to be used.

Most widely used is the *alloy-* or *fused-junction transistor*. A wafer of base material (generally *n*-type germanium) is held in a jig between two pellets of impurity (indium, for example). The structure is heated until the impurity melts (155° C for indium), and the molten impurity penetrates the base material, dissolving some of it. During cooling crystal regrowth results in a completed three-layer structure as shown in Fig. 2–11. By control of temperature, time, and pellet size it is possible to achieve various operating characteristics, but since rather high junction capacitance results from the process, the alloy-junction transistor generally does not perform well at the higher frequencies.

In the *diffusion* process, impurities of one conductivity type are made to diffuse at high temperature into the surface of a bar of opposite type, resulting in a *p-n* junction between the skin and the original bar. This technique forms the basis for the *drift* and *mesa* types to be discussed in Sect. 2–8.

The growing of junctions is accomplished by starting with a small *seed* of material cut from a previous operation. The seed is touched to the surface of a bath or *melt* of molten semiconductor and is slowly pulled from the melt. The size of the original seed grows because melt in the vicinity of the seed adheres to it and freezes during withdrawal. The characteristics of the melt can be changed during the pulling operation by adding impurities. The completed crystal is cut into diodes or transistors and leads are welded to the proper areas. In appearance, a *grown-junction* transistor resembles Fig. 1–1 and its dimensions are typically $0.01 \times 0.01 \times 0.1$ inch.

Also widely accepted is the *rate-grown* device, a transistor whose structure depends upon variations in growth rate. It is possible to dope a melt with both donors and acceptors, and grow single crystals from it. The crystal will be n-type if grown at a high rate and p-type if grown at a low rate because impurities differ in their solubility characteristics. By proper control of the growth rate, it is possible to produce alternate p and n regions in a single crystal.

Improved techniques such as those used for the manufacture of the *surface barrier* type have extended the operating frequency range of transistors. A very thin base wafer (0.0002 inch) with small electroplated contacts forming rectifying junctions has resulted in a transistor operable to frequencies in excess of 100 megacycles. This construction and operation are achieved by a manufacturing process that subjects a small piece of germanium to two jets of electrolyte, such as a solution of indium-chloride, which impinge upon opposite faces of the germanium base slab. Etching of the semiconductor is accomplished by passage of current through the electrolyte streams and the germanium. When the proper base thickness is achieved, current polarities are reversed and the jets plate metal emitter and collector contacts on either side of the base. The thin base region has the disadvantage of limiting power-handling capabilities.[2]

2–7. Other Transistor Types. Let us briefly consider the p-n-p-n *triode* and the *unipolar* transistor, for these devices serve to illustrate what can be accomplished when applying the foregoing physical principles to the design of semiconductor devices that differ from the basic triode. Although as yet neither has gained widespread use, each has greatly contributed to the reserve of semiconductor knowledge.

The p-n-p-n triode is, as the name implies, a four-layer structure and is commonly referred to as the *hook collector*. This addition of an n-type layer to the collector end of a p-n-p junction transistor can result in a device that exhibits high current gain in the common-base configuration; therefore $\alpha > 1$ for this transistor, and interesting characteristics result. An n-p-n-p device is also possible.[6]

Consider the device as shown in Fig. 2–12. Three p-n junctions exist; the second p-region is left floating in potential. This second p-region and the final n-region are referred to as the "hook collector" because of the hook noticeable in the energy-level diagram.

Holes injected by the emitter collect in the floating p-region, where they are trapped—unable to reach the collector because of the polarity of the collector-to-base bias. The floating p-region, because of the accumulation of trapped holes, will attain a positive potential, and the energy-level diagram will become altered because of increased hole potential energy in that region. Equilibrium occurs when one hole enters the floating p-region for every one that leaves.

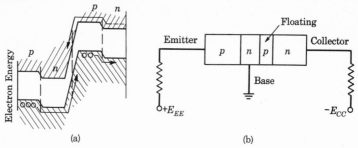

(a)   (b)

Fig. 2–12. p-n-p-n transistor and energy-level diagram.

The alteration of energy levels also affects electrons in the n-type collector, for they now find it easy to travel to the base. The sum of hole and electron currents is the total collector current. The essential action is the control of electron movement in the collector-base circuit by holes from the input (emitter) portion of the device. Frequency response for the hook collector is considered poor, and noise level and leakage currents are high.

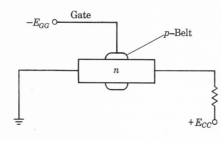

Fig. 2–13.   Unipolar transistor.

The *unipolar transistor*, also called the *field-effect transistor*, is illustrated in Fig. 2–13. A bar of n-type material is encircled by a p-type alloy belt. The resistance of the bar can be modulated by signals on the "gate." These signals essentially "sweep out" the area under the belt of carriers, thus "pinching off" the n-type bar to the desired degree. Certain advantages are claimed: input impedance is high, of the order of a megohm, and the frequency response is better than that of a junction triode.[14]

2–8. Operation at High Frequencies. The performance of junction transistors at high frequencies is seriously limited by several factors: collector-to-base capacitance loads the output and contributes to poor performance; *base-spreading* resistance, the ohmic resistance of the relatively long and narrow base path, also sets a limit upon the available gain of a transistor stage (see Chapter 9); deterioration of alpha at high frequencies, caused by the relative slowness of the diffusion process in the base region, prevents the collection process from following the emitter process well at high frequencies. In order to circumvent or minimize these limitations, the common junction triode has been subjected to many redesigns. Some of the modifications have proved highly successful and have resulted in satisfactory operation to frequencies in the hundreds of megacycles.

The *surface barrier transistor* previously discussed has been widely accepted. The *mesa transistor*, a microminiature device produced by vapor diffusion of a gas containing antimony into solid germanium to form the collector-base junction, is operable to 200 mc. The *drift transistor* uses a base region graded in conductivity, highly conductive near the emitter, and nearly pure germanium at the collector junction. Because an internal electric field is caused by the conductivity gradient, carriers will drift across the base region with high velocity instead of relying upon diffusion.

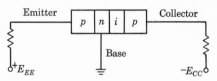

Fig. 2–14.   *p-n-i-p* transistor.

To reduce collector-to-base capacitance the *p-n-i-p transistor*,[5] shown in Fig. 2–14, has been proposed. An intrinsic or *i-layer* is located between the collector and base regions; this layer floats in potential. The *i*-layer serves to increase the width of the depletion region and consequently reduces junction capacitance, which is inversely proportional to the region's width. Otherwise, operation is similar to the junction triode.

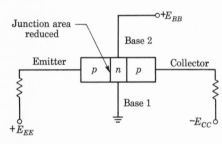

Fig. 2–15.   Junction tetrode.

If two connections are made to opposite sides of the base region of an ordinary junction transistor, and a biasing potential is applied between the two terminals, certain operational advantages are obtained. The structure is referred to as a *junction tetrode* or *double-base transistor*, and is shown in Fig. 2–15. The interbase bias voltage is large enough so that only a portion of the emitter junction is operating as an emitter; the remainder of the emitter is cut-off. Effective base resistance is thereby reduced because all transistor action occurs adjacent to one base contact; reduction in base resistance directly extends the maximum allowable operating frequency of junction transistors.

A semiconductor device that shows promise of extending amplifying operation to frequencies in the thousands of megacycles is the *spacistor tetrode*, shown diagrammatically in Fig. 2–16. High electric fields in the space-charge region are used to accelerate charge carriers—resulting transit time is much shorter than comparable carrier diffusion across the base of a transistor.[16, 17]

The emitting point is biased positively; the modulating point is biased to draw a negligible current because it is made negative with respect to the normal potential of the space-charge region to which it is attached (the modulating point and space-charge region form a reverse-biased diode). Thus practically no current will flow in the input circuit and an input impedance as high as 30 megohms can be achieved.

The modulating point is more positive than the emitting point, but none of the electrons in the emitting point—n-region—load path will be collected by the modulating point, for the reason stated in the preceding paragraph. The flow of carriers around that path is, however, dictated by the a-c signal input superimposed on the d-c level of the modulating point, because the field, due to the modulating point, penetrates throughout the space-charge region and can control emission from the emitting contact. The reverse bias

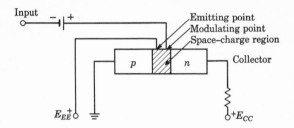

Fig. 2–16. Spacistor tetrode.

of E_{CC} on the p-n junction does not control current flow through the load—a reason why the output impedance may be many megohms.

The spacistor tetrode is capable of power amplifications of 9×10^6 or 70 db, and under matched conditions a voltage gain of 3000 has been achieved. Interelemental capacitances are very small.

2–9. Metallic Contact Devices. It has long been known that rectification or diode action can result from a metal-semiconductor contact. It is also possible to achieve an *ohmic* or *nonrectifying* contact between these materials, and all the devices discussed thus far employ such contacts.

Whether a particular contact is or is not rectifying depends upon the particular metal and semiconductor used. To formulate a general rule to be followed in determining the behavior of a contact, the *work function* of a material may be used as the test characteristic. The work function of a material may be defined as the amount of energy that must be added to an electron to cause it to be emitted from the surface of the material, or to permit it to escape completely from the domination of its parent. If we designate the work function of the metal as Φ_m and of the semiconductor as Φ_s, a contact will be ohmic if $\Phi_m < \Phi_s$ and rectify if $\Phi_m > \Phi_s$.[21] An ohmic condition can also result if the metal and the semiconductor can alloy, for it is then possible to achieve a gradual transition between materials. There are exceptions to these rules.

Commercial rectifiers using metal-to-semiconductor contact for their operation include the selenium and copper-oxide rectifiers and point-contact (crystal) diodes. The selenium rectifier uses the junction between selenium and cadmium, lead, or tin. The same metals are often used in contact with cuprous oxide in the copper-oxide rectifier. A point-contact diode is made from a small slab of semiconducting material, germanium for example, and a fine wire (whisker) that is sharpened to a point at one end. When a suitable spot for rectification is found on the surface of the slab, the unit is pulsed with a current to weld the wire to the slab. Naturally the power-handling capacity of such a device is limited by the wire size.

Historically, the first transistors were of the point-contact type.[1]   Today

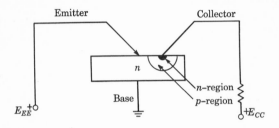

Fig. 2–17.   Point-contact transistor.

point-contact transistors are not generally accepted for amplifying applications because of the many advantages of the junction transistor. Their usefulness seems to lie in switching circuits; they can exhibit an alpha in excess of unity, but are noisy and difficult to manufacture.

The collector of the point-contact transistor shown in Fig. 2–17 is often a phosphor bronze wire. n- and p-regions are introduced into the germanium base by *forming*, the passage of large current pulses through the contact in the back direction. The emitter-base diode also makes use of point-contact rectification. Operation of the composite structure may be explained by the hook-collector theory.

2–10. Switching Devices.   Semiconductor devices that exhibit two stable operating states separated by a region of negative resistance are very useful circuit elements.

Only one p-n junction exists in the *unijunction transistor* or *double-base diode*, although it has three terminals, an emitter, and connections at each end of a long base bar, as is shown in Fig. 2–18. Application of a bias voltage to the base, in the absence of emitter signal or potential, results in a uniform voltage gradient along the base bar. At the emitter terminal the potential will be somewhat in excess of one-half E_{BB}, because of the physical position of the junction—it is closer to base number two.

Should E_{EE} now be applied and be of a magnitude greater than the potential previously existing at the emitter-base junction, holes are injected into the bar from the emitter. The potential distribution in the bar because of these injected carriers will be altered and the resistivity of the bar decreased. The

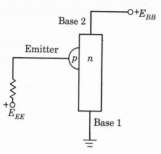

Fig. 2–18. Unijunction transistor.

voltage drop from emitter to base number one therefore decreases and emitter current increases regeneratively. The device may be returned to the OFF condition by applying a negative trigger pulse to the emitter. A sort of regenerative feedback resulting in a negative input resistance is achieved—a desirable condition for oscillation.

Unijunction transistors have been found useful as pulse amplifiers, multivibrators, and relaxation oscillators.

The *four-layer diode* is a two-terminal device that can operate in either of two states—an open or low-conductance state corresponding to a resistance of several megohms, and a closed or high-conductance state with a resistance of less than 20 ohms.[15] To switch from the open to the closed state, a voltage is applied to exceed the breakdown potential, and if sufficient holding current is available to keep it in the closed state the diode will exhibit only a small drop across its terminals. This p-n-p-n structure can be used as a sawtooth or a sine-wave generator, and in other circuits where bistable properties are advantageous.

Thyratron action, the control of high load power by a trigger pulse, is provided by the *silicon controlled rectifier* and the *thyristor*. The structure of the controlled rectifier is n-p-n-p, the cathode is n-type material, the anode is p-type, the *gate* is the internal p-region, and the internal n-region floats. The controlled rectifier will block current flow in either circuit direction until a gate signal of the correct magnitude causes *breakdown* and consequent large current flow, limited only by the load resistance. The gate loses control after breakdown and the device can be turned OFF only by removing the anode potential.

The thyristor is a three-terminal device exhibiting thyratron-like characteristics but may be turned ON and OFF by appropriate pulses to the base or gate terminal. A single pulse will turn the load circuit ON, allowing a high current to flow until an input pulse of the opposite polarity is applied.[11]

An additional mechanism of charge flow known as *tunneling* is possible in a semiconductor diode when the impurity concentrations are extremely high. A device that uses this phenomenon is the "Esaki" or *tunnel diode*. Carriers can tunnel through the junction barrier from the p-region valence band to the n-region conduction band and vice versa because there is a small but non-zero probability that this may be done according to the theories of quantum mechanics.

The volt-ampere characteristic of such a diode in the forward quadrant clearly exhibits a region of negative resistance. A negative resistance is useful for oscillation and also amplification. (Refer to Chapter 10 and Problem 8–23.)

2–11. Allied Semiconductor Devices. A family of active and passive circuit elements is available to the circuit designer, and it is indeed likely that the size of this family will grow to great proportions. Let us briefly examine the *silicon capacitor, Zener diode, thermistor, varistor,* and *photodiode.*

At a *p-n* junction the depletion or transition region widens with reverse potential and this in effect moves the two conduction areas apart and decreases the junction capacitance just as if the junction were two metal plates separated by a dielectric with a variable thickness. A silicon device that uses this phenomenon is called the *silicon capacitor.* A typical variation is 120 to 22 $\mu\mu$f for potentials from 0.1 to 25 volts.

The reverse breakdown characteristic of a junction diode makes it useful as a voltage reference element in electronic circuits. In the Zener region a very slight change in applied voltage will cause a large change in the reverse conductivity of the diode, so the diode will tend to maintain a fairly constant potential across its terminals while its current may vary by a considerable amount. *Zener diodes* available in many ratings have proved to be extremely useful circuit elements.

The thermistor is a thermally sensitive resistance, the temperature coefficient of which is large and negative. For many years thermistors, basically semiconductors, have been used to temperature-compensate circuits. As an example of sensitivity to ambient temperature, it is possible for a 10,000-ohm unit at 0° C to be 200 ohms at 100° C and 10 ohms at 300° C.

A resistor that exhibits a nonlinear relationship between the voltage applied to it and the current that it passes is called a *varistor.* The forward V-I curve of a diode presents such a nonlinear characteristic. Commerical varistors are available in high and low voltage and current ranges.

Just as semiconductors are sensitive to heat energy so are they also light-sensitive. A *photodiode* consists of a single *p-n* junction. Light energy will create electron-hole pairs and if such a diode is biased in the reverse direction, its conductivity will be altered by the incidence of light. The junction *phototransistor* is a three-layer structure, *n-p-n* for example, with only the two outer terminals brought to external terminations. Point-contact photosensitive devices are also available.

PROBLEMS

2–1. Does Eq. (2–1) predict reverse breakdown? Explain your answer.

2–2. Sketch the forward characteristic of a diode with a reverse saturation current of 10 μa for voltages to one volt. Calculate at least three points on the forward curve. Consider the temperature to be 300° K.

2–3. Sketch a curve, similar to Fig. 2–9, that compares silicon and germanium diodes. How does the width of the forbidden gap affect diode characteristics?

2-4. Evaluate the exponent in Eq. (2–1) at normal ambient temperature (293° K).

2-5. If the reverse current of a diode is made up of two components, the flow of minority carriers and a current due to surface leakage, explain how to determine I_R for use in Eq. (2–1).

2-6. The term *mobility* is used to designate the ease of carrier drift in a solid. Mobility is the ratio of drift velocity to electric field intensity:

$$\mu = \frac{v_d}{E} \qquad \frac{\text{cm/sec}}{\text{volt/cm}}.$$

Prove that the conductivity of a specimen can be expressed as $ne\mu$, n representing the density of free electrons that are assumed to be the only carriers.

2-7. In intrinsic germanium, hole mobility (μ_p) is 1800 cm²/volt-sec and electron mobility (μ_n) is 3800 cm²/volt-sec. If the measured conductivity of a specimen is 0.01 (ohm-cm)$^{-1}$, calculate the density of electron-hole pairs. (See Problem 2–6.)

2-8. Calculate the resistivity of a silicon specimen doped with 10^{16} donors per cubic centimeter. The sample is one inch long and has a 2 mm by 2 mm cross section. Determine the resistance of the bar between contacts placed at the ends of the long dimension and also between contacts placed at opposite sides of the short dimension. Consider electron mobility to be 1200 cm²/volt-sec at 300° K.

2-9. The number of thermally generated hole-electron pairs in intrinsic germanium is given by

$$n_i = 10^{16} T^{3/2} \epsilon^{-E_g/2kT} \qquad \frac{1}{\text{cm}^3}.$$

For temperatures of 200° K, 300° K, and 400° K calculate the density of pairs. E_g is the width of the forbidden gap.

2-10. Describe the operation of an *n-p-n* transistor by drawing an energy-level diagram similar to Fig. 2–10.

2-11. Why do minority carriers exist? Does your reasoning explain the difference in I_{CO} between silicon and germanium devices?

2-12. Describe the operation of a *p-n-p* transistor operated in the common-emitter configuration.

2-13. Explain why semiconductor devices made of silicon can operate at higher ambient temperatures than can germanium devices.

2-14. Consider the common-base output characteristics that depict I_{CO} ($I_E = 0$) as well as curves for other values of I_E (see Fig. 1–8). Since I_{CO} is caused by minority carriers and the remainder of the characteristic family results from majority carrier movement explain why both cause collector current in the same direction. A diagram may clarify your explanation.

2-15. The dependence of alpha upon base thickness has been investigated, with the following theoretical conclusions:

$$f_{\alpha b} = \frac{2.6}{W^2} \text{ for germanium } p\text{-}n\text{-}p$$

$$f_{\alpha b} = \frac{5.6}{W^2} \text{ for germanium } n\text{-}p\text{-}n$$

and

$$f_{\alpha b} = \frac{1.8}{W^2} \text{ for silicon transistors,}$$

where $f_{\alpha b}$ stands for the "alpha cutoff frequency," the frequency at which α has declined to $1/\sqrt{2}$ of its low-frequency magnitude, and W is base width in inches.[21] Compare operation of the three possible transistors with base widths of $\frac{1}{2}$, 1, and 2 mils.

2-16. Describe how it may be possible to utilize the Zener breakdown characteristic of a diode to provide voltage regulation in an electrical circuit.

2-17. Draw the energy-level diagram for an $n\text{-}p\text{-}n\text{-}p$ device showing the "hook." Consult an information source such as Reference 9 for additional information.

2-18. After consulting Reference 7, briefly discuss the need for, and the methods of, encapsulating junction transistors.

REFERENCES

1. Bardeen, J., and Brattain, W. H., "The Transistor, A Semiconductor Triode," *Phys. Rev.*, vol. 74 (July, 1948).
2. Bradley, W. E., "Principles of the Surface-Barrier Transistor," *Proc.* IRE, vol. 41 (Dec., 1953).
3. DeWitt, D., and Rossoff, A. L., *Transistor Electronics*, McGraw-Hill Book Co., Inc., New York, 1957.
4. Dunlap, Jr., W. C., *An Introduction to Semiconductors*, John Wiley & Sons, Inc., New York, 1957.
5. Early, J. M., "P-N-I-P and N-P-I-N Junction Transistor Triodes," *B.S.T.J.*, vol. 33 (May, 1954).
6. Ebers, J. J., "Four-Terminal P-N-P-N Transistors," *Proc.* IRE, vol. 40 (Nov., 1952).
7. Hunter, L. P., *Handbook of Semiconductor Electronics*, McGraw-Hill Book Co., Inc., New York, 1956.
8. Lo, A. W., *et al.*, *Transistor Electronics*, Prentice-Hall, Inc., Englewood Cliffs, New Jersey, 1955.
9. Martin, Jr., T. L., *Physical Basis for Electrical Engineering*, Prentice-Hall, Inc., Englewood Cliffs, New Jersey, 1957.
10. Middlebrook, R. D., *An Introduction to Junction Transistor Theory*, John Wiley & Sons, Inc., New York, 1957.

11. Mueller, C. W., and Hilibrand, J., "The Thyristor—a New High-Speed Switching Transistor," *IRE Transactions on Electron Devices*, vol. ED-5, (Jan., 1958).
12. Shea, R. F., *Principles of Transistor Circuits*, John Wiley & Sons, Inc., New York, 1953.
13. Shockley, W., *Electrons and Holes in Semiconductors*, D. Van Nostrand Co., Inc., New York, 1950.
14. Shockley, W., "A Unipolar 'Field Effect' Transistor," *Proc.* IRE, vol. 40 (Nov., 1952).
15. Shockley, W., "The Four-Layer Diode," *Electronic Industries and Tele-Tech*, vol. 16 (August, 1957).
16. Statz, H., and Pucel, R. A., "The Spacistor, a New Class of High Frequency Semiconducting Devices," *Proc.* IRE, vol. 45 (March, 1957).
17. Statz, H., Pucel, R. A., and Lanza, C., "High-Frequency Semiconducting Spacistor Tetrodes," *Proc.* IRE, vol. 45 (Nov., 1957).
18. Transistor Issue, *Proc.* IRE, vol. 40 (Nov., 1952).
19. Transistor Issue, *Proc.* IRE, vol. 46 (June, 1958).
20. *Transistors I*, Radio Corporation of America, Princeton, New Jersey, 1956.
21. van der Ziel, A., *Solid State Physical Electronics*, Prentice-Hall, Inc., Englewood Cliffs, New Jersey, 1957.
22. Warschauer, D. M., *Semiconductors and Transistors*, McGraw-Hill Book Co., Inc., New York, 1959.

Chapter 3

THE OPERATING POINT

This chapter begins the treatment of the transistor as an important part of the practical electronic circuit. Up to this point the transistor has been considered as an isolated component; now it is necessary to incorporate it into a complete circuit to do a specified job. Our first consideration will be the practical establishment of a suitable operating point; because several different circuits may be used, a comparison of the performance of the various circuits will be made.

Establishing the proper operating point for a transistor stage and maintaining that operating point despite unit-to-unit manufacturing variations, aging, or ambient temperature variations is of prime importance in modern electronic circuit design. As a consequence direct-current bias supplies for transistor circuits have been the subject of investigation during the first decade of the transistor.[1-8]

To establish an operating point for a transistor common-emitter circuit the necessary direct potentials and currents must be provided to locate at a suitable position in the active region of the collector characteristics. After an operating point is attained, time-varying or alternating excursions of input signal (base current, for example) of limited magnitude should cause output signal (collector current) variations of similar waveshape. If the corresponding output excursions are *clipped* or in other ways do not satisfactorily duplicate the input signal, then the operating point is probably unsatisfactory and must be repositioned on the collector characteristics.

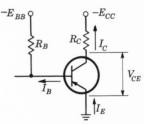

Fig. 3-1. Common-emitter amplifying stage.

Consider the circuit of Fig. 3-1. An operating point may be defined by a particular I_B and V_{CE}, or I_B and I_C, or I_C and V_{CE}, for specifying any of these quantity pairs will dictate a point on the output characteristics. Probably designation of I_B and V_{CE} is easiest to envision for it is necessary to control only the magnitude of the resistance R_B in the figure in order to determine I_B. The $I_B R_B$ product approximates the supply potential E_{BB} because the drop V_{BE} may be considered small. Collector current is directly dependent upon base current; the interrelation between these quantities was noted in Chapter 1:

$$I_C \cong \beta I_B + I_{CEO}. \tag{3-1}$$

V_{CE}, the other operating point coordinate, is dependent upon I_C and E_{CC} and R_C according to the relation

$$V_{CE} = E_{CC} - I_C R_C. \tag{3-2}$$

Now an operating point may be established by control of the elements R_B, R_C, E_{BB}, and E_{CC} as evidenced by the above discussion. The analogous situation in common-cathode vacuum-tube circuitry is the provision of direct plate-to-cathode and grid-to-cathode voltages, for these two potentials will locate a point on the tube's plate characteristics, and excursions in grid voltage about the operating or *quiescent* point will cause corresponding plate voltage (and plate current) changes.

3–1. Bias Stability. The transistor situation will now be discussed in detail. Refer to Fig. 3–2, where the operating point is noted as Q. A time-

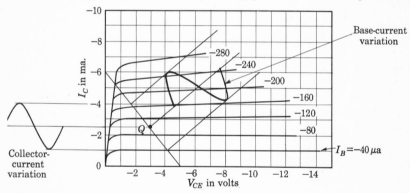

Fig. 3–2. Typical operation of the stage of Fig. 3–1. A sinusoidal base current results in a corresponding collector current of larger amplitude.

varying base current of about 120 μa peak-to-peak is causing a collector-current variation of 3 ma peak-to-peak. The collector current is a faithful reproduction of the signal and no clipping of the waveform due to the saturation or cutoff regions is evident. This is Class-A operation.

If a transistor of the same type but having different electrical characteristics (leakage, gain, or saturation) were inserted into the circuit, or if a different ambient temperature were encountered, operation as shown in Fig. 3–3 may result. Although the Q point still is at $I_B = 100$ μa, the introduction of a sinusoidal base-current signal of the same amplitude as previously considered (120 μa peak-to-peak) now results in a clipped collector-current waveform. The stage is being driven into the saturation region of the characteristics and output no longer follows input. The only difference between the two curves is that Fig. 3–3 describes a higher-gain unit. Because of the generally wide manufacturing tolerances on the parameters (β, in this in-

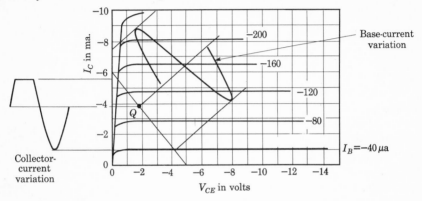

Fig. 3–3. Typical operation of the stage of Fig. 3–1 operating at the same base current as in Fig. 3–2. The transistor characteristics represent a higher gain unit.

stance), the problem discussed here is real, and must be solved by the circuit designer.

The question that naturally arises is: "How can we provide an operating point that will minimize the effects of manufacturing, aging, and temperature and thus limit distortion caused by these factors?" Study of Figs. 3–2 and 3–3 tends to show that stabilization of I_B is not the desired remedy to the operating point problem, for I_B was held constant in the above example. Note that the other operating-point coordinates did shift. If some point along the curve axes were to have been held constant, such as a particular value of I_C, then more satisfactory operation would have resulted. If, in Figs. 3–2 and 3–3, the Q point had been maintained at $I_C = 2.5$ ma instead of $I_B = 100$ μa, clipping would not have occurred. Gain will not be stabilized by this proposal, but methods for gain stabilization are available and will be treated later; our concern in this chapter is operating-point stability and suitability.

3–2. Variations. In Chapters 1 and 2 the transistor was spoken of as two back-to-back junction diodes and it was shown that the output current of the device is made up of two components, a leakage-current portion and an amplified input-signal portion. We may use these ideas to formulate an equivalent electrical circuit for a transistor, an equivalent that may be used in analyzing transistor circuits mathematically. Such an equivalent is shown in Fig. 3–4 for each of the practical configurations.

It has been noted that the emitter-base diode is always biased in the forward direction. Variations in the forward properties of that diode, while generally large, can often be adequately swamped by external circuit resistance. The collector-base diode is always biased reversely; its variations will

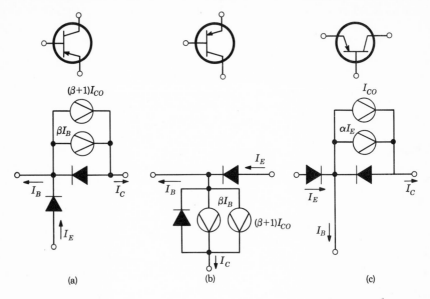

Fig. 3–4. Transistor configurations, and their simplified d-c equivalent circuits: (a) common-emitter; (b) common-collector; (c) common-base.

also be great, but because of the high value of resistance it presents, and the fact that this resistance accounts for the slope of the collector characteristics, a more-or-less second-order effect, we shall neglect it in the discussion that follows.

Let us center our attention upon the current generators of the equivalent circuits. The alpha parameter may differ by a few percent from unit to unit and therefore its tolerance would appear to be of little consequence in considering bias stability. A major contributor to instability is the $(1 - \alpha)$ term (as found in β); this term must somehow be swamped or its effects minimized. For a transistor with an α of 0.97, $1 - \alpha$ is 0.03. If α is 0.99 for a substitute transistor used in the given circuit, the $(1 - \alpha)$ term is now 0.01. Thus, with the numbers cited a 67% change occurs in $(1 - \alpha)$ while α changes by less than 2%.

Of great importance is change in I_{CO}. For germanium transistors I_{CO} generally varies according to the formula [3]

$$I_{CO} = A_0 \epsilon^{0.08(T-T_0)} \tag{3-3}$$

where A_0 is the measured value of I_{CO} at the reference temperature, T is the operating temperature of the collector junction in degrees Centigrade, and T_O is the reference temperature in degrees Centigrade, usually 25° C. The constant 0.08 represents an average determined from a large number of transistor tests. Typical of the variation to be expected in I_{CO} is that shown as

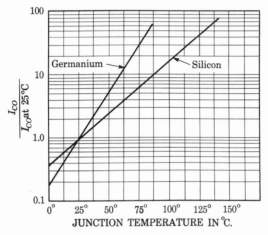

Fig. 3–5.   Typical variation of I_{CO} with temperature.

Fig. 3–5, which represents I_{CO} versus temperature for sample germanium and silicon transistors. About an 8% change per °C is to be expected in the leakage current of germanium units and about one half as much in silicon transistors. Leakage current in the common-emitter configuration varies as I_{CO}, for

$$I_{CEO} = (\beta + 1)I_{CO}. \tag{3-4}$$

Therefore magnitude change in I_{CEO} is much greater than I_{CO}.

Now in summary, the important unit-to-unit variations will be in the magnitude of the amplification factor and the magnitude of the leakage current. Consequently the zero input-current line of the characteristics will differ, as will the spacing between lines of constant input. Temperature will not have a strong effect upon α, but will greatly change leakage current. The resultant change in characteristics will be a ladder effect, with the height of the first rung (leakage) dependent upon temperature, the upper rungs moving up or down but their spacing more-or-less constant.

3–3. Circuit Studies.   The selection of an operating point depends upon a number of factors. Among these factors are the maximum signal excursions to be handled by the stage under consideration, the load on the stage, the available supply potentials, and the tolerable distortion in the signal. Gain can be optimized by appropriate choice of an operating point. Most manufacturers provide a "recommended operating point," and for low-power transistors this is usually at $I_C = 1$ ma, $V_{CE} = 5$ volts, but operation may just as well center about other points, and it is not necessary to follow the recommendation. No specific rules will be given here for selecting a point; rather by study of sample designs the reader will acquire a feeling for a choice based upon all the factors of the circuit design.

The selection of a biasing circuit can be made after study of the various schemes that have become popular. A number of these circuits are presented in the paragraphs that follow; they may be compared along the following lines:

1. Sensitivity to temperature and to manufacturing tolerances
2. Sensitivity to changes in supply voltages
3. Number of supplies required
4. Current drain on supplies
5. Number of circuit components
6. Input resistance presented to signal
7. Amount of degeneration (loss of gain)

Naturally, in any particular circuit all of the above factors will not be of equal importance, but, as we have previously seen, item number one can cause great difficulty and our major attention will be directed toward stabilizing the operating point.

Our study of the bias stability problem will commence with investigations of I_C, for we wish to make I_C independent of I_{CO} and $(1 - \alpha)$. When this is accomplished it still is possible that a-c stage gain will vary because of certain conditions, as stated in a subsequent chapter. However, a part of the overall problem will be solved if an amplifying stage can be prevented from being prematurely and unpredictably driven into saturation or cutoff.

What causes I_C to vary? In the following analysis of biasing methods one is impressed by the similarity of the equations for I_C—they all contain terms that include α, $(1 - \alpha)$, and I_{CO}. It will be seen that the effects of the $(1 - \alpha)$ terms can often be minimized. On the other hand terms involving I_{CO} are not easy to remove from the expressions for I_C. The relative merits of each of the circuits considered here can be studied.

The following assumptions are used for simplification of analysis:

1. Only the common-emitter connection will be studied.
2. The base-to-emitter voltage, V_{BE}, is negligible. In other words, the drops across the swamping resistors R_1 and R_2 are much greater than V_{BE}. If a more detailed study of behavior is required, corrections to the analyses

may be made. In almost all instances, however, V_{BE} will lie below 0.8 volt and generally below 0.2 volt for low-power transistors.

3. The collector-to-emitter voltage, V_{CE}, has negligible effect upon collector current. Thus, for the purposes of these analyses, I_C is composed of two components, $(\beta + 1)I_{CO}$ and βI_B, and depends upon collector voltage only insofar as I_B is dependent upon that voltage. The output resistance is assumed to be very large and constant. Although in reality its variations are great, the assumption nevertheless is generally valid.

4. The short-circuit current amplification factor α is constant over the practical range of possible operating points.

A circuit stability factor S has been defined and widely accepted and will be employed here.[6] It is a measure of the bias stability or circuit sensitivity primarily due to temperature. Mathematically,

$$S = \frac{\partial I_C}{\partial I_{CO}}. \tag{3-5}$$

Of course other stability factors are possible: we shall examine the change in I_C due to α, and due to supply-potential variations.

The value of the stability factor lies in its use as a measure of comparison among circuits. S as defined here cannot attain a magnitude below unity, the closer to unity the less the operating point will shift.

A transistor stage adequately biased with $S = 10$ and subjected to a temperature that changes I_{CO} by 40 μa will experience a resulting change in the operating point (I_C) of 400 μa. It is then the circuit designer's responsibility to determine if a 400 μa change is tolerable in light of expected signal magnitudes, etc.

Before considering the first of our sample circuits it is necessary to state that names have been ascribed to the various biasing circuits in order more clearly to compare their performance. These names are by no means universally used; however a system of nomenclature seems to be of value here.

3–4. Fixed Bias. Consider the practical common-emitter amplifying stage of Fig. 3–6a and its d-c equivalent circuit of Fig. 3–6b. Coupling capacitors are shown in order to isolate this stage from preceding and succeeding circuitry. The direct supply voltages for both the collector (E_{CC}) and the base (E_{BB}) are normally the same source, and therefore the circuit requires only one potential supply; a practical advantage over some alternate biasing circuits. This circuit essentially sets a constant base current, and thus extreme sensitivity to gain variations is to be expected. The resistances R_1 and R_2 improve performance by swamping variations in the input resistance of the transistor. These resistors have other important functions, which will be discussed.

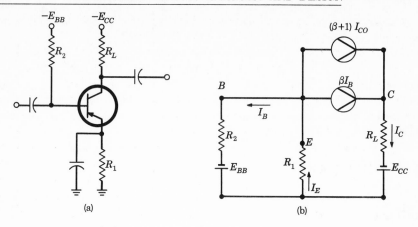

Fig. 3–6. Fixed biasing: (a) typical common-emitter amplifying stage with fixed biasing; (b) d-c equivalent circuit for (a).

Basic equations for this circuit are

$$\left.\begin{aligned} I_C &= I_E - I_B, \\ I_C &= \beta I_B + (\beta + 1)I_{CO}, \\ E_{BB} &= I_E R_1 + I_B R_2. \end{aligned}\right\} \quad (3\text{–}6)$$

These three equations may be solved for I_C:

$$I_C = \frac{\alpha E_{BB} + I_{CO}(R_1 + R_2)}{R_1 + R_2(1 - \alpha)}. \quad (3\text{–}7)$$

The effects of variations in α and I_{CO} can now be considered. To minimize effects of the $(1 - \alpha)$ term, we must set

$$R_1 \gg R_2(1 - \alpha), \quad (3\text{–}8a)$$

or

$$R_1 \geq 10R_2(1 - \alpha). \quad (3\text{–}8b)$$

The requirement posed by Eq. (3–8b) is practical only if E_{BB} is a low-voltage source separate from E_{CC}. If it is necessary to utilize E_{CC} for both supplies then Eq. (3–8b) cannot be satisfied. When employing fixed biasing we must often be content with a stage whose operating point is sensitive to changes in α and, in fact, a circuit with fixed bias is also extremely sensitive to changes in I_{CO}, as will be shown. However, this circuitry offers certain advantages; a minimum of components are needed, and input resistance is not measurably reduced by the bias scheme, for although R_2 parallels the transistor, it is generally of a sufficiently large magnitude so as not to effect the a-c input resistance of the stage. The need for only one power supply is also a necessity in certain applications.

Differentiation of Eq. (3–7) with respect to I_{CO} yields the following relation for stability factor:

$$S = \frac{\partial I_C}{\partial I_{CO}} = \frac{R_1 + R_2}{R_1 + R_2(1 - \alpha)}. \tag{3–9}$$

As has been stated, R_2 is generally of very large value, particularly if base current is obtained from E_{CC}, and consequently a fixed biased stage will often be adversely affected by any leakage current variations.

We may look at other sources of operating-point drift. Let

$$M = \frac{\partial I_C}{\partial E_{BB}}. \tag{3–10}$$

Then, for this circuit

$$M = \frac{\alpha}{R_1 + R_2(1 - \alpha)}. \tag{3–11}$$

If we define

$$N = \frac{\partial I_C}{\partial \alpha}, \tag{3–12}$$

then

$$N = \frac{(R_1 + R_2)E_{BB} + I_{CO}(R_1 + R_2)R_2}{[R_1 + R_2(1 - \alpha)]^2}. \tag{3–13}$$

The foregoing relationships are of little value unless typical magnitudes of the components and parameters are assumed. Therefore, let us consider a practical amplifying stage having the following characteristics:

$$I_C = 1 \text{ ma} \qquad I_B = 33 \text{ } \mu a \qquad R_L = 4700 \text{ ohms}$$

$$E_{BB} = E_{CC} = -8 \text{ volts} \qquad R_1 = 1000 \text{ ohms} \qquad \alpha = 0.97$$

The specified collector current was achieved with R_2 at a value of 210,000 ohms. The stability factors are therefore :

$$S = \frac{211 \text{ } K}{1 \text{ } K + (210 \text{ } K)(0.03)} = 28.9 \text{ } \mu a/\mu a,$$

and

$$M = 133 \text{ } \mu a/\text{volt}.$$

The sensitivity to alpha (N) cannot be determined from regular measurements of an operating stage because cutoff current I_{CO} appears in the expression for N; this transistor, when tested independently exhibited an I_{CO} of 10 μa. Thus

$$N = 0.04 \text{ ampere/unit} = 400 \text{ } \mu a/0.01 \text{ unit}.$$

We shall use these numbers to compare fixed biasing with other biasing schemes.

A few words are appropriately awarded to discussion of R_1. This resistor is technically unnecessary, for a fixed-bias stage will operate satisfactorily without bypassed emitter resistance. (The bypass capacitor is required to eliminate a-c degeneration in R_1, because that element is common to both the input and output loop. Generally the capacitor is chosen so that its reactance is less than 0.1 of R_1 at the lowest frequency the amplifier is called upon to handle.) It is obvious from Eq. (3–7) that R_1 helps to swamp the $(1 - \alpha)$ term and thus N is decreased, as well as S. With $R_1 = 0$ in the sample circuit, R_2 must increase in value to 237,000 ohms and the stability factors become

$$S = 33 \ \mu a/\mu a;$$

$$M = 136 \ \mu a/volt;$$

$$N = 487 \ \mu a/0.01 \ unit.$$

It might appear that if R_1 could be made extremely large, all problems would be solved. R_1, however, is an important factor in the d-c load line for the stage and will help determine signal-handling capabilities. The values of R_1 and R_L therefore are subject to a-c considerations and compromise; further discussion will be reserved for later in the chapter.

In summary, fixed biasing provides a simple and inexpensive means for establishing an operating point. The stability of the operating point is extremely poor when compared with that of other circuits. Bypassed emitter resistance improves the stability of the selected point.

3–5. Single-Battery Bias. If a resistor is added between the base terminal and ground in the common-emitter amplifying stage shown in Fig. 3–6a, the practical circuit and its d-c equivalent take on the forms shown in Fig. 3–7. The power supply to the base and the collector will almost always be common

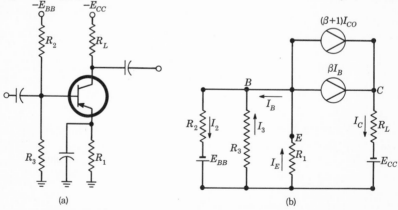

Fig. 3–7. Single-battery biasing; (a) typical common-emitter amplifying stage with single-battery biasing; (b) d-c equivalent circuit for (a).

in practical applications of this circuit. The resistor R_1 is again used to stabilize the stage.

Loop and nodal equations are:

$$\left.\begin{array}{r}
I_C = I_E - I_B, \\
I_C = \beta I_B + (\beta + 1)I_{CO}, \\
I_B = I_2 - I_3, \\
E_{BB} = I_3 R_3 + I_2 R_2, \\
0 = I_3 R_3 - I_E R_1.
\end{array}\right\} \qquad (3\text{--}14)$$

Solution of Eqs. (3–14) for I_C yields

$$I_C = \frac{\alpha R_3 E_{BB} + I_{CO}[R_1(R_2 + R_3) + R_2 R_3]}{R_1(R_2 + R_3) + (1 - \alpha)R_2 R_3}. \qquad (3\text{--}15)$$

To stabilize this current against changes in $(1 - \alpha)$ assume that $R_2 \gg R_3$, which is sometimes the case. Then if

$$R_1 R_2 \gg (1 - \alpha)R_2 R_3, \qquad (3\text{--}16a)$$

the requirement for insensitivity to $(1 - \alpha)$ becomes

$$R_1 \geq 10 R_3 (1 - \alpha). \qquad (3\text{--}16b)$$

This requirement can be achieved practically in some circuits.

Magnitude changes in I_{CO} again definitely affect collector current. A comparison can be made between so-called single-battery bias and fixed bias by considering the change in I_C due to variation in I_{CO}. For single-battery bias, from Eq. (3–15),

$$S = \frac{R_1(R_2 + R_3) + R_2 R_3}{R_1(R_2 + R_3) + (1 - \alpha)R_2 R_3}. \qquad (3\text{--}17a)$$

If we again consider R_3 small compared to R_2, then Eq. (3–17a) becomes

$$S = \frac{R_1 + R_3}{R_1 + R_3(1 - \alpha)} \quad \text{(for } R_2 \gg R_3\text{)}. \qquad (3\text{--}17b)$$

The assumption used here, that $R_2 \gg R_3$, is not necessarily true for all circuits. Generally R_2 is three to ten times greater; however extreme accuracy is seldom warranted in transistor circuit calculations because of the large parameter tolerances. This assumption, in the example that follows, where the resistance ratio is about four, accounts for a 15% error in S; for higher ratios the error would be considerably less.

The sample stage considered in the preceding section was also biased by the method of this section. The desired operation point was achieved with values of R_2 of 47,000 ohms and R_3 of 11,200 ohms, although an infinite number of combinations of these resistances is possible because the two can be thought of as a voltage divider. Using the approximate formula, Eq. (3–17b),

$$S = \frac{1\,K + 11.2\,K}{1\,K + (11.2\,K)(0.03)} = 9.1\ \mu a/\mu a$$

Thus in this circuit, single-battery biasing is approximately three times as stable with respect to I_{CO} as is fixed biasing. This represents a significant improvement, at the cost of just one resistive element.

$$M = \frac{\alpha R_3}{R_1(R_2 + R_3) + (1 - \alpha)R_2R_3} \tag{3–18}$$

$$= \frac{(0.97)(11.2\,K)}{(1\,K)(58.2\,K) + (0.03)(47\,K)(11.2\,K)} = 147\ \mu a/\text{volt}$$

and

$$N = \frac{(R_3E_{BB} + I_{CO}R_2R_3)(R_1R_2 + R_1R_3 + R_2R_3)}{[R_1(R_2 + R_3) + (1 - \alpha)R_2R_3]^2} \tag{3–19}$$

$$= 100\ \mu a/0.01\ \text{unit.}$$

A substantial improvement in operation is possible when single-battery bias rather than fixed bias is employed in a given circuit. This improvement is not always necessary, for the magnitude of S or M or N originally calculated for fixed biasing may be satisfactory for a particular application, and improvement in the magnitude of the factors may be of academic value only.

In summarizing the case for single-battery bias, we may say that operating point stability is considerably improved over that of fixed bias at the expense of one additional resistor. Only one d-c supply is required and bypassed emitter resistance is again recommended.

3–6. Emitter Bias. If the base of the common-emitter configuration is grounded, or returned to ground through a resistor of moderate size, and the emitter is connected to a separate potential supply as shown in Fig. 3–8, with the equivalent circuit for emitter bias, a most stable operating point can be achieved. R_1 and R_2 again help to swamp variations in the input diode. The basic equations for emitter bias are:

$$\left. \begin{aligned} I_C &= I_E - I_B, \\ I_C &= \beta I_B + (\beta + 1)I_{CO}, \\ E_{EE} &= I_ER_1 + I_BR_2. \end{aligned} \right\} \tag{3–20}$$

Solving for I_C:

$$I_C = \frac{\alpha E_{EE} + I_{CO}(R_1 + R_2)}{R_1 + R_2(1 - \alpha)}. \tag{3–21}$$

For stability with respect to α variations,

$$R_1 \geq 10R_2(1 - \alpha) \tag{3–22}$$

is the requirement.   This can be achieved if low-stage input impedance is not too undesirable.

The stability equations are identical with those for fixed bias except that E_{EE} appears, rather than E_{BB}.   Although the equations are similar, numerical values of the components will differ.

In the emitter-biased circuit, emitter current is being set, rather than base current.   Potential at the base will be close to ground, differing only by the

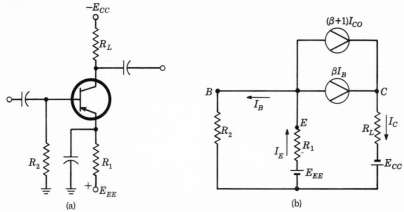

(a)   (b)

Fig. 3–8.   Emitter biasing: (a) typical common-emitter amplifying stage with emitter biasing; (b) d-c equivalent circuit for (a).

small drop $I_B R_2$.   Potential at the emitter terminal (V_E) is essentially that at the base ($V_{BE} < 0.5$ volt) so

$$I_E = \frac{E_{EE} - V_E}{R_1}, \tag{3–23a}$$

$$\cong \frac{E_{EE}}{R_1} \quad \text{(for R_2 small).} \tag{3–23b}$$

In this connection then, R_1 dictates the desired emitter (or collector) current, and R_2 serves just as a return for base current. R_2 could, for biasing pur-poses, be a short circuit, but no a-c amplification would then result.

To compare emitter biasing with the previously discussed methods, we shall assume that an 8-volt supply is used for E_{EE} and I_C is again required to be 1 ma.   If $R_2 = 10,000$ ohms, $R_1 = 8000$ ohms according to Eq. (3–23b), and

$$S = \frac{R_1 + R_2}{R_1 + R_2(1 - \alpha)} \tag{3–24}$$

$$= \frac{8\,K + 10\,K}{8\,K + (10\,K)(0.03)} = 2.17 \ \mu\text{a}/\mu\text{a}.$$

This compares very favorably with the typical numbers obtained for fixed biasing and single-battery biasing. Sensitivity to supply-voltage variations is about the same as that provided by the other schemes, but α variations have practically no effect upon the emitter-biased stage.

Suppose that transformer coupling is used between the preceding circuitry and the stage under consideration. The secondary of the transformer in Fig.

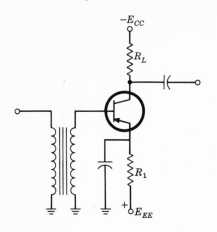

3–9 places the base terminal close to d-c ground, assuming negligible d-c resistance of the winding, and the equation for the operating point for this arrangement becomes:

$$I_C = \frac{\alpha E_{EE} + I_{CO}R_1}{R_1}. \quad (3\text{--}25)$$

Now α will give no difficulty because of the assumption that $R_2 = 0$, and S is given by

$$S = \frac{R_1{}^2}{R_1{}^2} = 1, \quad (3\text{--}26)$$

Fig. 3–9. Typical common-emitter amplifying stage with emitter biasing.

which indicates that the ultimate in operating-point stability can be achieved.

General conclusions to the discussion of emitter biasing—although the need for two d-c supplies of opposite polarity is often a definite disadvantage, a high degree of operating-point stability is guaranteed.

3–7. Self Bias. Self bias gets its name from the fact that the collector terminal is connected through an external resistor to the base terminal. This connection is shown in Fig. 3–10 with the approximate d-c equivalent. Because a lower voltage is available at the collector than with fixed biasing directly connected to E_{CC}, the value of R_2 will necessarily be smaller.

Because of the constant no-signal collector potential, an operating point is established at a particular base current. Should the collector static characteristics change for any reason, the base current will change somewhat because V_C, which can be said to be driving I_B, changes when the characteristics change. Thus with this circuit a constant I_B is not being set, because I_B will shift with output-circuit variations. The compensating effects of self bias are desirable, but from an a-c standpoint some gain will be lost in the feedback connection (R_2). Self biasing can take on several forms: the circuit may be as shown in Fig. 3–10; the base may be returned to ground through an additional resistor; or R_2 on occasion has been split into two components, with a capacitor to ground from the junction. The equations describing this

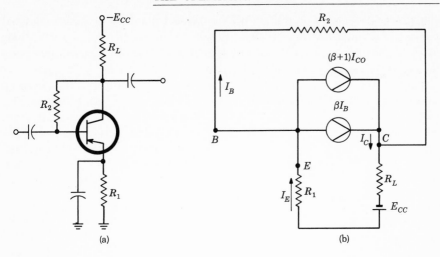

Fig. 3–10. Self biasing: (a) typical common-emitter amplifying stage with self bias; (b) d-c equivalent circuit for (a).

circuit are:

$$I_C = I_E - I_B,$$
$$I_C \cong \beta I_B + (\beta + 1)I_{CO},$$
$$E_{CC} = I_E R_1 + I_B R_2 + I_E R_L. \qquad \qquad \text{(3–27)}$$

The equation for I_C is

$$I_C = \frac{\alpha E_{CC} + I_{CO}(R_2 + R_1 + R_L)}{R_1 + R_L + (1 - \alpha)R_2}, \qquad (3\text{–}28)$$

which bears some similarity to Eq. (3–7) for fixed bias. For a stable design

$$(R_1 + R_L) \gg (1 - \alpha)R_2. \qquad (3\text{–}29\text{a})$$

This leads to the conclusion that if

$$(R_1 + R_L) \geq 10(1 - \alpha)R_2, \qquad (3\text{–}29\text{b})$$

the circuit will not be sensitive to the α parameter. It is possible to approximate this condition in some circuits.

Since R_2 is smaller here than in some other biasing circuits, this circuit is relatively less sensitive to I_{CO}. Emitter biasing, however, still results in a more stable operating point.

Conclusions to the discussion of self-bias operation are that only one supply voltage is necessary and that connecting the base resistor to the collector terminal rather than directly to a supply results in a more stable operating point. A-c operation, however, dictates the feasibility of this method.

3–8. Cutoff Bias. In the low-signal-level stages of some transistor circuits it may be advantageous to maintain as high an input impedance as possible, or to achieve a most economical design. By providing no path for quiescent base current we can still achieve Class-A operation if so desired. The diagram of Fig. 3–11 shows a cutoff-bias circuit and its d-c equivalent. The expression

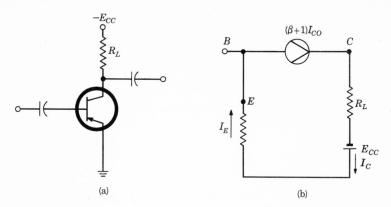

(a) (b)

Fig. 3–11. Cutoff biasing: (a) typical common-emitter amplifying stage with cutoff bias; (b) d-c equivalent circuit for (a).

for collector current may be written directly as

$$I_C = (\beta + 1)I_{CO} = \frac{I_{CO}}{1 - \alpha} = I_{CEO}. \tag{3–30}$$

Thus here we have a highly sensitive operating point, for collector current *is* I_{CEO}. As we noted in Chapter 1, it is possible to swing to I_{CO} as a lower limit on collector current, but distortion is prevalent in this low-current region. Nevertheless, consider a stage with $I_{CO} = 10\ \mu a$ and $\beta = 39$. Then the output current capability of such a stage is $I_{CEO} - I_{CO}$ or 390 μa peak. The allowable input signal would be 390/39 or 10 μa peak. These allowable swings are subject to temperature and α.

Cutoff bias has been successfully used for the input stage of multistage transistor amplifiers where the signal to be amplified is small.

3–9. Other Means of Setting the Operating Point. Many biasing circuits not included in this discussion have been used in various applications. Several are apparent in circuits considered in later chapters, and each may be studied on its own merits. It is felt, however, that the circuits previously described in this chapter are useful in the vast majority of applications, that their relative merits have been adequately explored, and that as new circuits are considered they can serve as a basis of comparison. The rather special biasing requirements for d-c amplifiers and power amplifiers will be treated in the text under those titles.

Common-base and common-collector circuits have not been discussed in this chapter. The use of these configurations is limited, and it is possible for the reader having experience with common-emitter circuits to bias these configurations fairly easily. Problems at the end of the chapter are intended to investigate these configurations further.

A newcomer to the transistor field may wonder why the cathode-biasing technique employed in vacuum-tube circuitry is not applicable to transistor

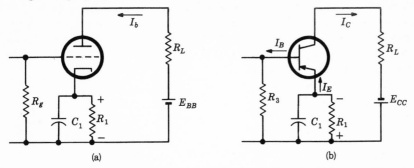

Fig. 3–12. (a) Cathode biasing for vacuum tube; (b) similar circuit for transistor stage.

circuits. Cathode bias for a tube is illustrated in Fig. 3–12a. Plate current flowing through resistor R_1 causes a potential drop across R_1 of the indicated polarity. Since negligible current is in R_g, the resulting grid-to-cathode bias is simply $I_b R_1$. Capacitor C_1 is chosen to have a small reactance compared with the resistance of R_1 at the lowest operating frequency.

A similar transistor circuit is that of Fig. 3–12b. If an emitter current is assumed, then the $I_E R_1$ drop would be of the polarity shown. This would tend to reverse-bias the emitter-base diode rather than provide the forward bias required for normal Class-A operation.

3–10. Drawing the Load Line. Refer again to Figs. 3–2 and 3–3, the common-emitter collector characteristics. The straight line passing through the Q point is known as a *d-c load line*. The procedure for establishing such a line for transistor-circuit analysis is almost identical to the methods normally employed with vacuum tubes. In a very general form we have seen that, for a simple stage such as is shown in Fig. 3–6,

$$I_C = f(I_B, V_{CE}). \tag{3–31}$$

The equation describing the collector circuit is

$$E_{CC} = I_C R_L + V_{CE} + I_E R_1. \tag{3–32a}$$

Since I_C and I_E are approximately equal, Eq. (3–32a) can be written as

$$E_{CC} \cong I_C(R_1 + R_L) + V_{CE}. \tag{3–32b}$$

Solution for I_C yields:

$$I_C \cong \frac{E_{CC}}{R_1 + R_L} - \frac{V_{CE}}{R_1 + R_L}. \qquad (3\text{-}33)$$

Equation (3–31) represents the collector characteristics of the transistor, and Eq. (3–33) describes a straight line with a slope of $-1/(R_1 + R_L)$ and abscissa intercept of E_{CC}. When Eq. (3–33) is superimposed upon the collector characteristics it is called the d-c load line. The operating point, or Q point, must lie on this line and also on the I_B (or I_C) line determined by biasing circuitry. As is apparent in Eq. (3–33), for all circuits using bypassed or unbypassed emitter resistors, the value of that resistance must be added to R_L to establish the load-line slope and I_C intercept.

When emitter biasing is used as in the circuit in Fig. 3–8, the collector circuit equation is:

$$E_{CC} + E_{EE} = I_C R_L + V_{CE} + I_E R_1. \qquad (3\text{-}34)$$

If, again, the approximation is made that I_C and I_E are equal, then

$$E_{CC} + E_{EE} \cong I_C(R_1 + R_L) + V_{CE}. \qquad (3\text{-}35a)$$

Thus

$$I_C \cong \frac{E_{CC} + E_{EE}}{R_1 + R_L} - \frac{V_{CE}}{R_1 + R_L}. \qquad (3\text{-}35b)$$

Equation (3–35b) describes a straight line with a slope of $-1/(R_1 + R_L)$, but now originating at an abscissa value of $E_{CC} + E_{EE}$. As could have been reasoned, collector and emitter voltage sources can be added algebraically to result in the originating point for the d-c load line.

The general rules for drawing the d-c load line for a common-emitter amplifier stage can be summarized as follows:

1. Sum all resistance in the emitter-collector circuit. The negative reciprocal of this total will be the slope of the line.

2. Sum all potential sources in the emitter-collector circuit. This will locate a point on the V_{CE} axis of the transistor collector characteristics curve.

3. Draw a straight line through the point determined in 2 with the slope determined in 1.

Example. A common-emitter stage works into a resistive load of 5000 ohms and has a bypassed emitter resistor of 1000 ohms. The collector supply potential is 12 volts. Draw the d-c load line and locate an operating point at $I_C = 1$ ma.

Summing resistance in the emitter-collector circuit results in 6000 ohms. The load line will have a V_{CE} intercept at $E_{CC} = 12$ volts and an I_C intercept at $E_{CC}/(R_L + R_1)$ or 2 ma. The line and Q are located as in Fig. 3–13.

In the foregoing sections investigations were made of the dependence of collector current upon the various circuit elements and parameters as well as temperature. But an operating point is defined by two quantities on the output characteristics, such as I_C and V_{CE}. Since the operating point must

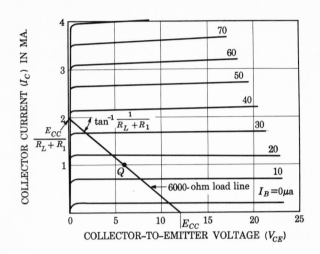

Fig. 3–13. D-c load line on collector characteristics for the example cited in the text.

lie on the load line, any change in I_C will result in a V_{CE} change; the load line or its equation may be used to locate this new V_{CE}.

3–11. Design of Biasing Circuitry. Design of the biasing circuitry for transistor amplifiers is not as straightforward as might be desired. It has been shown that the operating point will vary from the desired point because of parameter differences from one transistor to the next. When some of the more temperature-sensitive biasing circuitry is used, these parameter differences make the task of predicting biasing resistors difficult, if not impossible.

As an example of this difficulty, let us examine Eq. (3–7). If I_{CO} is assumed to be negligible, then

$$I_C \cong \frac{\alpha E_{BB}}{R_1 + R_2(1 - \alpha)}. \tag{3–36a}$$

$E_{BB} = 10$ volts, $R_1 = 1000$ ohms, $\alpha = 0.99$, and it is required to find the value of R_2 that will result in $I_C = 1$ ma.

$$R_2 = \frac{\alpha E_{BB} - I_C R_1}{I_C(1 - \alpha)} = 890,000 \text{ ohms.} \tag{3–36b}$$

If a value of 0.98 were used for α, which is still within the manufacturer's tolerance,

$$R_2 = 440,000 \text{ ohms.}$$

A one percent change in α resulted in a fifty percent change in the predicted value of R_2.

Probably a more accurate approach to the problem of predicting R_2 for a fixed-bias stage is to write the equation for the base-emitter loop. Then

$$E_{BB} = I_B R_2 + V_{BE} + I_E R_1. \tag{3-37a}$$

Now I_B can be determined from the collector characteristics at the Q point or from

$$I_B \cong \frac{I_C}{\beta}.$$

Since $I_E \cong I_C$, we may write

$$R_2 = \frac{\alpha(E_{BB} - V_{BE} - I_C R_1)}{I_C(1 - \alpha)}. \tag{3-37b}$$

Using the numbers previously employed, for $\alpha = 0.99$ and $V_{BE} = 0.2$ volts,

$$R_2 = 871,000 \text{ ohms;}$$

and for $\alpha = 0.98$,

$$R_2 = 431,000 \text{ ohms,}$$

which indicates that the spread in predicted values of R_2 is still intolerable even when V_{BE} is considered.

But suppose with the help of mathematics we investigate Eq. (3-36a) to see how much difficulty will be caused by a wrong value of R_2.

$$\frac{\partial I_C}{\partial R_2} = \frac{-\alpha E_{BB}(1 - \alpha)}{[R_1 + R_2(1 - \alpha)]^2}. \tag{3-38}$$

If the same numbers are again used, and R_2 has a nominal value of 890 K,

$$\frac{\partial I_C}{\partial R_2} = \frac{-(0.99)(10)(0.01)}{[1\,K + 890\,K(0.01)]^2} = -0.001 \ \mu\text{a/ohm}$$

A 100,000-ohm error in R_2 will account for a shift in I_C of about 100 μa, a significant change.

Thus it may be concluded that there is some folly in employing design equations for some types of biasing. Of course equations are perfectly good provided that the circuit parameters are accurately known, but if a spread is to be expected then a spread in required circuit resistance values will also be apparent. Nevertheless the reader will wish to be able to predict component sizes and as a first approximation any of the equations for collector current given in the chapter will be useful in the quest for the correct resistance values.

For the single-battery circuit, since two base circuit resistances are used, a certain amount of freedom of choice of R_3 is allowed. Consequently, in the material that follows, R_3 is usually chosen to be several times larger than the input resistance of the stage. For low-power stages, R_2 will generally be several times larger than R_3. Required values for resistors in circuits where mathematical prediction is inaccurate usually are determined by the building of sample stages with adjustable resistances and varying values until satisfactory operation is achieved. When emitter biasing is used, because of the insensitivity of that circuit to α, a very accurate prediction of the circuit resistances is possible.

When circuitry for establishing the operating point of a transistor amplifier is being designed the effects upon a-c operation should be carefully considered. The values chosen for R_2 and R_3 will affect the input impedance of the stage under consideration. Likewise, R_L, the d-c load resistor (also called the collector-return resistor), is an integral part of the a-c load of the stage. Choice of each of these must be weighed in light of a-c requirements.

3–12. Summary. Setting an operating point for a transistor stage is highly dependent upon the a-c requirements for that stage, but a compromise is almost always necessary when capacitive coupling is used, because the desired degree of freedom of choice for circuit elements is not often realized.

Maintaining a particular operating point, once it is set, is a problem dependent in part upon the circuit chosen. Since a number of circuits have been considered and the differences among them discussed, and a large number of equations formulated, the important equations have been tabulated in Table 3–1.

For direct-coupled multistage amplifiers, where no blocking capacitors are used to isolate the direct currents of each stage, the variation of collector current with temperature, supply voltage, and amplification factor may become quite severe, for variations in early stages are amplified by succeeding units. A great deal of stability is necessary in such circuits, and compensating networks are often employed. Compensating networks may be designed for the individual isolated circuits discussed here, although their use is not common when capacitive or transformer coupling is allowed. Direct-coupled amplifiers are treated in Chapter 8.

The discussion of the d-c portion of the transistor stage is now concluded and in the ensuing chapter a-c operation will be of primary concern. However, whenever a complete stage is to be analyzed or designed it is apparent that the interrelations between a-c operation and quiescent conditions must be known. We shall see that the operating point is an important part of each circuit to be studied.

TABLE 3–1. SUMMARY OF BIASING EQUATIONS

	Fixed Bias	Single Battery Bias	Emitter Bias	Self Bias
I_C	$\dfrac{\alpha E_{BB} + I_{CO}(R_1 + R_2)}{R_1 + R_2(1-\alpha)}$	$\dfrac{\alpha R_3 E_{BB} + I_{CO}[R_1(R_2 + R_3) + R_2 R_3]}{R_1(R_2 + R_3) + (1-\alpha)R_2 R_3}$	$\dfrac{\alpha E_{EE} + I_{CO}(R_1 + R_2)}{R_1 + R_2(1-\alpha)}$	$\dfrac{\alpha E_{CC} + I_{CO}(R_2 + R_1 + R_L)}{R_1 + R_L + (1-\alpha)R_2}$
$S = \dfrac{\partial I_C}{\partial I_{CO}}$	$\dfrac{R_1 + R_2}{R_1 + R_2(1-\alpha)}$	$\dfrac{R_1(R_2 + R_3) + R_2 R_3}{R_1(R_2 + R_3) + (1-\alpha)R_2 R_3}$	$\dfrac{R_1 + R_2}{R_1 + R_2(1-\alpha)}$	$\dfrac{R_2 + R_1 + R_L}{R_1 + R_L + (1-\alpha)R_2}$
$M = \dfrac{\partial I_C}{\partial E}$	$\dfrac{\alpha}{R_1 + R_2(1-\alpha)}$	$\dfrac{\alpha R_3}{R_1(R_2 + R_3) + (1-\alpha)R_2 R_3}$	$\dfrac{\alpha}{R_1 + R_2(1-\alpha)}$	$\dfrac{\alpha}{R_1 + R_L + (1-\alpha)R_2}$
$N = \dfrac{\partial I_C}{\partial \alpha}$	$\dfrac{\left\{(R_1 + R_2)E_{BB} + I_{CO}(R_1 + R_2)R_2\right\}}{[R_1 + R_2(1-\alpha)]^2}$	$\dfrac{\left\{\begin{array}{l}(R_3 E_{BB} + I_{CO}R_2 R_3) \\ \times (R_1 R_2 + R_1 R_3 + R_2 R_3)\end{array}\right\}}{[R_1(R_2 + R_3) + (1-\alpha)R_2 R_3]^2}$	$\dfrac{\left\{\begin{array}{l}(R_1 + R_2)E_{EE} \\ + I_{CO}(R_1 + R_2)R_2\end{array}\right\}}{[R_1 + R_2(1-\alpha)]^2}$	$\dfrac{\left\{\begin{array}{l}(R_1 + R_L + R_2)E_{CC} \\ + I_{CO}(R_2 + R_1 + R_L)R_2\end{array}\right\}}{[R_1 + R_L + (1-\alpha)R_2]^2}$

PROBLEMS

3-1. A transistor has a leakage current I_{CO} of 10 μa at 25° C. Use Eq. (3-3) to calculate the temperature rise necessary for I_{CO} to double its 25° C value. Will this same temperature rise pertain to a doubling of I_{CEO}?

3-2. Confirm Eq. (3-7) for fixed bias.

3-3. Confirm Eq. (3-15) for single-battery bias.

3-4. Confirm Eq. (3-21) for emitter bias.

3-5. Discuss each biasing scheme of this chapter from the standpoint of input resistance to alternating signals.

3-6. A certain fixed-bias stage with $R_2 = 110,000$ ohms and $\beta = 50$ is operating from a 10-volt supply and must exhibit a stability factor (S) of 10. Calculate the R_1 required. Is this a reasonable answer?

3-7. Sketch several other biasing schemes for common-emitter stages. Reference 3 may help.

3-8. Study and discuss the d-c supply power drain of each of the bias arrangements of this chapter.

3-9. Include V_{BE} in the equation for I_C for fixed biasing.

3-10. Calculations with laboratory confirmation indicate that, in a particular fixed-bias stage using silicon transistors, $R_1 = 1000$ ohms, $R_2 = 100,000$ ohms, $\alpha = 0.98$ and $I_{CO} = 0.1$ μa when the collector current is 3.27 ma. For a production run, resistors with ±20% tolerance are to be used. Calculate the operating point (I_C) shift if each resistor is at the upper end of its allowable range, and also at its lowest possible value.

3-11. To set an operating point for a single-battery biased common-emitter stage at 1 ma, the following data were taken of usable combinations of R_2 and R_3. The circuit feeds a 3600-ohm load and R_1 is 1000 ohms. The transistor has a β of 80 and I_{CO} of 7 μa. $E_{BB} = E_{CC} = 12.4$ volts.

R_2	R_3
200 K	115 K
150 K	60 K
110 K	35 K
40 K	10 K
21 K	5 K

Compare the various resistance pairs to determine which pair will result in a stage that shows a minimum of sensitivity to I_{CO} variations.

3-12. Using the same circuit as in the preceding problem, but with a $\beta = 22$ transistor, determine if a higher stability is achieved because required resistance values are lower. $R_2 = 18 K$ when $R_3 = 5 K$, and $R_2 = 32 K$ when $R_3 = 10 K$, for example.

3-13. Draw d-c load lines of 1000, 2000 and 5000 ohms on a sketch of the 2N344 collector characteristics (Appendix I), starting from $V_{CE} = -3$

volts. Locate operating points at $I_B = -50$ μa for each line. What angle, in degrees, does each load line make with the horizontal?

3–14. A vertical load line and a horizontal load line indicate what kind of loads?

3–15. Design an emitter-biased circuit in which the collector current does not change more than 0.5 ma for an increase of 200 μa in I_{CO}. The available supplies are $+15$ and -15 volts and the operating point must be at -10 volts and 1.5 ma. I_{CO} is initially negligible, $\alpha = 0.98$ and is substantially constant.

(a) What values should R_1 and R_2 be? What potential exists from base to emitter? The transistor is germanium.

(b) If α changed to 0.96 because of the same temperature variation that changed I_{CO}, would the values calculated in (a) be correct in order to limit the change in I_C to 0.5 ma? If not what can be done to the original design?

3–16. Derive the expression for I_C for a stage biased as shown in the accompanying figure.

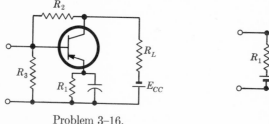
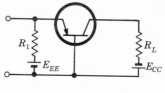

Problem 3–16.   Problem 3–17.

3–17. Consider the common-base circuit of the figure above. We desire $I_E = 1$ ma and $V_{CB} = 5$ volts. The load is 5000 ohms.

(a) Calculate the necessary values of E_{CC} and E_{EE} if R_1 is 1000 ohms.

(b) Derive an expression for I_C in terms of the circuit parameters.

(c) Derive an expression for $\partial I_C / \partial I_{CO}$.

(d) From your answer to (c), how can you achieve high stability in this circuit?

(e) What effects would a bypassed base resistance have upon the operation of this circuit?

(f) How would it be possible to operate a common-base circuit from one supply? Think.

(g) Discuss the circuit from the standpoint of a-c power lost in R_1 if the a-c input resistance of the transistor is 50 ohms.

3–18. For the common-collector circuit of Fig. A, $I_E = 1$ ma, $I_B = 100$ μa, $V_{EC} = 10$ volts and the load is 1000 ohms.

(a) Find R_2 if $E_{BB} = E_{EE}/2$.

(b) Derive an expression for I_E in terms of the circuit parameters.

(c) Derive an expression $\partial I_E / \partial I_{CO}$.

(d) From your answer to (c), how can high stability be achieved with this circuit?

(e) What effects would a bypassed collector resistance have upon this circuit?

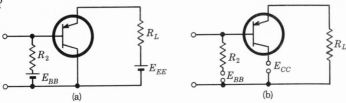

Problem 3-18.

(f) What polarities can E_{BB} and E_{CC} have in the common-collector stage of Fig. B above?

(g) How can the common-collector stage be operated from one supply?

(h) How will R_2 affect the a-c input resistance of the entire stage?

3-19. Derive an equation for θ, the angle between the d-c load line and the horizontal, as a function of R, and the scale factors of the plot.

3-20. The various biasing circuits (except self-bias) may be analytically treated by considering the transistor's base supply from a Thèvenin equivalent viewpoint. The generalized diagram of the accompanying figure can then be used for analysis of the different biasing techniques by altering or deleting elements in the figure. For example, for fixed bias from a single supply, $E_2 = 0$, $R_b = R_2$ and $E_1 = E_{CC}$.

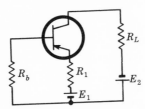

Problem 3-20.

(a) Derive an expression for I_C for the generalized biasing circuit.

(b) For fixed bias, single-battery bias, emitter bias and cutoff bias make a listing of the values of E_1, E_2 and R_b in terms of E_{CC}, E_{EE}, R_2 and R_3.

(c) Confirm Eqs. (3–7), (3–15), (3–21), and (3–30). Consider that $E_{BB} = E_{CC} = E_{EE}$.

REFERENCES

1. DeWitt, D., and Rossoff, A. L., *Transistor Electronics*, McGraw-Hill Book Co., Inc., New York, 1957.

2. Lo, A. W., *et al.*, *Transistor Electronics*, Prentice-Hall, Inc., Englewood Cliffs, New Jersey, 1955.
3. Hunter, L. P., *Handbook of Semiconductor Electronics*, McGraw-Hill Book Co., Inc., New York, 1956.
4. Riddle, R. L., and Ristenbatt, M. P., *Transistor Physics and Circuits*, Prentice-Hall, Inc., Englewood Cliffs, New Jersey, 1958.
5. Murray, R. P., "Design of Transistor RC Amplifiers," *IRE Trans.*, vol. AV-6, no. 3 (May–June, 1958).
6. Shea, R. F., "Transistor Operation: Stabilization of Operating Points," *Proc.* IRE, vol. 40 (Nov., 1952).
7. Shea, R. F., *Principles of Transistor Circuits*, John Wiley & Sons, Inc., New York, 1953.
8. Shea, R. F., *Transistor Circuit Engineering*, John Wiley & Sons, Inc., New York, 1957.

Chapter 4

EQUIVALENT CIRCUITS AND THEIR PARAMETERS

In order to predict the performance of a transistor circuit, the impedance levels it presents to a signal source and load and the signal amplification it provides may be determined either graphically or analytically if the appropriate information is available to the circuit designer. Graphical techniques are generally employed for analyzing high-signal-level stages and for checking the suitability of the operating point. The normal procedure for analyzing stages that are required to handle signals of small amplitude exclusively is to calculate performance using mathematical equations involving the small-signal parameters supplied by the manufacturer or determined by test.

General network theory is concerned with but five circuit elements: resistance, inductance, capacitance, and voltage and current sources. When a passive device, a transformer, for instance, is incorporated into an electrical circuit, its symbol is replaced by an equivalent circuit comprised of R, L, and C. The symbol for an active circuit element, a transistor or tube for example, can be replaced by the appropriate combination of R, L, C, and sources. To derive equations for circuit performance—gains and impedance levels—a drawing is made of the electrical equivalent for the entire network, and Kirchhoff's Laws, Ohm's Law, and the numerous network simplification procedures are utilized to obtain the required mathematical formulas. Substitution of the values of the known parameters and other circuit elements into such equations yields the required numerical results.

This chapter is devoted to the study of low-frequency equivalent circuits, where transistor capacitances and inductances do not materially affect operation and will therefore cover the major portion of the audio-frequency range, and encompass the entire field of control amplification. Discussion of the parameters of these circuits and studies of the practical configurations are to follow.

4-1. Equivalent Circuits. A very large number of different equivalent circuits for the transistor have been evolved to date, and as transistors enter higher frequency regions of operation, or are manufactured by different processes, new equivalents are born. Exactness in representation is somewhat responsible for the many equivalents, for an equivalent circuit for any device is subject to many refinements.

The d-c conditions in a transistor circuit were calculated in Chapter 3. Here we are concerned with a-c steady-state analysis and shall derive equations for the low-frequency current gain, voltage gain, power gain, and input and output resistance of single-stage amplifiers. Extension of these concepts to multistage amplifiers, with and without feedback, and to other communications circuits is reserved for the later chapters.

An equivalent circuit for the transistor (or any other device) will remain the same regardless of the circuit configuration in which it is employed, i.e. common-base, common-emitter, or common-collector. Once a particular equivalent circuit has been accepted from a technical standpoint, it will not vary. But conditions external to the transistor will differ because circuit applications differ. The equivalent circuit of a transistor derived for the common-base configuration can be used when employing the transistor in some other configuration just by connecting the three terminals of the transistor equivalent circuit to the proper places in the network.

It is sometimes more convenient to utilize alternate nomenclature when considering the various configurations. Thus β, the current-amplification factor relating excursions in collector current to those of base current, is most likely to be employed in discussing the common-emitter configuration (and also common-collector), while α, the ratio of variations in collector current to those of emitter current, is most often used in working with common-base stages. With the normal tools of circuit theory, it is possible to arrive at several different representations because of the interrelations among parameters.

It must be borne in mind that the equivalent circuits most often used are approximations in themselves, and that exact equivalents are unwieldy. Therefore, because of nonlinearities of characteristics and the lumping of distributed parameters, great accuracy in the calculation of the performance of transistor circuitry is unwarranted; simplifying assumptions should be utilized whenever practical.

Although a large variety of equivalent circuits for the junction transistor have been proposed, and have been put to good use by various organizations and individuals, for low-frequency applications manufacturers most often supply information pertaining to the parameters of the *current-generator equivalent tee* circuit and the *hybrid equivalent* circuit. Consequently, these representations will be used exclusively here—the *hybrid-π* equivalent is presented in Chapter 9.

4–2. Current-Generator Equivalent Tee. The diode equivalent circuit used in Chapter 3, which includes the current generators αI_E and I_{CO}, can be useful for a-c circuit analysis, provided that some modifications are made. Leakage current is a unidirectional and constant quantity and therefore not a factor in incremental studies. Designating instantaneous quantities by lower-case letters, the generator αI_E becomes αi_e, and the time-varying components of the circuit currents become i_c, i_b, and i_e. As a refinement, resistance will be added to each leg of the circuit to denote the finite resistance of the bulk material and semiconductor "barrier" resistance, and to provide a common

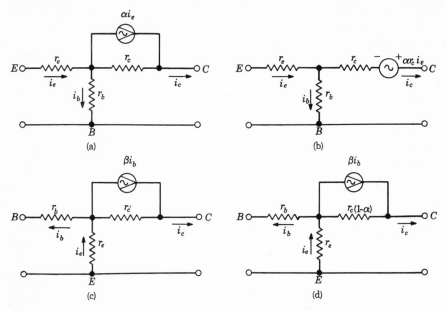

Fig. 4–1. (a) Common-base current-generator equivalent circuit; (b) common-base voltage-generator equivalent circuit; (c) common-emitter equivalent of (a); (d) common-emitter equivalent with all parameters in terms of (a).

element for the feedback of signal from output to input loop, an operational phenomenon.

The thoughts of the above paragraph, when compiled, result in the circuit of Fig. 4–1a. This is the current-generator equivalent tee; the name arises from the use of a current generator in the collector branch (a voltage-generator equivalent is also possible), and from the circuit diagram which is in the shape of the letter T.

For circuit studies it is often convenient to replace the current generator and parallel resistance with an equivalent voltage-generator, series-resistance combination according to the Thèvenin and Norton Theorems. The result of this interchange is the circuit of Fig. 4–1b. The interchange of sources is a useful tool, and it is recommended that the reader review his ability to perform this task. Simply, when making a source interchange, the value of the source resistance (or impedance) does not change but its location does, and a current generator of i becomes a voltage generator of magnitude iR. To reverse the procedure, a voltage generator of e becomes a current generator of e/R.

For the common-emitter connection, the equivalent circuits of Figs. 4–1a and 4–1b apply, but it is necessary to interchange the branches that include r_e and r_b. It is, however, customary to think of the collector current generator as dependent upon the input quantity i_b rather than i_e (Fig. 4–1c). To change from αi_e paralleling r_c to βi_b paralleling some new resistance r_c', we recall the summation of currents

$$i_e = i_c + i_b. \tag{4-1}$$

Then in making a source transformation of αi_e, the resulting voltage generator can be written as $\alpha(i_c + i_b)r_c$. But in series with this generator is r_c, and consequently an $i_c r_c$ voltage drop. If we combine the rise $\alpha i_c r_c$ with the drop $i_c r_c$, then $i_c r_c(1 - \alpha)$ is the composite drop due to collector current and $\alpha i_b r_c$ the total rise. Transforming these into a current-generator equivalent yields, for the generator,

$$\frac{e}{R} = \frac{\alpha i_b r_c}{r_c(1 - \alpha)} = \beta i_b,$$

and the resistance paralleling this source is

$$r_c' = r_c(1 - \alpha). \tag{4-2}$$

The generally accepted equivalent for common-emitter studies is Fig. 4–1d.

We now turn our attention to the derivation of performance equations for the three configurations.

Common-Emitter. Fig. 4–2 shows the current-generator equivalent tee network for the common-emitter configuration connected to a voltage source with source resistance of R_g and connected to a resistive load R_L. Of importance are relationships for current, voltage, and power gain, and input

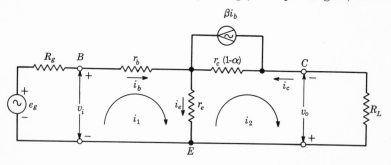

Fig. 4–2. A-c equivalent circuit for the common-emitter configuration with source and load terminations.

and output impedance. After the current source in the collector branch is replaced by an equivalent voltage source, loop equations may be written:

$$\left.\begin{aligned} v_i &= i_1(r_b + r_e) - i_2(r_e); \\ 0 &= -i_1[r_e - \beta r_c(1 - \alpha)] + i_2[r_e + r_c(1 - \alpha) + R_L]. \end{aligned}\right\} \quad (4\text{-}3)$$

The determinant D is

$$\begin{aligned} D &= (r_b + r_e)[r_e + r_c(1 - \alpha) + R_L] - r_e(r_e - \alpha r_c) \\ &= r_b[r_e + r_c(1 - \alpha) + R_L] + r_e(r_c + R_L); \end{aligned}$$

$$i_1 = \frac{\begin{vmatrix} v_i & -r_e \\ 0 & r_e + r_c(1 - \alpha) + R_L \end{vmatrix}}{D} = \frac{v_i[r_e + r_c(1 - \alpha) + R_L]}{D} \, ;$$

$$i_2 = \frac{\begin{vmatrix} r_b + r_e & v_i \\ -(r_e - \alpha r_c) & 0 \end{vmatrix}}{D} = \frac{v_i(r_e - \alpha r_c)}{D} .$$

Voltage Gain

$$\begin{aligned} A_v &= \left| \frac{v_o}{v_i} \right| = \left| \frac{i_2 R_L}{v_i} \right| = \frac{v_i R_L(\alpha r_c - r_e)/D}{v_i} \\ &= \frac{R_L(\alpha r_c - r_e)}{r_b[r_e + r_c(1 - \alpha) + R_L] + r_e(r_c + R_L)} . \end{aligned} \qquad (4\text{-}4)$$

Current Gain

$$\begin{aligned} A_i &= \left| \frac{i_2}{i_1} \right| = \frac{v_i(\alpha r_c - r_e)}{D} \cdot \frac{D}{v_i[r_e + r_c(1 - \alpha) + R_L]} \\ &= \frac{\alpha r_c - r_e}{r_e + r_c(1 - \alpha) + R_L} . \end{aligned} \qquad (4\text{-}5)$$

Power Gain

$$G = A_i \cdot A_v = \frac{\alpha r_c - r_e}{r_e + r_c(1 - \alpha) + R_L} \cdot \frac{R_L(\alpha r_c - r_e)}{r_b[r_e + r_c(1 - \alpha) + R_L] + r_e(r_c + R_L)}$$

$$= \frac{R_L(\alpha r_c - r_e)^2}{[r_e + r_c(1 - \alpha) + R_L]\{r_b[r_e + r_c(1 - \alpha) + R_L] + r_e(r_c + R_L)\}} . \qquad (4\text{-}6)$$

Input Resistance

$$R_i = \left| \frac{v_i}{i_1} \right| = \frac{v_i}{v_i[r_e + r_c(1 - \alpha) + R_L]/D}$$

$$= \frac{r_b[r_e + r_c(1 - \alpha) + R_L] + r_e(r_c + R_L)}{r_e + r_c(1 - \alpha) + R_L}. \tag{4-7}$$

Output Resistance

Look back from R_L, short-circuit e_g, and assume a driving voltage connected at v_o, then the loop equations are:

$$\left. \begin{array}{l} 0 = i_1(R_g + r_b + r_e) - i_2(r_e), \\ v_o = i_1[-r_e + \beta r_c(1 - \alpha)] + i_2[r_e + r_c(1 - \alpha)]. \end{array} \right\} \tag{4-8}$$

The determinant D' is

$$D' = (R_g + r_b + r_e)[r_e + r_c(1 - \alpha)] + r_e(-r_e + \alpha r_c),$$

$$i_2 = \frac{\begin{vmatrix} R_g + r_b + r_e & 0 \\ -r_e + \alpha r_c & v_o \end{vmatrix}}{D'} = \frac{v_o(R_g + r_b + r_e)}{D'},$$

therefore,

$$R_o = \left| \frac{v_o}{i_2} \right| = \frac{v_o}{v_o(R_g + r_b + r_e)/D'}$$

$$= \frac{(R_g + r_b + r_e)[r_c(1 - \alpha)] + r_e(R_g + r_b + \alpha r_c)}{R_g + r_b + r_e}. \tag{4-9}$$

An important conclusion to our mathematical study is that this configuration provides a current phase reversal, for i_2 is negative (r_c is actually much greater than r_e) and therefore flows oppositely to the arrow in Fig. 4-2. A phase reversal also exists between v_i and v_o. The assumed instantaneous directions of i_b, i_e, and i_c in Fig. 4-2 are true.

It may seem that a curve ball has been thrown. β was defined as the short-circuit current amplification factor for this configuration, yet from Eq. (4-5), when $R_L = 0$, which clearly represents a short circuit,

$$A_i = \frac{\alpha r_c - r_e}{r_e + r_c(1 - \alpha)}, \tag{4-10}$$

instead of

$$A_i = \beta = \frac{\alpha}{1 - \alpha}. \tag{4-11}$$

The discrepancy that exists can be clarified by stating that the βi_b current generator technically is in error, and to be more exact that generator should have some new nomenclature such as $\beta' i_b$. We may then define

$$\alpha' = \frac{\beta'}{\beta' + 1}. \tag{4-12}$$

Equation (4-10) can be correctly written as

$$A_i = \frac{\alpha' r_c - r_e}{r_e + r_c(1 - \alpha')}. \tag{4-13}$$

To find the value of α', equate Eqs. (4-11) and (4-13)

$$\frac{\alpha' r_c - r_e}{r_e + r_c(1 - \alpha')} = \frac{\alpha}{1 - \alpha},$$

and then

$$\alpha' = \frac{\alpha r_c + r_e}{r_c}. \tag{4-14}$$

When normal values for the parameters are inserted, Eq. (4-14) describes a difference between α and α' that amounts to less than 0.01%. It therefore

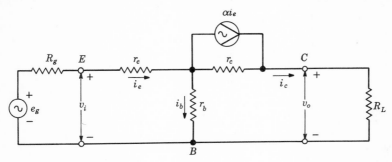

Fig. 4-3. A-c equivalent circuit for the common-base configuration with source and load terminations.

seems logical to call the current generator α, or β, rather than assign another symbol, for the accuracy of the equivalent circuit itself and the accuracy of measurement of the parameters each result in errors of considerably greater magnitude than the difference between the short-circuit current-amplification factor and the factor we have called α'.

Common-Base. Derivation of the formulas for the common-base configuration proceeds from the equivalent circuit of Fig. 4-1a with the transistor connected to a source and a load as shown in Fig. 4-3. The derived expressions are available in Table 4-2 and the reader is invited to verify them (see Problems 4-2 and 4-3). The common-base configuration does not provide phase reversal between input and output quantities.

Common-Collector. The circuit of Fig. 4–4 may be used to derive performance equations for the common-collector configuration. Formulas for the prediction of transistor operation in this orientation are listed in Table 4–3. The reader may verify them (see Problems 4–4 and 4–5). The common-collector orientation does not provide phase reversal between input and output quantities.

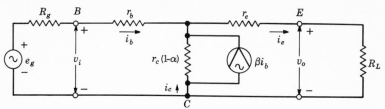

Fig. 4–4. A-c equivalent circuit for the common-collector configuration with source and load terminations.

Approximate Formulas. Tables 4–1, 4–2 and 4–3 are listings of the formulas derived for the three configurations. The so-called "complete" formulas, which themselves are based upon assumptions and approximations, are presented along with more "approximate" formulas, which are useful to gain a rapid insight into the circuit under consideration, without performing the more laborious task of solving the complete expression.

In deriving the approximate formulas, the following considerations are among those of importance: $r_c \gg r_b$, $r_c \gg r_e$, $r_c \gg R_L$, $r_c(1 - \alpha) \gg R_L$, $R_L \gg r_e$. These assumptions stem from knowledge of typical values for the parameters; one might expect to encounter values such as

$$r_b = 500 \text{ ohms}$$
$$r_e = 30 \text{ ohms}$$
$$r_c = 1,500,000 \text{ ohms}$$
$$\alpha = 0.975$$

Many other approximate relationships may be derived, some of which may more satisfactorily describe the operation of a particular transistor type or circuit.

It must be borne in mind that all equations presented herein pertain only to the circuits for which the formulas were derived. If series resistance were inserted into the emitter lead of the common-emitter configuration, for example, then r_e would have to be increased by the amount of that additional resistance, and certain approximate formulas might not hold; or, more specifically, the results of the use of the approximate formulas might be in error by an additional amount.

TABLE 4–1. COMMON-EMITTER FORMULAS FOR THE T-EQUIVALENT

	Complete Formulas	Approximate Formulas †
Voltage Gain, A_v*	$$\dfrac{R_L(\alpha r_c - r_e)}{\left\{\begin{matrix} r_b[r_e + r_c(1 - \alpha) + R_L] \\ + r_e(r_c + R_L) \end{matrix}\right\}}$$ (4–4)	$$\dfrac{\alpha R_L}{r_e + r_b(1 - \alpha)}$$ (4–4A)
Current Gain, A_i*	$$\dfrac{\alpha r_c - r_e}{r_e + r_c(1 - \alpha) + R_L}$$ (4–5)	$$\dfrac{\alpha}{1 - \alpha} = \beta$$ (4–5A)
Power Gain, G	$$\dfrac{R_L(\alpha r_c - r_e)^2}{\left\{\begin{matrix} [r_e + r_c(1 - \alpha) + R_L]\{r_b[r_e \\ + r_c(1 - \alpha) + R_L] + r_e(r_c + R_L)\} \end{matrix}\right\}}$$ (4–6)	$$\dfrac{\alpha^2 R_L}{(1 - \alpha)[r_e + r_b(1 - \alpha)]}$$ (4–6A)
Input Resistance, R_i	$$\dfrac{r_b[r_e + r_c(1 - \alpha) + R_L] + r_e(r_c + R_L)}{r_e + r_c(1 - \alpha) + R_L}$$ (4–7)	$$\dfrac{r_b(1 - \alpha) + r_e}{1 - \alpha}$$ (4–7A)
Output Resistance, R_o	$$\dfrac{\left\{\begin{matrix} (R_g + r_b + r_e)[r_c(1 - \alpha)] \\ + r_e(R_g + r_b + \alpha r_c) \end{matrix}\right\}}{R_g + r_b + r_e}$$ (4–9)	$$\dfrac{R_g r_c(1 - \alpha) + r_e r_c}{R_g + r_b + r_e}$$ (4–9A)

* Phase reversal.
† $r_c \gg r_e$, $r_c(1 - \alpha) \gg (R_L + r_e)$, $R_g \gg r_b$, $r_c \gg (R_g + r_b)$.

TABLE 4–2.   COMMON-BASE FORMULAS FOR THE T-EQUIVALENT

	Complete Formulas	Approximate Formulas †
Voltage Gain, A_v	$$\dfrac{(r_b + \alpha r_c)R_L}{r_b[R_L + r_c(1 - \alpha)] + r_e(r_b + r_c + R_L)}$$ (4–15)	$$\dfrac{\alpha R_L}{r_e + r_b(1 - \alpha)}$$ (4–15A)
Current Gain, A_i	$$\dfrac{r_b + \alpha r_c}{r_b + r_c + R_L}$$ (4–16)	α (4–16A)
Power Gain, G	$$\dfrac{(r_b + \alpha r_c)^2 R_L}{\left\{\begin{array}{l}(r_b + r_c + R_L)\{r_b[R_L + r_c(1 - \alpha)]\\ \quad + r_e(r_b + r_c + R_L)\}\end{array}\right\}}$$ (4–17)	$$\dfrac{\alpha^2 R_L}{r_e + r_b(1 - \alpha)}$$ (4–17A)
Input Resistance, R_i	$$\dfrac{r_b[R_L + r_c(1 - \alpha)] + r_e(r_b + r_c + R_L)}{r_b + r_c + R_L}$$ (4–18)	$r_e + r_b(1 - \alpha)$ (4–18A)
Output Resistance, R_o	$$\dfrac{r_b(R_g + r_e - \alpha r_c) + r_c(R_g + r_b + r_e)}{R_g + r_b + r_e}$$ (4–19)	$$\dfrac{r_c[R_g + r_b(1 - \alpha) + r_e]}{R_g + r_b + r_e}$$ (4–19A)

† $r_c \gg r_b$, $r_c(1 - \alpha) \gg R_L$, $r_c \gg (R_g + r_e)$.

TABLE 4–3.   COMMON-COLLECTOR FORMULAS FOR THE T-EQUIVALENT

	Complete Formulas	Approximate Formulas †
Voltage Gain, A_v	$$\frac{r_c R_L}{r_b(r_e + R_L) + r_c[r_e + R_L + r_b(1 - \alpha)]}$$ (4–20)	1 (4–20A)
Current Gain, A_i	$$\frac{r_c}{r_c(1 - \alpha) + r_e + R_L}$$ (4–21)	$\dfrac{1}{1 - \alpha}$ (4–21A)
Power Gain, G	$$\frac{r_c^2 R_L}{\left\{ \begin{array}{l} [r_c(1 - \alpha) + r_e + R_L]\{r_b(r_e + R_L) \\ \quad + r_c[r_e + R_L + r_b(1 - \alpha)]\} \end{array} \right\}}$$ (4–22)	$\dfrac{1}{1 - \alpha}$ (4–22A)
Input Resistance, R_i	$$\frac{r_b(r_e + R_L) + r_c[r_e + R_L + r_b(1 - \alpha)]}{r_c(1 - \alpha) + r_e + R_L}$$ (4–23)	$\dfrac{R_L}{1 - \alpha}$ (4–23A)
Output Resistance, R_o	$$\frac{r_e(R_g + r_b + r_c) + r_c(1 - \alpha)(R_g + r_b)}{R_g + r_b + r_c}$$ (4–24)	$r_e + (1 - \alpha)(R_g + r_b)$ (4–24A)

† $r_c(1 - \alpha) \gg R_L$, $R_L \gg [r_e + r_b(1 - \alpha)]$, $r_c \gg (R_g + r_b)$.

4–3. Matrix Parameters. A two-terminal-pair device may be treated as a black box and general equations written relating the terminal quantities, e_1, i_1, e_2 and i_2. A general representation of such a device is shown in Fig. 4–5. Within the box is a linear, active, bilateral network—here a transistor. Because the external conditions are measurable, the device within the box can be characterized by a set of four parameters; these parameters are the coefficients in the pair of simultaneous equations that may be written to relate the external quantities. For example, the box of Fig. 4–5 can be described by

$$\left.\begin{aligned} e_1 &= z_{11}i_1 + z_{12}i_2; \\ e_2 &= z_{21}i_1 + z_{22}i_2. \end{aligned}\right\} \quad (4\text{–}25)$$

Five other equation pairs may be written to relate the terminal quantities:

$$\left.\begin{aligned} i_1 &= y_{11}e_1 + y_{12}e_2; \\ i_2 &= y_{21}e_1 + y_{22}e_2. \end{aligned}\right\} \quad (4\text{–}26)$$

$$\left.\begin{aligned} e_1 &= h_{11}i_1 + h_{12}e_2; \\ i_2 &= h_{21}i_1 + h_{22}e_2. \end{aligned}\right\} \quad (4\text{–}27)$$

$$\left.\begin{aligned} i_1 &= g_{11}e_1 + g_{12}i_2; \\ e_2 &= g_{21}e_1 + g_{22}i_2. \end{aligned}\right\} \quad (4\text{–}28)$$

$$\left.\begin{aligned} e_1 &= a_{11}e_2 - a_{12}i_2; \\ i_1 &= a_{21}e_2 - a_{22}i_2. \end{aligned}\right\} \quad (4\text{–}29)$$

$$\left.\begin{aligned} e_2 &= b_{11}e_1 - b_{12}i_1; \\ i_2 &= b_{21}e_1 - b_{22}i_1. \end{aligned}\right\} \quad (4\text{–}30)$$

The above relationships may also be written in matrix form (see Problem 4–9).

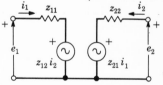

Fig. 4–5. Black box showing positive directions for external quantities.

Fig. 4–6. Equivalent circuit using z-parameters.

For each of the above equation pairs it is possible to draw an equivalent electrical circuit, a circuit that could be considered to be the contents of the box of Fig. 4–5. The equivalent circuit that satisfies Eqs. (4–25) is shown in Fig. 4–6 and has been called the z-equivalent. In a like manner equivalent circuits for the other equations can be drawn, and many variations are possible, particularly when one considers the equivalence of sources.

Let us momentarily discuss the z-equivalent, since the defining equations and the circuit are available. It is possible to derive the relationships for circuit gains and input and output resistances as has been done for the current-generator equivalent tee. The short-circuit current gain is easily arrived at, for when $e_2 = 0$, from Eqs. (4-25)

$$\frac{i_2}{i_1} = -\frac{z_{21}}{z_{22}}. \tag{4-31}$$

The derivation of the performance equations for all of the matrix equivalents is left to the reader. The equations are presented in Appendix II.

The discussion in this section has been rather general and, in fact, can apply to devices other than the transistor. For transistor work one of the preceding representations has emerged as an industry standard; attention will now be focused upon the *hybrid equivalent*.

4-4. The Hybrid Equivalent Circuit. The *hybrid* or *h*-parameters have become the most used for describing the characteristics of the transistor. They are the coefficients in Eqs. (4-27), which describe a four-terminal network. Repeated here

$$e_1 = h_{11}i_1 + h_{12}e_2; \tag{4-32}$$

$$i_2 = h_{21}i_1 + h_{22}e_2. \tag{4-33}$$

When considering a transistor in the common-base configuration, as in Fig. 4-7a, the h-parameter equivalent circuit can take on the form of Fig. 4-7b

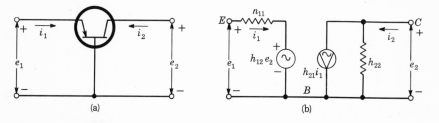

Fig. 4-7. Common-base configuration: (a) four-terminal network; (b) equivalent circuit for (a).

in order to satisfy Eqs. (4-32) and (4-33). Since the defining equations must obey Kirchhoff's Laws, h_{11} must be an impedance, and h_{22} an admittance, while h_{12} and h_{21} are dimensionless. For low-frequency analysis, h_{11} and h_{22} will be resistive.

The ease of measurement of the h-parameters has contributed to their widespread adoption. If the output terminals are a-c short-circuited, then $e_2 = 0$ and

$$h_{11} = \frac{e_1}{i_1}. \tag{4-34}$$

Also

$$h_{21} = \frac{i_2}{i_1}. \tag{4-35}$$

Opening the a-c input circuit reduces i_1 to zero and gives

$$h_{12} = \frac{e_1}{e_2}, \tag{4-36}$$

and

$$h_{22} = \frac{i_2}{e_2}. \tag{4-37}$$

Therefore h_{11} may be called the "input impedance with output short-circuited," and h_{22} is the "output admittance with input open-circuited." Likewise, h_{12} is the "voltage feedback ratio with input open-circuited," and h_{21} is the "current amplification with output short-circuited." It is interesting to note that

$$h_{21} = -\alpha, \tag{4-38}$$

both being defined under short-circuit loading. α is preceded by a negative sign because of the direction assigned to i_2 in Fig. 4-7a; in the common-base configuration current flowing into the emitter terminal actually results in collector current out of the collector terminal.

The short and open circuits referred to in the preceding paragraph for the measurement of transistor parameters may be accomplished in the laboratory by the insertion of suitable capacitors and inductors. A large-valued capacitor across an output terminal pair will short-circuit an a-c signal, but will not disturb quiescent conditions. Likewise, a large-valued choke in an input bias current supply will essentially open that circuit to a-c.

In order to standardize transistor nomenclature, the American Institute of Electrical Engineers (AIEE) and the Institute of Radio Engineers (IRE) have recommended the following parameter symbols:

$$h_{ib} = h_{11} \text{ (input impedance)}$$

$$h_{rb} = h_{12} \text{ (voltage feedback ratio)}$$

$$h_{fb} = h_{21} \text{ (current amplification)}$$

$$h_{ob} = h_{22} \text{ (output admittance)}.$$

The subscript b refers in each case to the parameter derived from the common-base configuration. Since the numerical subscripts are still in use and of course exist in the literature, it is necessary to be familiar with both systems. Some amount of duplication will be presented in this book.

Adherence to the defining Eqs. (4–32) and (4–33) when considering the common-emitter and common-collector configurations would result in new families of parameters. For those connections the AIEE-IRE symbols are h_{ie}, h_{re}, h_{fe}, and h_{oe}; and h_{ic}, h_{rc}, h_{fc}, and h_{oc}, with the second subscript in each case representing the configuration employed, i.e. e for common-emitter and

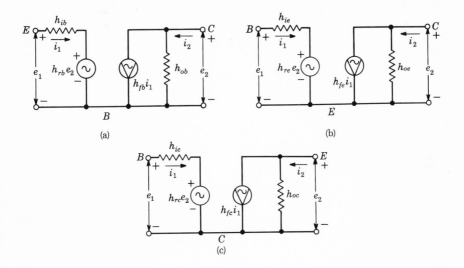

(a)   (b)

(c)

Fig. 4–8. h-parameter equivalent circuits: (a) common-base; (b) common-emitter; (c) common-collector.

c for common-collector. Fig. 4–8 depicts equivalent circuits employing this nomenclature.

We have thus far used the symbols with numerical subscripts for a common-base stage exclusively. Since a common-emitter or -collector stage can also be described by Eqs. (4–32) and (4–33), a distinction must be made based upon transistor orientation. Generally, h_{11b}, etc. are used for the parameters we have up to now called h_{11}, etc.; likewise h_{11e}, etc., and h_{11c}, etc., exist.

It is interesting to note that the equivalent circuits of Fig. 4–8 do not differ, because they all must satisfy the defining equations. Only the parameter nomenclature varies because of configuration, and it is therefore possible to derive performance equations in terms of general parameters h_i, h_r, h_f, and h_o, and then, with these formulas, calculate circuit operation by inserting the specific parameters that correspond to the circuit configuration being analyzed.

We shall now investigate the general hybrid equivalent with the help of the circuit of Fig. 4–9. If we transform the collector branch current generator $h_f i_1$ and parallel admittance h_o to a voltage generator $(h_f/h_o)i_1$ with series

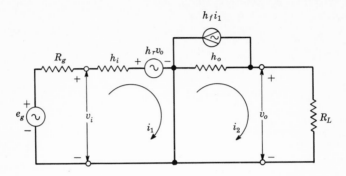

Fig. 4–9. A-c equivalent circuit for the general configuration with source and load terminations.

admittance h_o, then loop equations are

$$v_i = i_1 h_i + i_2 h_r R_L;$$
$$0 = i_1 \frac{h_f}{h_o} + i_2 \left(\frac{1}{h_o} + R_L\right). \tag{4-39}$$

The determinant D is

$$D = \frac{h_i(1 + R_L h_o) - h_r h_f R_L}{h_o},$$

$$i_1 = \frac{\begin{vmatrix} v_i & h_r R_L \\ 0 & \dfrac{1}{h_o} + R_L \end{vmatrix}}{D} = \frac{v_i(1 + R_L h_o)/h_o}{D},$$

$$i_2 = \frac{\begin{vmatrix} h_i & v_i \\ h_f/h_o & 0 \end{vmatrix}}{D} = \frac{-v_i h_f/h_o}{D}.$$

Voltage Gain

$$A_v = \left|\frac{v_o}{v_i}\right| = \left|\frac{i_2 R_L}{v_i}\right| = \frac{v_i R_L(h_f/h_o)/D}{v_i}$$

$$= \frac{h_f R_L}{h_i + R_L(h_i h_o - h_r h_f)}. \tag{4-40}$$

Current Gain

$$A_i = \left| \frac{i_2}{i_1} \right| = \frac{v_i(h_f/h_o)/D}{v_i[(1 + R_L h_o)/h_o]/D}$$

$$= \frac{h_f}{1 + R_L h_o}. \qquad (4\text{-}41)$$

Power Gain

$$G = A_i \cdot A_v = \frac{h_f}{1 + R_L h_o} \cdot \frac{h_f R_L}{h_i + R_L(h_i h_o - h_r h_f)}$$

$$= \frac{h_f{}^2 R_L}{(1 + R_L h_o)[h_i + R_L(h_i h_o - h_r h_f)]}. \qquad (4\text{-}42)$$

Input Resistance

$$R_i = \left| \frac{v_i}{i_1} \right| = \frac{v_i}{v_i[(1 + R_L h_o)/h_o]/D}$$

$$= \frac{h_i(1 + R_L h_o) - h_r h_f R_L}{1 + R_L h_o}. \qquad (4\text{-}43)$$

Output Resistance

Look back from R_L, short-circuit e_g, and assume a voltage source connected at v_o; then the loop equations are

$$\left. \begin{array}{l} 0 = i_1(h_i + R_g) + v_o h_r; \\[2mm] v_o = -i_1 \left(\dfrac{h_f}{h_o} \right) - i_2 \left(\dfrac{1}{h_o} \right). \end{array} \right\} \qquad (4\text{-}44)$$

The determinant D' is

$$D' = -\frac{h_i + R_g}{h_o},$$

$$i_2 = \frac{\begin{vmatrix} h_i + R_g & -v_o h_r \\ -h_f/h_o & v_o \end{vmatrix}}{D'} = \frac{v_o(h_i + R_g - h_r h_f/h_o)}{D'},$$

$$R_o = \left| \frac{v_o}{i_2} \right| = \frac{v_o}{v_o(h_i + R_g - h_r h_f/h_o)/D'}$$

$$= \frac{h_i + R_g}{h_o(h_i + R_g) - h_r h_f}. \qquad (4\text{-}45)$$

With the preceding equations it is possible to calculate the performance of a common-base stage by simply inserting h_{ib}, h_{rb}, h_{fb}, and h_{ob}, whereas to predict the circuit operation of a common-emitter connected transistor we should use h_{ie}, h_{re}, h_{fe}, and h_{oe}. The common-collector configuration would be treated similarly. Table 4–4 is a convenient summary of the formulas derived.

TABLE 4–4. FORMULAS FOR THE HYBRID EQUIVALENT

Voltage Gain, A_v	$\dfrac{h_f R_L}{h_i + R_L \Delta^h}$ (4–40)
Current Gain, A_i	$\dfrac{h_f}{1 + R_L h_o}$ (4–41)
Power Gain, G	$\dfrac{h_f{}^2 R_L}{(1 + R_L h_o)[h_i + R_L \Delta^h]}$ (4–42)
Input Resistance, R_i	$\dfrac{h_i + R_L \Delta^h}{1 + R_L h_o}$ (4–43)
Output Resistance, R_o	$\dfrac{h_i + R_g}{\Delta^h + R_g h_o}$ (4–45)

$$\Delta^h = h_i h_o - h_r h_f$$

It is somewhat cumbersome to provide a complete set of twelve parameters for each transistor type. Consequently, it has become more-or-less standard for manufacturers to supply just the common-base h-parameters. The user can either mathematically solve for the other sets, or can rearrange the com-

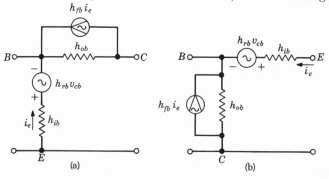

Fig. 4–10. Repositioning of the terminals of the common-base equivalent circuit of Fig. 4–8 for: (a) common-emitter analysis; (b) common-collector analysis.

mon-base equivalent circuit by transferring terminals. Both methods will be employed in subsequent paragraphs.

Our next goal will be to derive a series of relations among the three sets of h-parameters. To study the other connections, we shall rearrange the terminals of the common-base circuit of Fig. 4–8a. This repositioning is shown in Fig. 4–10. In (a) of that figure, we have the equivalent common-emitter circuit in terms of common-base parameters. To find h_{ie} and h_{fe}, recall that

$$h_{ie} = \frac{e_1}{i_1},$$
$$h_{fe} = \frac{i_2}{i_1}$$

for output short-circuited.

The output short-circuit results in the network of Fig. 4–11a. A further simplification to that of Fig. 4–11b can be made with a knowledge of typical parameter values. h_{rb} normally has a value of 10^{-3} or 10^{-4}, and h_{ob} usually

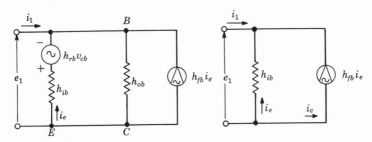

Fig. 4–11. Circuits for derivation of relationships between common-base and common-emitter parameters: (a) Fig. 4–10a with output short-circuited; (b) further simplification.

represents a resistance of 10^5 or 10^6 ohms. These two parameters will be removed for simplicity and then

$$-i_1 = i_e + h_{fb}i_e$$
$$e_1 = -i_e h_{ib}$$

(4–46)

Since

$$h_{ie} = \frac{e_1}{i_1} = \frac{-i_e h_{ib}}{-i_e(1 + h_{fb})},$$

(4–47)

then

$$h_{ie} = \frac{h_{ib}}{1 + h_{fb}}.$$

(4–48)

We know that

$$h_{fe} = \frac{i_c}{i_1} = \frac{i_e h_{fb}}{-i_e(1 + h_{fb})},$$

(4–49)

so

$$h_{fe} = \frac{-h_{fb}}{1 + h_{fb}}. \tag{4-50}$$

In a similar manner equations for h_{re} and h_{oe} as well as the common-collector parameters may be derived (see Problems 4–22 and 4–23). Table 4–5 presents a summary of these relations among parameters.

TABLE 4–5. RELATIONS AMONG PARAMETERS

Relations Between Common-Base and Common-Emitter Parameters	Relations Between Common-Base and Common-Collector Parameters
$h_{ie} \cong \dfrac{h_{ib}}{1 + h_{fb}}$	$h_{ic} \cong \dfrac{h_{ib}}{1 + h_{fb}}$
$h_{re} \cong \dfrac{h_{ib}h_{ob} - h_{rb}h_{fb} - h_{rb}}{1 + h_{fb}}$	$h_{rc} \cong 1$
$h_{fe} \cong \dfrac{-h_{fb}}{1 + h_{fb}}$	$h_{fc} \cong \dfrac{-1}{1 + h_{fb}}$
$h_{oe} \cong \dfrac{h_{ob}}{1 + h_{fb}}$	$h_{oc} \cong \dfrac{h_{ob}}{1 + h_{fb}}$

The results of the preceding paragraph may also be used to derive formulas for the common-emitter configuration in terms of the more familiar common-base parameters. Or, it is possible to utilize the circuit of Fig. 4–10a, and by connecting the collector terminal to a load and the base terminal to a

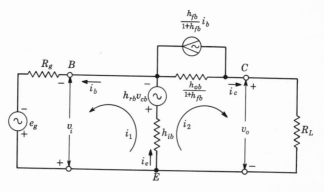

Fig. 4–12. A-c equivalent circuit for the common-emitter configuration with source and load terminations.

signal source, write and solve the circuit equations for terminal properties of the common-emitter connection in terms of common-base parameters.

Refer to Fig. 4–12. After making a source interchange in the collector branch, the Kirchhoff equations are:

$$v_i = i_1 \left(h_{ib} - \frac{h_{fb}h_{rb}}{h_{ob}} \right) + i_2 \left[h_{ib} - \frac{(1 + h_{fb})h_{rb}}{h_{ob}} \right];$$

$$0 = i_1 \left[h_{ib} + \frac{(1 - h_{rb})h_{fb}}{h_{ob}} \right] + i_2 \left[h_{ib} + R_L + (1 - h_{rb}) \left(\frac{1 + h_{fb}}{h_{ob}} \right) \right]. \qquad (4\text{--}51)$$

The determinant D is

$$D = \frac{h_{ib}(1 + R_L h_{ob}) - h_{rb}h_{fb}R_L}{h_{ob}}$$

Voltage Gain

$$A_v = \left| \frac{v_o}{v_i} \right| = \left| \frac{i_2 R_L}{v_i} \right|$$

$$= \frac{R_L[h_{ib}h_{ob} + (1 - h_{rb})h_{fb}]}{h_{ib}(1 + R_L h_{ob}) - h_{rb}h_{fb}R_L} \qquad (4\text{--}52)$$

Current Gain

$$A_i = \left| \frac{i_2}{i_1} \right|$$

$$= \frac{h_{ib}h_{ob} + (1 - h_{rb})h_{fb}}{h_{ob}(h_{ib} + R_L) + (1 - h_{rb})(1 + h_{fb})} \qquad (4\text{--}53)$$

Power Gain

$$G = A_i \cdot A_v$$

$$= \frac{R_L[h_{ib}h_{ob} + (1 - h_{rb})h_{fb}]^2}{[h_{ob}(h_{ib} + R_L) + (1 - h_{rb})(1 + h_{fb})][h_{ib}(1 + R_L h_{ob}) - h_{rb}h_{fb}R_L]}$$

$$(4\text{--}54)$$

Input Resistance

$$R_i = \left| \frac{v_i}{i_1} \right|$$

$$= \frac{h_{ib}(1 + R_L h_{ob}) - h_{rb}h_{fb}R_L}{h_{ob}(h_{ib} + R_L) + (1 - h_{rb})(1 + h_{fb})} \qquad (4\text{--}55)$$

Output Resistance

The method previously used with the T-circuit results in

$$R_o = \frac{h_{ib} + R_g[h_{ib}h_{ob} + (1 - h_{rb})(1 + h_{fb})]}{h_{ob}(h_{ib} + R_g) - h_{rb}h_{fb}} \qquad (4\text{--}56)$$

While not obvious from the equations, there is current and voltage phase reversal with this connection. This reversal is apparent when one realizes that h_{fb} is a negative number. The reader may prefer to make the substitution $\Delta^{h_b} = h_{ib}h_{ob} - h_{rb}h_{fb}$ where applicable.

TABLE 4–6. COMMON-EMITTER FORMULAS FOR THE HYBRID EQUIVALENT

	Complete Formulas †	Approximate Formulas ⊙
Voltage Gain, $A_v{}^*$	$\dfrac{R_L(h_{ib}h_{ob} + h_{fb})}{h_{ib}(1 + R_Lh_{ob}) - h_{rb}h_{fb}R_L}$ (4–52)	$\dfrac{h_{fb}R_L}{h_{ib}(1 + R_Lh_{ob})}$ (4–52A)
Current Gain, $A_i{}^*$	$\dfrac{h_{ib}h_{ob} + h_{fb}}{h_{ob}(h_{ib} + R_L) + (1 + h_{fb})}$ (4–53)	$\dfrac{h_{fb}}{h_{ob}R_L + (1 + h_{fb})}$ (4–53A)
Power Gain, G	$\dfrac{R_L(h_{ib}h_{ob} + h_{fb})^2}{\left\{ \begin{array}{l}[h_{ob}(h_{ib} + R_L) + (1 + h_{fb})] \\ \times\ [h_{ib}(1 + R_Lh_{ob}) - h_{rb}h_{fb}R_L]\end{array} \right\}}$ (4–54)	$\dfrac{h_{fb}{}^2R_L}{\left\{ \begin{array}{l}h_{ib}(1 + R_Lh_{ob}) \\ \times\ [R_Lh_{ob} + (1 + h_{fb})]\end{array} \right\}}$ (4–54A)
Input Resistance, R_i	$\dfrac{h_{ib}(1 + R_Lh_{ob}) - h_{rb}h_{fb}R_L}{h_{ob}(h_{ib} + R_L) + (1 + h_{fb})}$ (4–55)	$\dfrac{h_{ib}(1 + R_Lh_{ob})}{R_Lh_{ob} + (1 + h_{fb})}$ (4–55A)
Output Resistance, R_o	$\dfrac{h_{ib} + R_g[h_{ib}h_{ob} + (1 + h_{fb})]}{h_{ob}(h_{ib} + R_g) - h_{rb}h_{fb}}$ (4–56)	$\dfrac{h_{ib} + R_g(1 + h_{fb})}{h_{ob}(h_{ib} + R_g) - h_{rb}h_{fb}}$ (4–56A)

* Phase reversal.

† $(1 - h_{rb})$ factors omitted.

⊙ $(1 + h_{fb}) \gg h_{ib}h_{ob}$, $R_L \gg h_{ib}$, $h_{ib} \gg h_{rb}h_{fb}R_L$.

4–5. Parameters. The two equivalent circuits presented thus far in this chapter, the current-generator equivalent tee and the hybrid equivalent are, at best, approximations to transistor behavior, for nonlinearities have been linearized, and reactances neglected. More exact equivalents have been derived to study operation of the device; they can be found in the literature.[1, 10] From these studies it is evident that all of the h-parameters are, in reality, complex numbers: h_{ib}, h_{rb} and h_{fb} can be described in terms of the "alpha cutoff frequency," the signal frequency at which the α parameter has decreased by 3 db. For the analysis and design of low-frequency circuits, however, it is sufficient to know that the h-parameters represent both ohmic and semiconductor types of resistance, that they are dictated, in the main, by the physical width of the base region, and are ideally functions of ambient temperature and direct emitter current. Since base width depends upon collector junction voltage, parameters will vary with that potential.

The addition of capacitances to the transistor equivalent circuits thus far considered will be discussed in a later chapter.

T- and h-Parameters. The T- and h-parameters must be related, for the two equivalent circuits were used to describe the same device—the transistor; and the gain and resistance equations must be identical, whether expressed in r's or h's. Our goal at this point is to find the relations between the two sets of parameters. To simplify the problem we shall consider only the common-base h-parameters; Table 4–5 will then give us h-parameters for the other configurations, if desired.

It has already been noted that

$$h_{fb} = -\alpha \qquad (4\text{--}38)$$

If the equations from Tables 4–2 and 4–4 for input resistance are compared and, for simplicity, R_L set to zero, then

$$R_i = h_{ib} = \frac{r_b r_c(1 - \alpha) + r_e(r_b + r_c)}{r_b + r_c} \qquad (4\text{--}57)$$

from which

$$h_{ib} \cong r_e + r_b(1 - \alpha) \qquad (4\text{--}58)$$

Letting R_g approach an open-circuit condition yields, from the two R_o equations available,

$$\frac{1}{h_{ob}} \cong r_c \qquad (4\text{--}59)$$

If we substitute the three parameter interrelations now available into one of the formulas containing h_{rb} in Table 4–4, then, to complete the list,

$$h_{rb} \cong \frac{r_b}{r_c} \qquad (4\text{--}60)$$

These equations are tabulated in Table 4–7 which also includes T-parameters in terms of h's. The reader is invited to verify the remaining equations (Problem 4–24).

TABLE 4–7. APPROXIMATE RELATIONS BETWEEN h-PARAMETERS AND T-PARAMETERS

$h_{ib} = r_e + r_b(1 - \alpha)$	$r_e = h_{ib} - \dfrac{h_{rb}}{h_{ob}}(1 + h_{fb})$
$h_{rb} = \dfrac{r_b}{r_c}$	$r_b = \dfrac{h_{rb}}{h_{ob}}$
$h_{fb} = -\alpha$	$r_c = \dfrac{1}{h_{ob}}$
$h_{ob} = \dfrac{1}{r_c}$	$\alpha = -h_{fb}$

Curves and Parameters. Because either a set of curves or a set of parameters may be used to specify an active circuit element such as the transistor, the curves and parameters must be related. Considering the common-base connection with collector voltage and emitter current as independent variables, the functional relationships among variables are

$$i_C = f(i_E, v_{CB});$$
$$v_{EB} = f(i_E, v_{CB}). \tag{4-61}$$

For differential changes in the quantities, the differential change in i_C is

$$di_C = \frac{\partial i_C}{\partial i_E}\,di_E + \frac{\partial i_C}{\partial v_{CB}}\,dv_{CB} \tag{4-62}$$

and the differential change in v_{EB} is

$$dv_{EB} = \frac{\partial v_{EB}}{\partial i_E}\,di_E + \frac{\partial v_{EB}}{\partial v_{CB}}\,dv_{CB}. \tag{4-63}$$

Differential changes represent a-c components

$$di_C = i_c \qquad\qquad dv_{CB} = v_{cb}.$$
$$di_E = i_e \qquad\qquad dv_{EB} = v_{eb}.$$

The operating range over the characteristics may be considered as linear if the changes are small; therefore the partial derivatives are constants, and symbols have already been assigned for them:

and

$$i_c = h_{fb}i_e + h_{ob}v_{cb} \tag{4-64}$$
$$v_{eb} = h_{ib}i_e + h_{rb}v_{cb}. \tag{4-65}$$

In Chapter 1 a pictorial definition of alpha was given, and it was shown to be the incremental ratio of collector to emitter current at $v_{CB} = $ constant. From the same characteristics the slope of the lines of constant total emitter current yields h_{ob}; correlation of this statement is evident from Eqs. (4–62) and (4–64)

$$h_{ob} = \frac{\partial i_C}{\partial v_{CB}}\bigg|_{i_e=0}. \tag{4-66}$$

To determine the two remaining parameters of the set graphically, one must have the input characteristics of emitter current versus emitter-to-base voltage for various collector-to-base potentials. Such a curve is Fig. 1–8b. h_{ib} is the slope of the lines of constant v_{CB} and mathematically

$$h_{ib} = \frac{\partial v_{EB}}{\partial i_E}\bigg|_{v_{cb}=0} \tag{4-67}$$

From the same characteristics,

$$h_{rb} = \frac{\partial v_{EB}}{\partial v_{CB}}\bigg|_{i_e=0}. \tag{4-68}$$

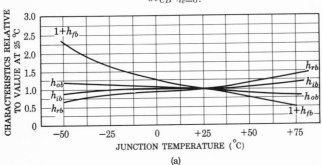

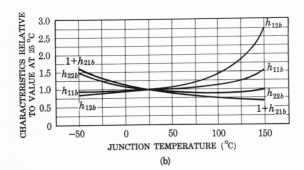

Fig. 4–13. (a) Variation of the h-parameters of a germanium transistor with junction temperature; (b) variation of the h-parameters of a silicon transistor with junction temperature.

Variation of Parameters with Temperature. To some extent each of the parameters of any transistor equivalent circuit exhibits temperature sensitivity. When the internal or junction temperature varies over a considerable

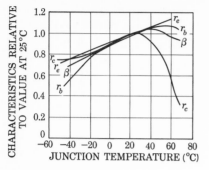

range, definite steps must be taken to compensate a circuit for changes in these parameter values.

As can be seen from examination of Fig. 4–13, variations in the parameters of a typical silicon transistor generally follow the same pattern as those of the typical germanium transistor. The h_{ib} and h_{rb} parameters for the silicon transistor exhibit their greatest sensitivity at temperatures where germanium cannot operate.

Fig. 4–14. Variation of the *T*-parameters of a germanium transistor with junction temperature.

A typical family of curves showing variations in the *T*-parameters is shown in Fig. 4–14. The major reduction that occurs in r_c can be extremely unwelcome. Likewise variations in the other parameters present problems to gain stability and tend to alter input and output impedances. To overcome the effects of temperature variations on parameters, feedback networks and compensating circuitry are often employed.

Variation of Parameters with Operating Point. The parameters of the transistor are sensitive to biasing conditions. The quiescent collector-to-base voltage and the quiescent emitter current each account for specific factors that alter the nominal values of the parameters. Nominal parameter values for low-power transistors are most often given for operation at $I_E = 1$ ma and $V_{CB} = 5$ volts; should the application require operation at a dif-

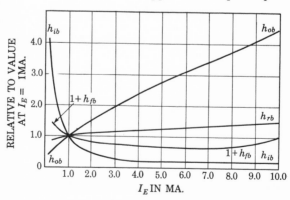

Fig. 4–15. Variation of the *h*-parameters with emitter current for a typical transistor.

ferent point (as it most often does), the nominal parameter values should be multiplied by the manufacturer's correction factors. Typical correction information is shown in Figs. 4–15 and 4–16. It is standard procedure for a

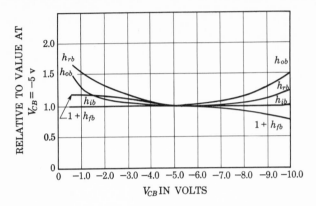

Fig. 4–16. Variation of the h-parameters with collector voltage for a typical transistor.

manufacturer to provide graphs indicating the variation of the parameters of each transistor type.

Example. For the transistor whose parameter variations are shown in Figs. 4–15 and 4–16, determine h_{ob} at $V_{CB} = 10$ volts and $I_E = 0.5$ ma. Nominal h_{ob} is 0.5 micromho.

From the I_E curve at 0.5 ma, the h_{ob} multiplication factor is 0.65. From the V_{CB} curve at 10 volts, the h_{ob} multiplication factor is 1.5. Therefore at the specified operating point

$$h_{ob} = (0.5)(0.65)(1.5) = 0.49 \text{ micromho.}$$

Effect of Manufacturing Tolerances. A most troublesome variation in parameters occurs because of production tolerances. The spread in possible values for the parameters of a single transistor type when it leaves the manufacturers is illustrated by the typical numbers quoted below:

Parameter	Minimum	Design Center	Maximum
h_{ib} in ohms	30	40	90
h_{ob} in micromhos	0.1	0.4	1.5
h_{rb}	$50(10^{-6})$	$500(10^{-6})$	$1500(10^{-6})$
h_{fb}	-0.97	-0.98	-1.0

While for any particular sample it is unlikely that all parameters will be at their maximum or at their minimum values, nevertheless the circuit designer must not exclude this possibility. Thus if we examine the effect of these production variations upon the operation of a sample amplifying stage, greater insight will be possible into the problem of gain stability.

Example 1. Using the numbers quoted above, calculate the power gain of a common-emitter stage for the design center and the two extremes. The stage is feeding a 20,000-ohm load.

From Eq. (4-54)

$$G = \frac{R_L[h_{ib}h_{ob} + h_{fb}]^2}{[h_{ob}(h_{ib} + R_L) + (1 + h_{fb})][h_{ib}(1 + R_Lh_{ob}) - h_{rb}h_{fb}R_L]}.$$

With design center parameters,

$$G = 13.7 \times 10^3, \text{ or } 41.4 \text{ db.}$$

With minimum parameters,

$$G = 19.0 \times 10^3, \text{ or } 42.8 \text{ db.}$$

With maximum parameters,

$$G = 5.4 \times 10^3, \text{ or } 37.3 \text{ db.}$$

It is easy to see that a very large gain spread is possible. For most applications, it would be foolhardy to fail to include stabilizing feedback.

Example 2. Consider the effects of operation at $-50°$ C upon the stage of Example 1.

We must correct the parameters for such low-temperature operation. Under the assumption that Fig. 4-13a applies to this transistor, the correction factors are:

for h_{ib}, 0.9   for h_{ob}, 1.2

for h_{rb}, 0.7   for $1 + h_{fb}$, 2.3

The corrected parameters, when Eq. (4-54) is employed, result in less spread. With design center parameters,

$$G = 7.6 \times 10^3, \text{ or } 38.8 \text{ db.}$$

With minimum parameters,

$$G = 8.8 \times 10^3, \text{ or } 39.4 \text{ db.}$$

With maximum parameters,

$$G = 5.3 \times 10^3, \text{ or } 37.2 \text{ db.}$$

There appears to be a general tendency among manufactured units for h_{ib} and h_{rb} to be high when h_{fb} is high and for h_{ob} to decrease with increasing h_{fb}; however, in some types h_{ob} increases with h_{fb}. It may be concluded, then, that the use of general rules relating these quantities may be unwise, and that in examining gain variation due to manufacturing tolerances it may be advantageous to include all possible extremes. From study of the power-gain equation for the common-emitter stage, h_{fb} appears squared in the numerator and for high gain a large value of that parameter is necessary; the major effects of h_{ib}, h_{ob}, and h_{rb} are in the denominator; for high gain these three parameters must have a low value. If a selection is made from the previous list of those parameters that would result in *maximum* gain,

$$h_{ib} = 30 \text{ ohms,}$$

$$h_{ob} = 0.1 \text{ micromho,}$$

$$h_{rb} = 50 \times 10^{-6},$$

$$h_{fb} = -1.0,$$

and thus

$$G = 323 \times 10^3.$$

The parameters that would result in a *minimum* gain are

$$h_{ib} = 90 \text{ ohms,}$$

$$h_{ob} = 1.5 \text{ micromhos,}$$

$$h_{rb} = 1500 \times 10^{-6},$$

$$h_{fb} = -0.97,$$

and therefore

$$G = 2.6 \times 10^3.$$

Better than a 100:1 gain spread is possible because of the effects of manufacturing tolerances.

4–6. Comparison of Configurations. It was stated earlier that the common-emitter configuration is the most widely accepted and that emphasis would be placed upon that type of connection; this emphasis was apparent in the chapter devoted to biasing. It is natural to question the reasons behind the popularity of common-emitter circuitry, so a comparison of the configurations is in order.

The three configurations have been compared and the results depicted in Figs. 4–17 through 4–21. Typical parameter values of

$$h_{ib} = 50 \text{ ohms,}$$

$$h_{rb} = 5 \times 10^{-4},$$

$$h_{fb} = -0.98,$$

$$h_{ob} = 1 \text{ micromho}$$

were used in the equations previously derived for A_v, A_i, G, R_i, and R_o, and expected performance calculated. Load resistance was considered to be the independent variable except for the calculation of transistor output resistance. Output resistance depends upon the source and is not a function of load.

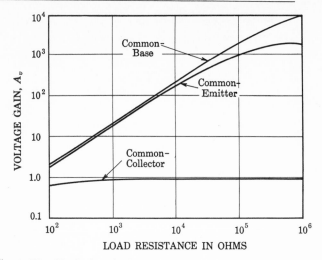

Fig. 4–17. Typical variation of voltage gain with load resistance.

Voltage Gain. The common-emitter and the common-base configurations provide essentially the same voltage gain, as evidenced by the curves of Fig. 4–17. A common-collector stage will never exhibit voltage gain greater than unity. It remains near unity for most high values of load resistance.

Current Gain. The common-emitter and common-collector configurations exhibit similar current-gain curves; they generally drop off for higher values of load resistance. These variations are depicted in Fig. 4–18. The common-

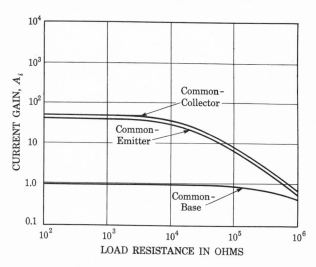

Fig. 4–18. Typical variation of current gain with load resistance.

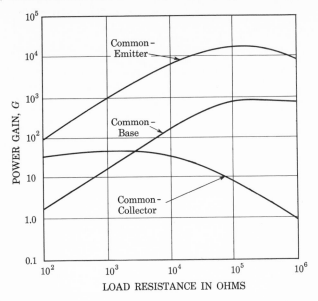

Fig. 4–19. Typical variation of power gain with load resistance.

base configuration is incapable of current amplification above the value of h_{fb} $(-\alpha)$.

Power Gain. Multiplication of the current gain and the voltage gain for each connection results in the power gain curves of Fig. 4–19. Since the common-emitter stage shows the greatest power gain for all values of load resistance, it is most frequently used.

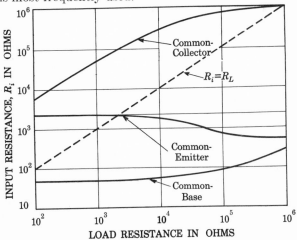

Fig. 4–20. Typical variation of input resistance with load resistance.

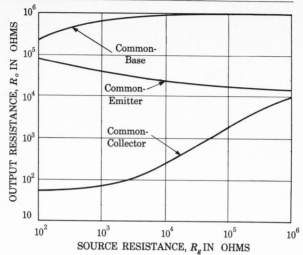

Fig. 4–21. Typical variation of output resistance with source resistance.

Input Resistance. The curves of Fig. 4–20 depict input resistance for the various configurations. The highest resistance is presented by the common-collector circuit although the common-emitter circuit with unbypassed resistance between emitter terminal and ground would present higher input resistances than shown in the figure. The curves, it must be remembered, apply only to the transistor under consideration; alteration of the circuit by feedback or otherwise will alter the values of gain and resistance presented in the curves.

Output Resistance. Output resistance is not a function of R_L, but rather depends upon R_g; consequently Fig. 4–21 presents R_o versus R_g. The common-emitter connection yields intermediate values of output resistance and its variations are not too extreme for most applications.

4–7. Stabilization of Gain. The effects of temperature extremes and manufacturing tolerances upon the gain of a transistor stage were evident in the sample calculations of Section 4–5. Greater than a 100:1 spread in gain resulted; and a greater spread is possible with parameters of a different transistor type or other temperature extremes. Gain calculations for a multistage amplifier will tend to show an even greater degree of lack of predictability. The problem is one of making the gain of constructed amplifiers similar to that calculated by the designer using nominal parameter values.

Use of degenerative local feedback provides a partial solution to the repeatability problem. The gain of a stage is reduced when using feedback, but gain spread is also reduced.

For the common-emitter configuration, local feedback can take on two forms: an unbypassed resistor in series with the emitter terminal, or a resistor

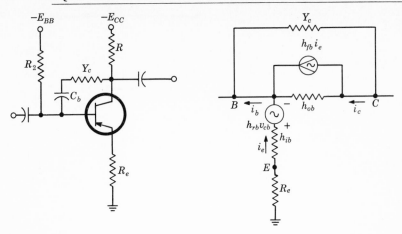

Fig. 4–22. Local feedback for gain stabilization: (a) location of R_e and Y_c in a physical circuit; (b) equivalent for (a) from Fig. 4–10.

between collector and base terminals. Occasionally both are employed in the same circuit. Consider the circuit and equivalent shown in Fig. 4–22. The emitter resistance R_e can be thought of as swamping variations in h_{ib}; the collector-to-base admittance Y_c is bypassing h_{ob} by providing a lower resistance path. (The capacitor C_b blocks d-c to keep from altering the original biasing of the stage.)

Since R_e and Y_c are respectively in series and parallel with h_{ib} and h_{ob} these elements can be easily incorporated into the formulas for operation; here the approximate formulas of Table 4–6 are modified:

$$A_v = \frac{h_{fb}R_L}{(h_{ib} + R_e)[1 + R_L(h_{ob} + Y_c)]}, \tag{4-69}$$

$$A_i = \frac{h_{fb}}{(h_{ob} + Y_c)R_L + (1 + h_{fb})}, \tag{4-70}$$

$$G = \frac{h_{fb}^2 R_L}{(h_{ib} + R_e)[1 + R_L(h_{ob} + Y_c)][R_L(h_{ob} + Y_c) + (1 + h_{fb})]}, \tag{4-71}$$

$$R_i = \frac{(h_{ib} + R_e)[1 + R_L(h_{ob} + Y_c)]}{R_L(h_{ob} + Y_c) + (1 + h_{fb})}, \tag{4-72}$$

$$R_o = \frac{h_{ib} + R_e + R_g(1 + h_{fb})}{(h_{ob} + Y_c)(h_{ib} + R_e + R_g) - h_{rb}h_{fb}}. \tag{4-73}$$

For examples of the effects of this *local* feedback upon circuit operation, the reader is referred to Chapters 5 and 7. A more complete treatment of feedback theory is reserved for Chapter 8.

4–8. Gain Considerations. Thus far in the chapter the voltage amplification of a simple transistor stage has been defined by the ratio of the voltage
at the collector terminal to the voltage at the base terminal. This definition
gives a valid picture of the contribution of the transistor to overall voltage
gain, but the circuit designer is sometimes more concerned with the ratio of
load voltage to source voltage. In a like manner, concern may be centered
about the ratio of load current to source current rather than gain as given by
the preceding gain expressions, which involve collector current and base
current.

If a transistor is being fed from a source with high internal resistance compared to its input resistance, as is true in the circuit of Fig. 4–23a, the voltage

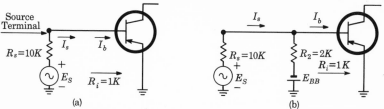

Fig. 4–23. Diagrams for sample gain calculations.

available at its base, based upon the numbers indicated in the diagram, is

$$\frac{R_i}{R_s + R_i} E_s = \frac{E_s}{11}.$$

A considerable attenuation is evident. In the figure all of the current leaving
the source enters the transistor base (base-biasing resistance is assumed large
compared with R_i). The efficiency of the circuit under discussion is of course
related to the maximum-power-transfer theorem; matching of resistance levels
is necessary for optimum performance.

If the method of base bias is as shown in Fig. 4–23b, a greater power loss is
evident. The signal voltage at the base is

$$\frac{R_i R_2/(R_i + R_2)}{R_s + R_i R_2/(R_i + R_2)} E_s = \frac{E_s}{16}$$

and the base current is

$$\frac{R_2}{R_i + R_2} I_s = \frac{2}{3} I_s.$$

In a like fashion loss of signal can occur in the collector-load circuit, and
in the next section examples are given. Certainly from this brief discussion
it can be seen that the amplification required from a circuit must be clearly
defined, and that the loss of gain due to passive circuit elements warrants
attention.

Other power gain expressions have evolved and are used in the literature to measure how efficiently a transistor stage fits into a network containing a specific signal source and a specific load.

The ratio of actual power delivered to a load to power available from the signal generator is known as *transducer gain*. Available power, or the maximum power the source is capable of supplying, depends upon impedance matching. Under conditions where the source (E_s) sees a load equal to its internal resistance (R_s), then

$$P_{\text{avail}} = \frac{E_s{}^2}{4R_s} \tag{4-74}$$

and the transducer gain (G_t) is

$$G_t = \frac{P_o}{P_{\text{avail}}} = \frac{E_o{}^2/R_L}{E_s{}^2/4R_s}. \tag{4-75}$$

With the substitutions that $P_o = I_o{}^2 R_L$ and $E_s = I_s(R_s + R_i)$,

$$G_t = \frac{4I_o{}^2 R_L R_s}{I_s{}^2(R_s + R_i)^2} \tag{4-76a}$$

or

$$G_t = \frac{4A_i{}^2 R_L R_s}{(R_s + R_i)^2} \tag{4-76b}$$

Equation (4-76b) may be useful when comparing several amplifiers in a circuit with fixed generator resistance.

Available power gain (G_a) is defined as the ratio of power available from the transistor to power available from the signal source. Available power depends upon output matching, and

$$G_a = \frac{E_{co}{}^2/4R_o}{E_s{}^2/4R_s} = \frac{E_{co}{}^2 R_s}{E_s{}^2 R_o}, \tag{4-77}$$

where E_{co} is the open-circuit or no-load output voltage and R_o is the output resistance.

If both the input and output of the transistor are matched, *maximum available gain* (MAG) will result. Under these conditions, for a specific transistor, no greater power amplification can occur.

$$MAG = \frac{I_o{}^2 R_o}{I_s{}^2 R_i} = A_i{}^2 \frac{R_o}{R_i} = A_i{}^2 \frac{R_L}{R_s} \tag{4-78}$$

for $R_L = R_o$ and $R_s = R_i$. To achieve this optimum of operation, impedance-matching devices may have to be employed. This is generally not done at audio frequencies for the cost of such devices (transformers) may prohibit the achievement of optimum performance in certain applications, and the low cost of transistors may dictate that an additional stage is less costly. Every transistor type has an MAG; this gain is independent of the actual load or source, although matching is assumed.

Other expressions for the power gains discussed here are given in Problems 4–29, 4–30, and 4–31.

Example. A source with an open-circuit voltage of 1 mv and an internal resistance of 1000 ohms supplies a transistor with input resistance of 500 ohms and $G = 10{,}000$. Find G_t.

$$P_i = \frac{E_s^2 R_i}{(R_s + R_i)^2} = \frac{(10^{-3})^2(500)}{(1000 + 500)^2} = 0.222 \times 10^{-9} \text{ w}$$

$$P_o = P_i G = (0.222 \times 10^{-9})(10^4) = 2.22 \times 10^{-6} \text{ w}$$

$$P_{\text{avail}} = \frac{E_s^2}{4R_s} = \frac{(10^{-3})^2}{4(1000)} = 0.250 \times 10^{-9} \text{ w}.$$

Then

$$G_t = \frac{P_o}{P_{\text{avail}}} = \frac{2.22 \times 10^{-6}}{0.25 \times 10^{-9}} = 8880.$$

The transducer gain and the power gain are nearly equal, indicating a fairly efficient input circuit. If $R_i = R_s$, then $G = G_t$.

4–9. Examples of Single-Stage Calculations

Example 1. It is desired to analyze the circuit of Fig. 4–24 to determine A_v, A_i, and G of the transistor stage and to determine the operating point.

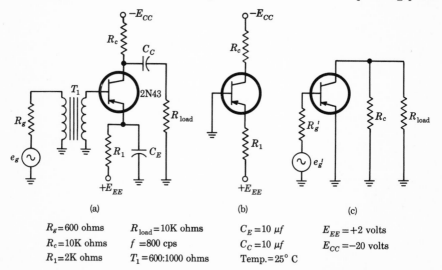

(a)   (b)   (c)

$R_g = 600$ ohms	$R_{\text{load}} = 10\text{K}$ ohms	$C_E = 10\ \mu f$	$E_{EE} = +2$ volts
$R_c = 10\text{K}$ ohms	$f = 800$ cps	$C_C = 10\ \mu f$	$E_{CC} = -20$ volts
$R_1 = 2\text{K}$ ohms	$T_1 = 600{:}1000$ ohms	Temp. $= 25°$ C	

Fig. 4–24. Analysis of single-stage amplifier, Example 1: (a) complete circuit; (b) d-c portion; (c) a-c portion.

A good starting point is investigation of the operating point; this means solving the d-c circuit. Since the base terminal is essentially at ground potential (transformer secondary resistance assumed negligible) and since the emitter-to-base potential drop can be considered negligible, it can be concluded that the emitter terminal is also at d-c ground, and

$$I_E \cong \frac{E_{EE}}{R_1} = \frac{2}{2\,K} = 1 \text{ ma.}$$

$I_C \cong I_E$; therefore $I_C = 1$ ma, and the drop across R_c is

$$I_C R_c = (1 \times 10^{-3})(10 \times 10^3) = 10 \text{ volts.}$$

Therefore

$$V_{CE} = E_{CC} - I_C R_c = 20 - 10 = 10 \text{ volts.}$$

Thus the operating point is defined by

$$I_C = 1 \text{ ma} \quad \text{and} \quad V_{CE} = 10 \text{ volts.}$$

To obtain the a-c parameters, we can make use of the design-center values tabulated for the 2N43:

$$h_{ib} = 29 \text{ ohms} \qquad h_{fe} = 42$$
$$h_{rb} = 5 \times 10^{-4} \qquad h_{ob} = 0.8 \text{ micromho.}$$

No correction is needed for emitter current; however, at 10 volts the following correction factors must be used:

for h_{fe}, 1.1;   for h_{rb}, 0.75;   for h_{ob}, 0.75;   for h_{ib}, 1.

Therefore the corrected parameters are

$$h_{ib} = 29 \text{ ohms} \qquad h_{fe} = 46$$
$$h_{rb} = 3.75 \times 10^{-4} \qquad h_{ob} = 0.6 \text{ micromho}$$
$$h_{fb} = -0.979.$$

The a-c load (R_L) upon the stage is R_c in parallel with R_{load} (when C_c is large enough for its reactance to be negligible). Thus $R_L = 5\,K$ ohms. Operation of the circuit is calculated from the approximate formulas of Table 4–6:

$$A_v = \frac{h_{fb}R_L}{h_{ib}(1 + h_{ob}R_L)} = 169,$$

$$A_i = \frac{h_{fb}}{h_{ob}R_L + (1 + h_{fb})} = 40.8,$$

$$G = A_v A_i = 6900, \text{ or } 38.4 \text{ db.}$$

The gain calculations pertain only to the transistor; to include the entire circuit we observe that not all of the alternating collector current flows to R_{load}; in fact only one half of i_c gets to the required resistor. All of the alternating collector voltage is available at R_{load}; therefore the actual figures are

$$A_v = 169$$

$$A_i = 20.4$$

$$G = 3450, \text{ or } 35.4 \text{ db.}$$

These figures do not include the performance of the coupling transformer. Since R_{load} is known and cannot be changed, and since the degree of mismatch is unimportant in this example, it is unnecessary to calculate R_o of the stage. Should the calculation be made, R_g must be reflected into the base circuit by consideration of the transformer turns ratio. Calculating R_i is also unnecessary except as a check of the suitability of the coupling transformer.

Further information could be gleaned by graphical methods. Plotting of d-c and a-c load lines and observations of their limits could indicate the maximum possible Class-A output voltage, current, and power, and yield information concerning overload capacity and distortion. Frequency response could also be determined; these topics will be discussed in Chapter 5.

Example 2. Analyze the circuit of Fig. 4–25 to determine A_v, A_i, and G. Again starting by investigating the d-c circuit paths we notice that R_1 is

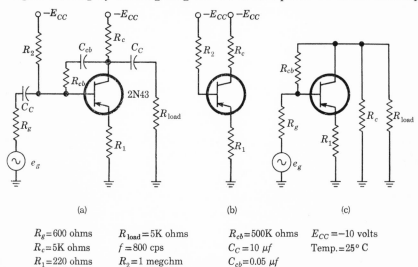

(a)   (b)   (c)

$R_g = 600$ ohms	$R_{load} = 5K$ ohms	$R_{cb} = 500K$ ohms	$E_{CC} = -10$ volts
$R_c = 5K$ ohms	$f = 800$ cps	$C_C = 10$ μf	Temp. = 25° C
$R_1 = 220$ ohms	$R_2 = 1$ megohm	$C_{cb} = 0.05$ μf	

Fig. 4–25. Analysis of single-stage amplifier, Example 2: (a) complete circuit; (b) d-c portion; (c) a-c portion.

rather small; consequently $I_E R_1$ will be small, so that the base potential will differ from ground potential by less than one volt. If we consider the base to be at ground potential, then

$$I_B \cong \frac{E_{CC}}{R_2} = \frac{10}{10^6} = 10 \ \mu\text{a}.$$

If a d-c load line starting at -10 volts is drawn on the output characteristics of the 2N43 transistor and the slope of that line made equal to $-1/R_c$ or, in this instance, approximately $-1/5 \ K$, then I_B of 10 μa corresponds to an operating point at

$$I_C \cong 1.0 \text{ ma} \quad \text{and} \quad V_{CE} \cong 5 \text{ volts}.$$

The published nominal parameters need not be corrected for this operating point. However there is series emitter resistance and collector-to-base shunting admittance, so the gain formulas must be modified to include the effects of this local feedback. The a-c load on this stage is $2.5 \ K$, the resistance of the parallel combination of R_c and R_{load}.

$$A_v = \frac{h_{fb} R_L}{(h_{ib} + R_e)[1 + (h_{ob} + Y_c)R_L]} = 9.8,$$

$$A_i = \frac{h_{fb}}{R_L(h_{ob} + Y_c) + (1 + h_{fb})} = 32.5,$$

$$G = A_v A_i = 318, \text{ or } 25.0 \text{ db}.$$

One half of the collector current reaches R_{load}; therefore, the actual figures for the stage are

$$A_v = 9.8,$$

$$A_i = 16.25,$$

$$G = 159, \text{ or } 22.0 \text{ db}.$$

There is essentially no power loss in the base circuit. By utilizing the a-c load-line techniques to be explained in Chapter 5 we could also obtain other information concerning this circuit.

4–10. Instantaneous Analysis. Often it is desirable to analyze circuit operation by assuming that instantaneous signals of certain polarities are introduced at a circuit input for the purpose of determining the resulting changes in voltages and currents at some other place in a composite circuit. A technique of this type is often utilized for vacuum-tube circuit analysis, and an extension of the method to transistors is desirable.

Consider the p-n-p transistor shown in Fig. 4–26a. The directions of normal d-c currents and potentials are shown on the diagram. Collector characteristics for the transistor, Fig. 4–26b, include the load line and the operating point. The load line is determined by R_1 and R_L in series, and applies to both d-c and a-c analyses. R_1 is included in the diagram for completeness.

Let us now introduce an a-c source at the input terminals of the network, and assume that terminal A of that source is, at the moment of inspection, more positive than terminal B (Fig. 4–26c). The source will thus attempt to cause a current i_s to flow *into* the transistor base, or in other words, the source

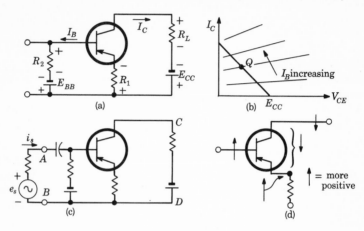

Fig. 4–26. Instantaneous analysis.

will reduce the instantaneous value of base current. Turning our attention back to (b) of the figure we may note that a reduction in base current causes a corresponding reduction in the magnitude of collector current and a corresponding increase in the magnitude of the collector-emitter voltage. Emitter current likewise will be reduced.

Now examine the altered circuit potentials. The voltage from D to C of Fig. 4–26c was, in the absence of signal, equal to $(-E_{CC} + I_C R_L)$. The positive-going base signal has, as described above, reduced collector current. Therefore the D to C potential $(-E_{CC} + I_C R_L)$ is now more negative because of that reduction. It can easily be seen that a phase reversal has occurred, because a positive-going input has resulted in a more negative-going output.

A corresponding reduction in emitter current will result when conditions are as described above, and this, for a circuit with resistance in the emitter lead, will cause the drop across R_1 to decrease, and the emitter terminal will become more positive.

Now suppose that we adopt a shorthand notation to specify the operation discussed here. Using an arrow pointed upward to indicate a potential that is instantaneously becoming more positive, it is possible to draw Fig. 4–26d. This figure shows that when the base is subjected to a positive-going signal, the collector potential becomes more negative. The emitter potential is now more positive than previously if an emitter resistance is included in the circuit. The effects of an unbypassed emitter resistance such as R_1 in the diagram may be clearly understood. The assumed input signal has increased the emitter potential, allowing a reduced signal from base-to-emitter, an indication of negative feedback.

Some may prefer analyzing transistor circuits currentwise. Base current instantaneously flowing toward the base (reducing the normal bias current) causes a reduced collector current, or one that is instantaneously flowing toward the collector, and an emitter current away from the emitter terminal. Of course in all cases these a-c excursions are superimposed upon the normal direct currents. It is possible to extend this type of reasoning to other configurations and naturally to the n-p-n unit. It is suggested that the reader work out a system of analysis that he finds most satisfactory to explain the operation.

4–11. Summary. The transistor has been described by several equivalent circuits, the parameters of which have been briefly discussed, and the importance of the topics of Chapters 1 and 3 have been brought to light in the analysis of simple single-stage circuits. The ties between semiconductor physics and the subject of parameter values and variations have not been thoroughly covered here. Such relationships are available in the more advanced texts.[1, 6, 10]

The reader may feel that the transistor is a vastly complex and unpredictable device after having been informed of parameter corrections and variations that abound at every turn. Certainly the device is complex, but successful circuits are not extremely difficult to create. The manufacturer's production control is steadily improving and gain spread due to this cause is being overcome. Temperature sensitivity is a problem; the solution seems to be dependent upon the individual engineer's experience with compensating circuitry. Feedback, the subject of Chapter 8, is an important remedy for some problems.

The next hurdle to be met in this transistor study is the design of simple single-stage amplifying circuits, and the extension of our knowledge to coupling circuits and to operation at the higher audio frequencies.

PROBLEMS

4–1. Prove that the power gain of a transistor stage can be expressed as

$$G = A_i{}^2 R_L / R_i,$$

or as

$$G = A_v{}^2 R_i / R_L.$$

4-2. Verify Eqs. (4–15), (4–16), (4–17) and (4–18) for the common-base orientation.

4-3. Verify Eq. (4–19) for the common-base orientation.

4-4. Verify Eqs. (4–20), (4–21), (4–22) and (4–23) for the common-collector configuration.

4-5. Verify Eq. (4–24) for the common-collector configuration.

4-6. Use the typical values of T-parameters listed in Sec. 4–2 to calculate the voltage gain, current gain, and input resistance of a common-emitter stage feeding a 2000-ohm load. Compare the answers obtained from using the complete equations with those obtained from the approximate equations of Table 4–1.

4-7. A transistor being operated common-emitter and feeding a 5000-ohm load has $\alpha = 0.99$, $r_b = 100$ ohms, $r_c = 2 \times 10^6$ ohms and $r_e = 40$ ohms. What is the input resistance and voltage amplification at low frequencies?

4-8. Calculate the current amplification and input and output resistance of a simple transistor circuit feeding a 1000-ohm load from a 1000-ohm source. $\beta = 50$, $r_b = 500$ ohms, $r_e = 30$ ohms and $r_c = 10^6$ ohms. Consider the three practical configurations.

4-9. Write the six pairs of black-box equations in matrix form.

4-10. Draw equivalent circuits for Eqs. (4–26) and Eqs. (4–28).

4-11. Draw equivalent circuits for Eqs. (4–29) and Eqs. (4–30).

4-12. Analyze the common-collector circuit with common-base parameters shown in the accompanying diagram in order to confirm the gain and resistance equations which are presented in the table.

COMMON-COLLECTOR FORMULAS FOR THE h-EQUIVALENT*

Voltage Gain, A_v	$\dfrac{R_L}{h_{ib} + R_L}$
Current Gain, A_i	$\dfrac{1}{h_{ob}(h_{ib} + R_L) + (1 + h_{fb})}$
Power Gain, G	$\dfrac{R_L}{(h_{ib} + R_L)[h_{ob}(h_{ib} + R_L) + (1 + h_{fb})]}$
Input Resistance, R_i	$\dfrac{h_{ib} + R_L}{h_{ob}(h_{ib} + R_L) + (1 + h_{fb})}$
Output Resistance, R_o	$\dfrac{h_{ib}(1 + R_g h_{ob}) + R_g(1 + h_{fb})}{1 + R_g h_{ob}}$

* $(1 - h_{rb})$ factors omitted.

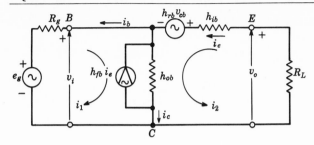

Problem 4–12.

4–13. Confirm the formulas given in Problem 4–12 by using the formulas of Table 4–3 and the parameter relations of Table 4–7.

4–14. Confirm the formulas given in Problem 4–12 by using the formulas of Table 4–4 and the parameter relations of Table 4–5.

4–15. It is desired to investigate the common-collector configuration with local feedback from output (emitter) to input (base). Use the h-matrix equivalent circuit and derive an expression for current gain in terms of the common-base h-parameters and the feedback resistance R_X.

4–16. A common-base stage couples a low-resistance source to a load of 50,000 ohms. If $h_{ib} = 32$ ohms, $h_{fb} = -0.96$, $h_{rb} = 2 \times 10^{-4}$, and $h_{ob} = 10^{-6}$ mho, find the input and output resistance of this transistor, and the voltage gain provided by the circuit.

4–17. Draw a practical circuit and specify all test equipment, switches, batteries, etc., for the laboratory measurement of the common-base h-parameters of a low-power transistor at 400 cps. Show how to compute the parameters from meter readings.

4–18. Consider a 2N43 to be operated common-emitter at the recommended point. Calculate the maximum and minimum current gain to be expected. The load is 10,000 ohms and the temperature is 25° C.

4–19. What effect will a 40° C rise in ambient temperature have upon the operation of the circuit of Problem 4–18?

4–20. What is the power gain of a 2N344 with $h_{fe} = 25$ and $R_L = 2000$ ohms? Calculate the voltage and current gains of this common-emitter circuit.

4–21. For a transistor in the common-base configuration investigate the effects of a resistor in the base lead and one from collector-to-emitter.

4–22. Prove the relationships between h_{re} and h_{oe} and the common-base h-parameters.

4–23. Prove the relationships between the common-collector and common-base h-parameters.

4–24. Prove the relationships listed in Table 4–7 that include the T-parameters expressed as functions of common-base h-parameters.

4–25. For the transistor whose parameter variations are shown in Figs. 4–15 and 4–16, determine all common-base parameters at $I_E = 8$ ma and $V_{CB} = 2$ volts. Nominal values are $h_{ib} = 40$ ohms, $h_{fb} = -0.95$, $h_{rb} = 5 \times 10^{-4}$ and $h_{ob} = 10^{-6}$ mho.

4–26. The curves representing power gain versus load resistance each reach a maximum at a particular value of load resistance. This value of load resistance may be determined by differentiating the appropriate gain formulas with respect to R_L. Impedance matching thus could describe this effect. Impedance matching, however, is not used to any great extent in low-frequency transistor circuitry because of other considerations such as the widespread use of R-C coupling, where the difference in magnitude between R_o and R_i prevents impedance matching. Derive an expression for R_L for maximum power gain for the common-emitter configuration in terms of the h-parameters.

4–27. Repeat Problem 4–26 for the common-base configuration.

4–28. Repeat Problem 4–26 for the common-collector configuration.

4–29. Prove that, for any configuration, transducer gain may be given by

$$G_t = \frac{4R_L R_g h_f{}^2}{[R_g R_L h_o + R_g + (h_i h_o - h_r h_f)R_L + h_i]^2}.$$

4–30. Prove that, for any configuration, available gain may be given by

$$G_a = \frac{h_f{}^2 R_g}{[(h_i h_o - h_r h_f) + R_g h_o][R_g + h_i]}.$$

4–31. Prove that, for any configuration, maximum available gain may be given by

$$MAG = \frac{h_f{}^2}{[(h_i h_o - h_r h_f)^{1/2} + (h_i h_o)^{1/2}]^2}.$$

4–32. For the transistor of Problem 4–20, by how much will the circuit gains change if an unbypassed emitter resistance of 100 ohms is used?

4–33. In the calculation of the gains of the circuit of Fig. 4–24, approximate formulas were used. Using complete equations, determine the error resulting from the use of the approximate relations.

4–34. Make a listing similar to Table 4–6 for the common-emitter configuration with feedback resistors R_e and Y_c.

4–35. A transistor with $f_{ab} = 0.5$ mc has the following low-frequency h-parameters: $h_{ib} = 50$ ohms, $h_{rb} = 10^{-4}$, $h_{fbo} = -0.98$, $h_{ob} = 2 \times 10^{-6}$ mho. Express the common-emitter h-parameters in complex form at 10,000 cps. $h_{fb} = h_{fbo}/(1 + jf/f_{ab})$, with h_{fbo} the low-frequency or reference value of that parameter.

4–36. Explain how to determine the common-emitter h-parameters graphically.

4–37. Very occasionally a transistor is employed in the reverse common-base configuration. Power gain of less than unity is thereby achieved, so this connection is not useful for amplification. Although no applications are treated here, as an exercise derive the formulas for A_v, A_i, R_i, and R_o from the T-equivalent circuit.

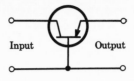

Problem 4–37.

4–38. Use the T-equivalent circuit to investigate the effects of unbypassed emitter-lead and base-lead resistance upon circuit gains and resistance levels.

4–39. The curves of Figs. 4–17 through 4–20 can be approximated by straight lines intersecting at "break" values of R_L. Each of the complete A_v, A_i, G, and R_i equations can be put in the form

$$\frac{a + bR_L}{c + dR_L}.$$

Breaks in the straight line approximations will occur at $R_L = a/b$ and $R_L = c/d$.

(a) From Table 4–6 determine formulas that will predict the breaks in the common-emitter performance versus R_L curves.

(b) Repeat part (a) for the common-base curves.

REFERENCES

1. DeWitt, D., and Rossoff, A. L., *Transistor Electronics*, McGraw-Hill Book Company, Inc., New York, 1957.
2. Early, J. M., "Design Theory of Junction Transistors," *Bell System Technical Journal*, vol. 32 (Nov., 1953).
3. Hunter, L. P., *Handbook of Semiconductor Electronics*, McGraw-Hill Book Company, Inc., New York, 1956.
4. Hurley, R. B., *Junction Transistor Electronics*, John Wiley & Sons, Inc., New York, 1958.
5. Kambouris, G. N., "Low Frequencies Vary T-Parameters," *Electronic Industries*, vol. 17 (Dec., 1958).
6. Lo, A. W., *et al.*, *Transistor Electronics*, Prentice-Hall, Inc., Englewood Cliffs, New Jersey, 1955.
7. Riddle, R. L., and Ristenbatt, M. P., *Transistor Physics and Circuits*, Prentice-Hall, Inc., Englewood Cliffs, New Jersey, 1958.
8. Shea, R. F., *Principles of Transistor Circuits*, John Wiley & Sons, Inc., New York, 1953.
9. Shea, R. F., *Transistor Audio Amplifiers*, John Wiley & Sons, Inc., New York, 1955.
10. Shea, R. F., *Transistor Circuit Engineering*, John Wiley & Sons, Inc., New York, 1957.

Chapter 5

SINGLE-STAGE AMPLIFIER DESIGN

The designer of a transistor amplifier must have a usable knowledge of the information presented in Chapters 1 through 4—the basic definitions, transistor-operation theory, biasing techniques, parameter variations, and the methods of predicting gain and circuit impedances. In addition, he must know the specifications for the particular circuit to be designed; those specifications may take on various forms. For most practical designs information of the following types is necessary:

1. Desired gain (voltage, current, or power)
2. Input and output signal levels
3. Carrier frequency and phase-shift or frequency response
4. Input impedance
5. Operating and storage temperature range
6. Load and source characteristics
7. Available supply potentials
8. Cost, weight, and size requirements
9. Other environmental conditions
10. Distortion
11. Life expectancy

After collection of the pertinent requirements the design may be initiated.

This chapter is devoted to the design of single-stage, low-power audio and control amplifiers. Before proceeding with sample designs, we shall discuss the choice of a particular transistor, coupling circuitry, a-c load-line analysis, and the basic considerations of operation at the higher audio frequencies.

5–1. Choice of a Transistor. What transistor type should be used for a hi-fi preamplifier, a motor-driving stage, an aircraft installation, a computer, a radio-frequency amplifier, etc.? These questions arise daily. The answers to them are available from the manufacturers' literature and from tests performed by the interested circuit designer.

All transistor types are classified by the manufacturer according to the

114

intended application, i.e., audio, intermediate-frequency, oscillator, switching, high-power, general-purpose, etc. To narrow the field, we can choose all those transistors that pertain to our application. Then a study of circuit specifications will allow a choice of semiconductor material and finally the particular transistor can be chosen for the job.

Silicon vs. Germanium. The transistor circuit designer must choose between silicon and germanium units for most of his applications. Study of the peculiarities of each will usually result in certain advantages of one material over the other—in general, the choice is obvious for a particular application.

A major difference between the two materials is the width of their respective energy gaps. The larger gap for silicon results in a much lower leakage current (I_{CO}), but often at the expense of greater resistive parameters and a lower current-amplification factor. A brief operational comparison is given here:

1. Temperature—Silicon units operate satisfactorily at temperatures of 175° C or higher, whereas operation with germanium is impossible above a junction temperature of about 90 to 100° C. Both types can be operated at the low temperatures, −55° C for example.

2. Cutoff currents—Silicon transistors have leakage currents 100 or more times lower than the I_{CO} of comparable germanium units.

3. Current-amplification factor—Whereas both materials can be used to manufacture transistors with high alphas at 25° C, the change of alpha with temperature is generally more noticeable in silicon transistors.

4. Collector voltage—Higher maximum collector-voltage ratings are available in present silicon units.

5. Saturation resistance (R_{CS})—Silicon devices may exhibit several hundred ohms of collector-to-emitter resistance when in the full ON or saturated condition. R_{CS} for germanium units is much lower.

6. Cost—Germanium transistors are available at considerably lower cost (1959).

The Particular Transistor. Hundreds of transistor types are available to the circuit designer just as hundreds of vacuum-tube types are available, and a choice must be made; usually this choice must come near the beginning of each circuit design.

Choosing the correct transistor involves familiarization with available products; knowledge of the relative advantages of silicon and germanium must result in a material decision. After the material has been selected, the following items should be considered:

1. Current-amplification factor—High-, medium-, and low-alpha types are available.

2. Maximum collector-operating voltage—Ratings range from 3 to 300

volts. This rating is sometimes called BV_{CE}, minimum collector-to-emitter breakdown voltage at a specific collector current.

3. Maximum collector-power dissipation—This limitation is usually specified at 25° C (77° F).

4. Maximum junction temperature—When the transistor is operated with junction temperature at the specified maximum, the allowable collector-power dissipation is zero. Between the limiting junction temperature and 25° C a linear relationship usually exists between maximum power dissipation and operating temperature.

5. Maximum collector current.

6. Alpha cutoff frequency (f_{ab})—The frequency at which alpha is down to 0.707 of its reference-frequency value.

7. Physical size, mounting dimensions.

8. Cost.

9. Noise factor—Low-noise transistors are available for special applications.

10. Leakage current—Low-leakage units may be selected during manufacture.

11. Variation of parameters—Types can be compared according to the extent of parameter variations due to production tolerances and ambient temperature excursions.

5–2. Coupling. As has been stated, the transistor is capable of voltage and current amplification. Should an application require primarily voltage amplification (or power amplification), then, from study of the gain equations and the sample graphs of the preceding chapter, the stage must be terminated in a high-resistance load. On the other hand, if current amplification is of primary concern, a low value of load resistance is mandatory. In the vast majority of circuits, the general requirement is to raise the signal-power level. It is generally desirable to work into high-resistance loads to achieve maximum power transfer, but often this is impossible because of other considerations, which will be apparent from the discussion of coupling circuitry.

The joining of a low-frequency stage to its signal source or load can be accomplished for both vacuum tube and transistor with transformers or resistance-capacitance circuitry. The advantages and disadvantages of each method are discussed in the paragraphs to follow.

Coupling Transformers. It was shown in Chapter 3 that a high level of operation-point stability is achieved with transformer coupling. This is by no means the only advantage of transformers; their ability to transform impedances is of particular importance. If we consider an ideal transformer, the power levels of primary and secondary will be equal, and thus

$$V_1 I_1 = V_2 I_2. \tag{5–1}$$

The magnetomotive-force equation applies,

$$N_1 I_1 = N_2 I_2. \tag{5-2}$$

N_1 and N_2 denote the number of primary and secondary turns, respectively. From Ohm's Law,

$$Z_1 = \frac{V_1}{I_1}, \tag{5-3a}$$

and

$$Z_2 = \frac{V_2}{I_2}. \tag{5-3b}$$

Substitution of Eqs. (5–1), (5–2) and (5–3b) into (5–3a) yields

$$Z_1 = \left(\frac{N_1}{N_2}\right)^2 Z_2. \tag{5-4}$$

In a practical sense Eq. (5–4) enables the circuit designer to achieve any required a-c load on a given transistor by choosing the proper turns ratio of the transformer coupling the transistor to a given load.

It is true, however, that coupling transformers are by no means ideal. Fig. 5–1a presents the transformer as a complex circuit configuration of re-

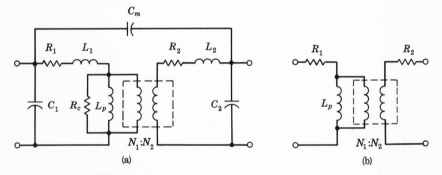

(a)   (b)

Fig. 5–1.   Transformer equivalent circuits: (a) complete circuit for iron-core transformer; (b) approximation useful at low frequencies.

sistance, inductance, and capacitance. C_1 and C_2 represent distributed winding capacitances; L_1 and L_2 are leakage inductances; R_1 and R_2 are winding resistances; R_c is representative of core losses. The capacitance C_m exists between primary and secondary windings. L_p is a measure of primary inductance and is of interest when the magnetizing current is studied. The only ideal portion of an actual transformer is shown by the windings N_1 and N_2.

For low-frequency use, the equivalent circuit of Fig. 5–1a may be approximated by the circuit of Fig. 5–1b. Considering each component separately, the following observations may be made:

1. The winding resistances R_1 and R_2 must generally be kept low to minimize losses. The slope of the d-c load line is directly determined by R_1 for transistor collector potential is usually fed through this transformer winding. Resistances of typical interstage transformers range from 200 to 1000 ohms per winding.

2. L_p should generally be large. If $2\pi f L_p$ is more than twice the reflected load resistance $(N_1/N_2)^2 R_L$, the a-c load line will approach the desired straight line. Should L_p be small or should R_L be removed, the transistor works into a reactive load; operation on the resulting elliptical load line will often damage the transistor by causing its ratings to be exceeded.

As with transformer-coupled vacuum-tube stages, low-frequency response falls off because of a decreasing ωL_p; at the high end of the audio-frequency spectrum, resonances within a transformer may cause a response "hump"; a general decrease in response is apparent for frequencies beyond the "hump" because of lowered shunt capacitive reactances and increased leakage reactance.

To specify an interstage transformer, it is common to supply information of the following types:

1. Impedance ratio (or turns ratio)
2. Maximum a-c power delivered to the primary
3. Maximum unbalanced direct current in the windings
4. Minimum primary inductance (at a specified voltage level, frequency, and d-c unbalance)
5. Maximum permissible power loss (or efficiency)
6. Frequency response

An efficiency percentage can describe power loss; an insertion-loss factor in decibels may be supplied, or voltage regulation can be used as a figure of merit.

$$\text{Regulation} = \frac{V_{SO} - V_{SF}}{V_{SF}}. \tag{5-5}$$

V_{SO} and V_{SF} stand for no-load and full-load secondary voltages respectively. V_{SO} can also be used to signify the secondary voltage at full load if no losses are experienced. Since

$$V = \sqrt{PR}, \tag{5-6}$$

then

$$\text{Regulation} = \frac{\sqrt{P_{SO}R} - \sqrt{P_{SF}R}}{\sqrt{P_{SF}R}} \tag{5-7a}$$

$$= \frac{\sqrt{P_{SO}} - \sqrt{P_{SF}}}{\sqrt{P_{SF}}}. \tag{5-7b}$$

P_{SO} is the no-loss full-load secondary power and P_{SF} is the actual secondary power at full load. If a 3-db loss is to be considered, then $P_{SO} = 2P_{SF}$, for one half of the input power is lost, and

$$\text{Regulation (3-db loss)} = \frac{\sqrt{2P_{SF}} - \sqrt{P_{SF}}}{\sqrt{P_{SF}}} \qquad (5\text{-}8)$$

$$= 0.414, \text{ or } 41.4\%.$$

Similarly

$$\text{Regulation (2-db loss)} = 26\%.$$

$$\text{Regulation (1-db loss)} = 12\%.$$

Interstage transformers are very useful for coupling transistor circuits. A high level of circuit efficiency is attainable, and the few components simplify circuit design, although transformer disadvantages such as weight, physical size, cost, and availability may rule them out in some designs. A 2- to 3-db loss can be expected for the average miniature coupling transformer.

Capacitive Coupling. Because input resistance of common-emitter stages is low (500 to 2000 ohms) large coupling capacitors must be employed if acceptable frequency response is necessary, and if phase shift is not to be excessive at the lower frequencies. Advances in the art of capacitor manufacture have resulted in high-capacitance, low-voltage electrolytics that have become widely adopted by circuit designers. It is commonplace to find 50-microfarad capacitors joining stages of a transistor amplifier.

The circuit shown in Fig. 5–2a and its equivalent in Fig. 5–2b can form the

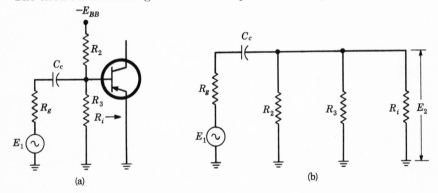

Fig. 5–2. Typical input circuit: (a) actual schematic; (b) low-frequency a-c equivalent for (a).

basis for several sample calculations. Should a voltage source of internal resistance R_g be driving the stage shown, phase shift could be calculated by utilizing conventional circuit theory. Assume $R_2 \gg R_3$, and use voltage-division principles

$$E_2 = E_1 \frac{R_3 R_i/(R_3 + R_i)}{R_3 R_i/(R_3 + R_i) + R_g - jX_c}. \qquad (5\text{–}9)$$

The voltage-transfer function is

$$\frac{E_2}{E_1} = \frac{R_3 R_i}{R_3 R_i + R_g R_3 + R_g R_i - jX_c(R_3 + R_i)}. \qquad (5\text{–}10)$$

Phase shift is determined by the complex denominator, and is

$$\theta = \tan^{-1} \frac{X_c(R_3 + R_i)}{R_3 R_i + R_g R_3 + R_g R_i}. \qquad (5\text{–}11)$$

θ is a positive angle, or, stated otherwise, the coupling network provides a phase lead of output voltage with respect to the source.

When the transistor is fed from a previous common-emitter stage, R_g could be represented by R_o, and a current generator of I_o would parallel it, as depicted in Fig. 5–3. The necessary coupling capacitor can again be determined

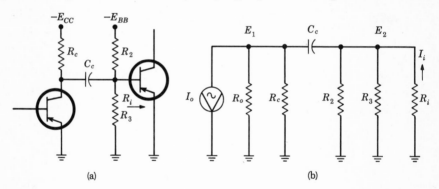

Fig. 5–3. Typical R-C coupled circuit: (a) actual schematic; (b) low-frequency a-c equivalent for (a).

by solving the a-c equivalent circuit. The value of R_o is often large compared with R_c, and R_2 large compared with R_3; for simplicity R_o and R_2 will be omitted from the work that follows. The current generator and parallel R_c can be replaced by an equivalent-voltage source, and, by voltage-division principles,

$$E_2 = (I_o R_c) \frac{R_3 R_i/(R_3 + R_i)}{R_c + R_3 R_i/(R_3 + R_i) - jX_c}. \qquad (5\text{–}12)$$

It is obvious that

$$E_2 = I_i R_i.$$

Therefore the resulting current-transfer function is

$$\frac{I_i}{I_o} = \frac{R_3 R_c}{R_3 R_c + R_i R_c + R_3 R_i - j X_c (R_3 + R_i)}. \tag{5-13}$$

When investigating phase shift, we find that

$$\theta = \tan^{-1} \frac{X_c (R_3 + R_i)}{R_3 R_c + R_i R_c + R_3 R_i}. \tag{5-14}$$

The frequency response of a coupling network can be of importance in the design of audio amplifiers. For networks of the type shown in Fig. 5–3 for which Eq. (5–13) applies approximately, the frequency response will be 3 db down (half-power point) when the denominator of Eq. (5–13) has the form $A + jA$, or when

$$X_c (R_3 + R_i) = R_3 R_c + R_i R_c + R_3 R_i.$$

Therefore

$$f_{3\text{ db}} = \frac{R_3 + R_i}{2 \pi C (R_3 R_c + R_i R_c + R_3 R_i)}. \tag{5-15}$$

For accuracy in calculations one must be aware of any assumptions used. In the preceding work R_o and R_2 were not to affect the resulting equations; however, there are some practical circuits where these parameters are important and should be thoroughly investigated. In the preceding work the transistor's input impedance was assumed to be resistive (R_i). When by-passed-emitter resistance is used, input impedance will be sensitive to frequency, and low-frequency response thus limited. This condition warrants study.

Consider that the emitter of the second transistor in the circuit of Fig. 5–3 is connected to ground through R_1 bypassed by C_1. The circuit load can no longer be represented by R_i alone, but must also include R_1 and C_1. An expression for the input impedance of the transistor is

$$Z_i \cong R_i + \frac{[\beta + 1] R_1}{1 + j \omega C_1 R_1}. \tag{5-16}$$

If the effects of the coupling capacitor are not considered, and our attention focussed entirely upon C_1, the lower half-power frequency for the circuit including bypassed emitter resistance is given by

$$f_{3\text{ db}} \cong \frac{[\beta + 1] R_1 + R_i + R_T}{2 \pi C_1 R_1 [R_i + R_T]}. \tag{5-17}$$

R_T is the equivalent resistance of the parallel combination of R_c, R_o, R_2, and R_3. Proof of Eqs. (5–16) and (5–17) is left to the reader (Problem 5–12).

Example. Consider a typical stage having the following characteristics:

$$R_i = 1500 \text{ ohms} \qquad\qquad R_g = 600 \text{ ohms}$$

$$R_c = 10{,}000 \text{ ohms}$$

$$R_3 = 10{,}000 \text{ ohms} \qquad\qquad f = 400 \text{ cps}$$

It is desired to find a value for C that will result in a phase shift of 5° or less when the transistor is employed in the circuits of Fig. 5–2 and Fig. 5–3.

For the circuit of Fig. 5–2, Eq. (5–11) can be rearranged to the form

$$X_c = \frac{\tan \theta (R_3 R_i + R_g R_3 + R_g R_i)}{R_3 + R_i},$$

from which

$$C = 2.4 \ \mu\text{f}.$$

For the circuit of Fig. 5–3, rearrangement of Eq. (5–14) gives

$$X_c = \frac{\tan \theta (R_3 R_c + R_i R_c + R_3 R_i)}{R_3 + R_i},$$

so

$$C = 0.4 \ \mu\text{f}.$$

Any value of capacitance in excess of these values will result in less than a 5° phase shift.

If the low-frequency response of the Fig. 5–3 circuit is desired, and a 5-μf coupling capacitor used, then the frequency at which the response is 3 db down from its mid-frequency value is given by Eq. (5–15):

$$f_{3 \text{ db}} = 2.8 \text{ cps}.$$

Suppose that 20 μf is bypassing 1000 ohms in the emitter branch of the load transistor, and its current amplification factor is 50. The lower half-power frequency for this circuit is 70 cps according to Eq. (5–17).

From the numbers cited, emitter bypassing is obviously the limiting area in most low-frequency response studies.

5–3. High-Frequency Considerations. The parameters of the transistor begin to take on complex form at the upper end of the audio-frequency spectrum, and to calculate circuit performance successfully corrections must be made to the low-frequency equivalent circuits.

Collector Capacitance. One of the important considerations is output capacitance. The collector-to-base capacitance in the common-base equivalent, C_{ob}, parallels the aforementioned conductive h_{ob}, and has a nominal value of only 10 to 50 $\mu\mu$f. In the common-emitter orientation the corresponding transistor output capacitance with input circuit open is considerably larger; C_{ob} must be multiplied by the $(1 + h_{fb})^{-1}$ factor and, therefore, 200 to 2000 $\mu\mu$f is to be expected. To maintain a consistent set of symbols, C_{oe} will be used to designate collector-to-emitter capacitance in the common-emitter configuration.

C_o is not a constant, but is subject to variations due to the same factors that caused the T- and h-parameters to vary, namely temperature, emitter current, collector potential, frequency, and manufacturing techniques. Typi-

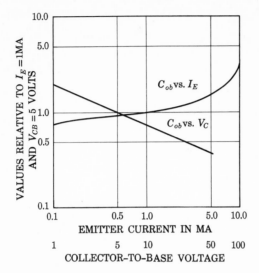

Fig. 5–4. Variation of collector capacitance with operating point.

cal variations of this parameter are given in Fig. 5–4. It is customary to specify C_o at a high frequency, usually not that at which the other parameters are specified.

The common-base and common-emitter equivalent circuits including C_{ob} are depicted in Fig. 5–5. To include the effects of collector capacitance in

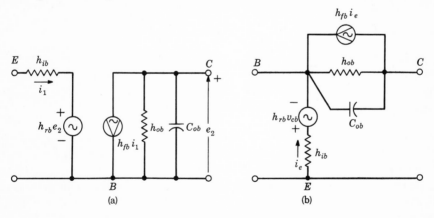

Fig. 5–5. Transistor equivalent circuits including collector capacitance: (a) common-base; (b) common-emitter (see Fig. 4–10a).

the operational formulas of Chapter 4, one needs only to add an admittance of $j\omega C_{ob}$ to all h_{ob} terms.

Alpha Variation. C_o is not the only factor that results in operational differences at high frequencies. The magnitude of h_{fb} varies with frequency according to the relation

$$h_{fb} = \frac{h_{fbo}}{1 + j(f/f_{ab})}, \qquad (5\text{--}18)$$

where h_{fbo} indicates the reference or low-frequency value of the parameter, and f_{ab} symbolizes the "alpha cutoff frequency," the frequency at which the magnitude of the current-amplification factor has decreased to 0.707 of its low-frequency value. The symbol f_{ae} will be used to represent the "beta cutoff frequency."

The common-emitter short-circuit current-amplification factor h_{fe} varies according to

$$h_{fe} = \frac{h_{feo}}{1 + j(f/f_{ae})}, \qquad (5\text{--}19)$$

but h_{fe} is a function of h_{fb}

$$h_{fe} = \frac{-h_{fb}}{1 + h_{fb}}. \qquad (5\text{--}20)$$

Therefore

$$h_{fe} = \frac{-h_{fbo}/[1 + j(f/f_{ab})]}{1 + h_{fbo}/[1 + j(f/f_{ab})]}. \qquad (5\text{--}21a)$$

Simplifying

$$h_{fe} = \frac{-h_{fbo}}{1 + h_{fbo} + j(f/f_{ab})}. \qquad (5\text{--}21b)$$

h_{fe} in Eq. (5–21b) will be down by 3 db when

$$1 + h_{fbo} = f/f_{ab}, \qquad (5\text{--}22)$$

or at

$$f = (1 + h_{fbo})f_{ab}. \qquad (5\text{--}23)$$

Hence

$$f_{ae} = (1 + h_{fbo})f_{ab}. \qquad (5\text{--}24)$$

The $(1 + h_{fbo})$ term has a nominal value of less than 0.1. It may be concluded that the common-emitter configuration is inferior to common-base circuitry when high-frequency operation is considered, for the former configuration experiences a decline in its current-amplification parameter at a much lower frequency. Nevertheless because it is basically a higher-gain configuration, common-emitter stages are used in many high-frequency applications.

Eq. (5–18), the variation of alpha with frequency, and Eq. (5–19), which explains the variation of beta with frequency, are of the same form and when graphed can be represented by the same curve. Fig. 5–6 depicts the change in magnitude of the amplification factor, expressed as a ratio and measured in decibels, versus the denominator term f/f_α, which is com-

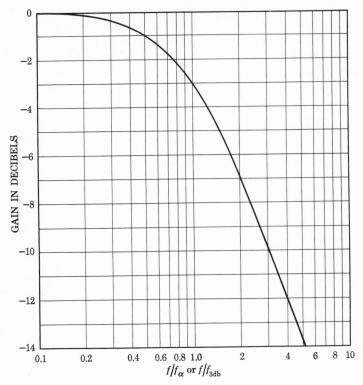

Fig. 5–6.

mon to each of the equations cited. When the abscissa value is the alpha cutoff frequency where f/f_α is unity, the ordinate corresponding to this abscissa is -3 db. A 3-db loss indicates that alpha has diminished to 0.707 of its mid-frequency value, and also means that the entire stage, if approximations may be used, has suffered a 3-db loss in current gain.

Operation Prediction. All of the h-parameters are frequency sensitive, and therefore should each be available in complex form, $h = A + jB$, or their frequency function should be available, $h = f(\omega)$, the gain and impedance equations of Chapter 4 could be utilized for performance calculations. It is not usual for such complete information to be available, but some idea of performance can be derived from the inclusion of alpha variation and collector capacitance in the equations. The equations are somewhat unwieldy, even when only these two corrections are made, but they will be used to gain some insight into performance at the higher frequencies. The hybrid-π equivalent circuit, introduced in Chapter 9, lends itself to quick calculations more readily than the h-equivalent and will be used for further studies.

At the present we are restricted to the audio-frequency range, and for simplicity shall consider low-resistance loads (less than 5000 ohms) exclusively, for high-resistance circuits have the further disadvantage that wiring and stray capacitances are then important, and performance deteriorates as frequency rises. Actually any parallel capacitance will serve to reduce both voltage and current circuit gains. In the circuit of Fig. 5–7a a current source,

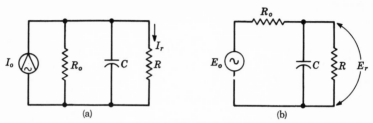

Fig. 5–7. R-C circuits under study.

I_o, with parallel resistance, R_o, is feeding a parallel R-C load; the amount of the current I_o that reaches R at any frequency can be determined easily by a summation of currents at the significant node. Therefore

$$\frac{I_r}{I_o} = \frac{R_o}{R + R_o + j\omega C R_o R}. \tag{5–25}$$

The resistive-load current decreases by 3 db when

$$\omega C R_T = 1,$$

where R_T is the equivalent resistance of all parallel resistive elements

$$[R_T = R R_o / (R + R_o)].$$

Hence

$$f_{3\,db} = \frac{1}{2\pi C R_T}. \tag{5–26}$$

Should an equivalent voltage source be substituted to arrive at the circuit form of Fig. 5–7b,

$$\frac{E_r}{E_o} = \frac{R}{R + R_o + j\omega C R_o R}, \tag{5–27}$$

and

$$f_{3\,\mathrm{db}} = \frac{1}{2\pi C R_T} \tag{5-28}$$

with R_T defined as previously. Because Eqs. (5–25) and (5–27) are of the general form of Eq. (5–18) the curve of Fig. 5–6 may be used to estimate loss due to parallel capacitance. It is necessary to calculate $f_{3\,\mathrm{db}}$ and enter the curve at any frequency ratio $f/f_{3\,\mathrm{db}}$ in order to find the loss due to such capacitances.

Now if frequency variant h_{fb} and capacitance C_{ob} are introduced into the approximate common-emitter expressions in terms of common-base parameters, and a low value of R_L is assumed, then current gain is

$$A_i \cong \frac{h_{fbo}}{1 + h_{fbo} + jf/f_{ab}}, \tag{5-29}$$

indicating that current gain diminishes rapidly with increasing frequency.

The input-impedance expression, Eq. (4–55A), becomes

$$Z_i \cong \frac{h_{ib}[1 + R_L(h_{ob} + j\omega C_{ob})]}{R_L(h_{ob} + j\omega C_{ob}) + (1 + h_{fb})}. \tag{5-30}$$

Modified for low-resistance loads, C_{ob} has little effect, and

$$Z_i \cong \frac{h_{ib}(1 + jf/f_{ab})}{1 + h_{fbo} + jf/f_{ab}}. \tag{5-31}$$

This expression has the same denominator as the current-gain formula, Eq. (5–29), so both are diminishing at the same rate. At the beta cutoff frequency, $f = f_{ab}(1 + h_{fbo})$ and

$$Z_i \cong \frac{h_{ib}\underline{/-45°}}{\sqrt{2}\,(1 + h_{fbo})}.$$

An impedance of this form can result from a parallel R-C circuit with $R = h_{ib}/(1 + h_{fbo})$ and $X_c = h_{ib}/(1 + h_{fbo})$ at the specific frequency considered. Therefore the effective input capacitance may be approximated by

$$C_{in} \cong \frac{1}{\omega_{ab} h_{ib}}, \tag{5-32}$$

when load resistance and C_{ob} are both low-valued. The "Miller effect" in transistors, which accounts for an even higher input capacitance, is discussed in Chapter 9.

Voltage gain for the transistor alone is given by the Eq. (4–52), or by

$$A_v = A_i \frac{Z_L}{Z_i}.$$ (5–33)

Combining Eqs. (5–29), (5–31), and (5–33) yields

$$A_v \cong \frac{h_{fbo}}{1 + h_{fbo} + jf/f_{ab}} \cdot \frac{R_L(1 + h_{fbo} + jf/f_{ab})}{h_{ib}(1 + jf/f_{ab})}$$

$$\cong \frac{h_{fbo}R_L}{h_{ib}(1 + jf/f_{ab})}.$$ (5–34)

This equation, for common-emitter circuitry, shows only slight variation of voltage gain with frequency when compared with the current-gain and input-impedance expressions.

Should the output resistance formula, Eq. (4–56), be altered to include C_{ob} and h_{fb}, then from study of the equation at a usable frequency, say the beta cutoff frequency, it can be shown that output capacitance is small, and is dependent upon C_{ob}. In fact, output capacitance is more nearly of the magnitude of C_{ob} than C_{oe}, even for high source resistance.

From studies of this sort, some general conclusions may be drawn:

1. Input impedance of a junction transistor is highly dependent upon signal frequency, for the transistor looks, to its signal source, like a parallel R-C circuit.

2. Voltage gain of the transistor itself is fairly independent of frequency, but the gain of an entire circuit will deteriorate at low frequencies because of drops across coupling capacitors, and at high frequencies shunting capacitance and the circuit-source resistance (in series with Z_i) will effectively reduce gain.

3. Current gain is dictated by f_{ae}, and will consequently fall off because of that phenomenon. At very low frequencies, bypass and coupling capacitors will not be efficient in their function and currents will find easier paths through biasing resistances and collector-return resistance; lowered overall circuit current gain results.

4. Output impedance will tend to be reduced as signal frequencies rise, and output capacitance will generally be a contributor but not the prime factor in limiting high-frequency response.

We are now able to summarize transistor operation for the audio-frequency range by making use of the discussion of the preceding sections. Examination of Fig. 5–8 indicates that the audio band could conveniently be separated into three frequency ranges, the low-, mid-, and high-audio ranges. The gain falloff at low frequencies with transformer coupling is due to primary inductance; with R-C coupling the increased reactance of the blocking capacitors is to blame. At the high end of the audio band, loss of gain in transformer-coupled stages is primarily due to leakage inductance, its increased reactance is in series with the load. For both R-C and transformer-coupled stages, stray capacitances and alpha reduction cause a decrease in delivered signal at the higher frequencies.

At this point in the text no specific method will be advanced for the prediction of high-frequency operation. Naturally a transistor with a high $f_{\alpha b}$

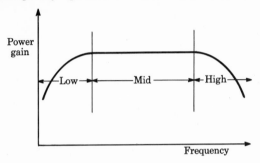

Fig. 5–8. Separation of the audio spectrum into three convenient ranges and typical amplifier response.

will behave better than one with a low value of that parameter, circuits with high load and source resistances will tend to perform more poorly than low-resistance circuits, but in general transistor operation in the audio-frequency range is very satisfactory.

5–4. Load Lines. Every amplifying stage sees two different loads—one a load presented to its d-c output, and the other the load presented to the a-c component of its output. In Chapter 3 rules were presented for drawing a d-c load line on the output characteristics curve. Summation of all the resistance in the emitter-to-collector circuit dictates the slope of the line; the line originates at $E_{CC} + E_{EE}$ and terminates at $(E_{CC} + E_{EE})/\Sigma R$. The quiescent or operating point is established by circuitry that provides a constant base or collector current.

The a-c load on a stage can be established by summing the impedance of all the a-c circuit elements in the emitter-to-collector circuit. This task is usually simplified by considering that all by-pass and coupling capacitors are short circuits to an a-c signal.

To illustrate the handling of loads and the drawing of load lines, consider the circuit of Fig. 5–9. The d-c loading is comprised of the series combination of R_1, R_e and R_c. The a-c load is R_e plus the parallel combination of R_c, R_2 and R_i of the second stage.

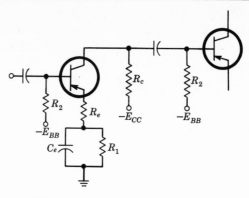

Fig. 5–9.　Circuit for text example.

If the parameters of the circuit of Fig. 5–9 are

$$R_e = 220 \text{ ohms} \qquad R_c = 10 \ K \text{ ohms} \qquad R_2 = 120 \ K \text{ ohms}$$

$$R_1 = 2.2 \ K \text{ ohms} \qquad R_i = 10 \ K \text{ ohms},$$

the d-c load line has a slope that is the negative reciprocal of $220 + 2.2 \ K + 10 \ K$, or 12,420 ohms, and the slope of a-c line is the negative reciprocal of

$$220 + \frac{1}{1/10 \ K + 1/120 \ K + 1/10 \ K}$$

or 4800 ohms.　A-c load lines must pass through the Q point and are not established by axes intersections.

In Fig. 5–10, d-c and a-c load lines are drawn on an output characteristics

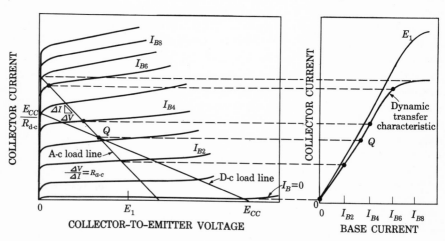

Fig. 5–10.　D-c and a-c load lines on output characteristics, and construction of dynamic transfer characteristic.

curve. After the d-c line linking E_{CC} and $E_{CC}/R_{\text{d-c}}$ is positioned and the Q point located, the a-c line may be drawn through Q with the appropriate slope. For some purposes a dynamic transfer characteristic is valuable. Projection of the points of intersection of the a-c load line and lines of constant base current to an $I_C\text{-}I_B$ curve is easily accomplished. From the transfer characteristic linearity of operation is easily studied, and operating point suitability therefore clearly established. The characteristic is said to be dynamic for it is derived from the load line and does not assume a constant collector potential. A static characteristic at potential E_1 is also shown in the figure.

5–5. Design of Single-Stage Low-Power Amplifiers. As stated earlier in this chapter, it must be assumed that certain specifications are known concerning any circuit to be designed; usually the value of the load is specified, often the available supply voltages are obtainable, and the required power or voltage gain is known. In this last regard, some information must be available pertaining to the transducer or signal-source output; transistor stages can exhibit input impedances of from tens of ohms to hundreds of thousands of ohms and it is important that the degree of loading of the transducer be considered or impedance matching be considered, or in some way a specification of input impedance be made. Of particular value is the output equivalent circuit of the signal source, whether it be a microphone, synchro, or other element. This equivalent can take the form of a voltage generator in series with a source impedance (often resistive), according to Thèvenin's Theorem.

For the transistor, high input impedance always rules out high power gain. A high input impedance can be obtained from the emitter-follower connection or from the common-emitter connection with large unbypassed-emitter resistance. This latter method is widely accepted. It must be borne in mind that the input impedance of a particular stage is reduced by base-bias schemes. Fixed-biasing, single-battery biasing, emitter-biasing and self-biasing tend to reduce input impedance by paralleling the transistor input with resistive elements. For maximum input impedance emitter-biasing with transformer coupling or cutoff-biasing present the most satisfactory circuitry.

The usual design procedure, for a common-emitter stage, is to specify the input resistance required and solve the input resistance equation for h_{ib}. The h_{ib} term includes all unbypassed-emitter resistance. The gain of that stage must be considered to be of importance secondary to R_i.

High-Impedance Circuit Design Example

Object. Design a low-power transistor stage with an input resistance of 200,000 ohms. The transistor to be used has parameter values of

$$h_{ib} = 50 \text{ ohms} \qquad h_{ob} = 2 \times 10^{-6} \text{ mho}$$

$$h_{rb} = 10 \times 10^{-4} \qquad h_{fb} = -0.97$$

The load to be fed is 10,000 ohms. Consider that corrections have been made to the parameters because of temperature and operating point, and use a common-emitter stage with emitter biasing. Base current may flow through the source, which is of fairly low d-c resistance. Consider signal levels to be extremely small.

Solution. This problem has been simplified to the point where it is only necessary to calculate the required value of $h_{ib} + R_e$ and to determine the resulting gain. From the expression for input resistance, Eq. (4–55) modified to include R_e,

$$h_{ib} + R_e = \frac{R_i(h_{ob}R_L + 1 + h_{fb}) + h_{rb}h_{fb}R_L}{1 + h_{ob}(R_L - R_i)}$$

$$= 16{,}150 \text{ ohms},$$

and

$$R_e = 16{,}100 \text{ ohms}.$$

The power gain to be expected will be checked using the approximate formula

$$G = \frac{h_{fb}{}^2 R_L}{(h_{ib} + R_e)(1 + R_L h_{ob})(R_L h_{ob} + 1 + h_{fb})}$$

$$= 11.4,$$

which is very low, but it must be remembered that the primary concern in this design is to achieve a high input impedance.

R-C Amplifier Design Example

Object. Design a transistor amplifying stage to meet the following requirements:

1. Frequency response: 40 to 20,000 cps
2. Load resistance: 1000 ohms
3. Input impedance: 500 (minimum) to 2000 (maximum) ohms
4. Power gain: 25 db (minimum)
5. Source characteristics: impedance—2000 ohms (resistive); maximum output—10 mv
6. Temperature: 30 ± 5° C
7. D-c potential available: −15 volts

Solution. Since a good frequency response is the primary concern, let us employ R-C coupling and use the 2N414 transistor, which behaves well throughout the audio range. A silicon unit is unnecessary since wide temperature variations are not expected.

Single-battery bias will be used because it offers high stability, and the circuit selected is shown in Fig. 5–11. We shall choose a tentative operating point at $V_{CE} = -6$ volts and $I_C = 1$ ma. No corrections to the nominal parameters are necessary at that point.

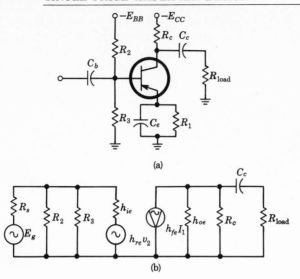

(a)

(b)

Fig. 5–11. Circuit design example: (a) schematic; (b) equivalent.

From the manufacturer

$$h_{ib} = 25 \text{ ohms} \qquad\qquad h_{ob} = 0.62 \ \mu\text{mho}$$

$$h_{fe} = 60 \qquad\qquad f_{\alpha b} = 7 \text{ mc}$$

$$h_{rb} = 0.5 \times 10^{-3} \qquad\qquad C_{ob} = 12 \ \mu\mu\text{f}$$

If we choose $R_c = 6000$ ohms then very little a-c power will be lost in that resistor, and R_1 must then be 3000 ohms to satisfy the d-c collector circuit equation

$$E_{CC} = I_C R_c + I_E R_1 + V_{CE}.$$

We can make $R_3 = 10{,}000$ ohms, and, since we wish I_C to be 1 ma, R_2 will be large enough so it will not affect calculations to any great extent. A brief check of bias stability is in order. From Eq. (3–16b), the criterion is

$$R_1 \geq 10R_3(1 - \alpha).$$

In this instance $R_1 = 3 \ K$ and $10R_3(1 - \alpha) = 1.6 \ K$; therefore the criterion is met.

A few preliminary calculations are necessary in order to obtain the proper parameters for use in the various formulas:

$$h_{fb} = \frac{-h_{fe}}{1 + h_{fe}} = \frac{-60}{61} = -0.984,$$

$$R_L = \frac{R_c R_{\text{load}}}{R_c + R_{\text{load}}} = \frac{(6\ K)(1\ K)}{6\ K + 1\ K} = 857 \text{ ohms,}$$

$$R_g = \frac{R_s R_3}{R_s + R_3} = \frac{(2\ K)(10\ K)}{2\ K + 10\ K} = 1670 \text{ ohms,}$$

$$f_{ae} = (1 + h_{fb})f_{ab} = (0.016)(7) = 112 \text{ kc.}$$

These figures enable us to calculate the operation of the transistor alone:

$$A_v = \frac{h_{fb} R_L}{h_{ib}(1 + R_L h_{ob})} = 33.8,$$

$$A_i = \frac{h_{fb}}{h_{ob} R_L + (1 + h_{fb})} = 59.6,$$

$$G = (33.8)(59.6) = 2020,$$

$$R_i = \frac{h_{ib}(1 + R_L h_{ob}) - h_{rb} h_{fb} R_L}{R_L h_{ob} + (1 + h_{fb})} = 1540 \text{ ohms,}$$

$$R_o = \frac{h_{ib} + R_g(1 + h_{fb})}{h_{ob}(h_{ib} + R_g) - h_{rb} h_{fb}} = 33,300 \text{ ohms.}$$

At mid-frequencies, the current entering the transistor base is the following fraction of that which leaves the signal source:

$$\frac{R_3}{R_i + R_3}.$$

In this example 86.5% of the source output gets to the base. Load current is the following fraction of the a-c collector current

$$\frac{R_c}{R_c + R_{\text{load}}}.$$

Thus 85.8% of the collector current is available to the load.

All of the collector voltage is available across the load; however the source output is split between R_s and the parallel combination of R_i and R_3 according to

$$\frac{R_3 R_i/(R_3 + R_i)}{R_s + R_3 R_i/(R_3 + R_i)}$$

which when simplified, equals

$$\frac{R_3 R_i}{R_3 R_i + R_s(R_3 + R_i)}.$$

For this example, only 40% is across the transistor input terminals.

Using the values previously cited, the overall performance at mid-frequencies is

$$A_{iT} = (0.865)(0.858)(59.6) = 44.3,$$

$$A_{vT} = (0.40)(33.8) = 13.5,$$

$$G = (44.3)(13.5) = 600, \text{ or } 27.8 \text{ db.}$$

A_{vT} is here defined as the ratio of collector voltage to source voltage E_g, and A_{iT} is the ratio of load current to source current.

The reduction in current gain due to alpha variation at 20,000 cycles is read from Fig. 5–6 as less than 0.1 db. Acceptable high-frequency performance could have been predicted from knowledge of the $f_{\alpha b}$ and C_o of the transistor, and from the fact that low load and source resistances were employed.

When the real portion of the denominator of Eq. (5–10) is set equal to the imaginary portion, it will yield the 3-db down point at the low-frequency (40 cps) end of the spectrum:

$$R_3 R_i + R_s R_3 + R_s R_i = X_c(R_3 + R_i).$$

Then

$$X_c = 3340 \text{ ohms,}$$

and

$$C = \frac{1}{2\pi 40\,(3340)} = 1.2 \ \mu\text{f.}$$

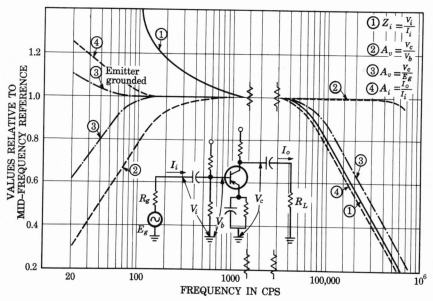

Fig. 5–12. Test data on amplifier similar to text example.

A ten-microfarad capacitor would be fine for this application. Similar calculations indicate that 10 μf would be acceptable for load coupling and 100 μf for emitter resistance bypassing; it is to be remembered that all three are important at the low frequencies and will contribute to gain fall-off.

The measured frequency response for an amplifier very similar to this design is shown in Fig. 5–12. Operation of the entire circuit is highly dependent upon source resistance.

5–6. Effects of the Operating Point upon Gain. The parameters of the transistor are sensitive to operating point, for, as evidenced by the curves and discussion of the last chapter, corrections must be made to the nominal parameters when operating with collector voltage and emitter current differing from the manufacturer's recommended values. It is true for certain transistors that astute operation-point selection, when feasible, permits a maximization of gain, or provides a means for gain adjustment, and in certain instances may be useful in meeting the gain specifications for a particular circuit design.

Let us numerically investigate the variation in performance due to emitter quiescent current selection. From the manufacturer's design center parameters and his correction information, a listing has been made for the 2N43 transistor. A large variation in h_{ib} is evident from the numbers cited and it

EMITTER CURRENT IN MILLIAMPERES

	0.1	0.2	0.5	1.0	4.0	7.0	10.0
h_{ib}	230	120	55	29	9	5.8	4.6
$h_{rb} \times 10^{-4}$	3.8	4.2	4.6	5	6.5	7.5	8.0
h_{fb}	−0.966	−0.968	−0.974	−0.977	−0.986	−0.988	−0.988
$h_{ob} \times 10^{-6}$	0.32	0.36	0.55	0.80	2.4	3.6	5.0

is to be suspected that this will result in a substantial change in input impedance and voltage gain. Common-emitter current amplification will be affected by the changing $(1 + h_{fb})$ factor.

With a 1000-ohm load assumed, calculations based upon the parameters listed above serve to predict the performance of a single common-emitter stage. The results of such calculations and test results based upon a built-up stage are displayed as Fig. 5–13. (A_v is here used to signify the load-voltage to base-voltage ratio.) It is necessary in such a study to hold V_{CE} constant (5 volts throughout) for this potential also has a strong effect upon gains and resistance levels. The collector-supply voltage therefore differed at each investigated operating point according to

$$E_{CC} = V_{CE} + I_C R_L,$$

so

$$E_{CC} = 5 + I_E(1000).$$

The circuit designer has the gain and resistance levels of a transistor at his control. By using a large quiescent current he can achieve higher-gain circuitry, at the price of high standby current and lowered input resistance and possibly the need for a higher direct voltage supply. One practical application of the material of this section is in the automatic gain control systems used in communications receivers and discussed in Chapter 8.

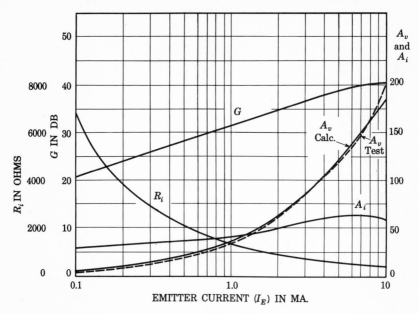

Fig. 5–13. Performance *vs.* emitter current for a typical transistor.

5–7. Summary. Because the single-stage transistor amplifier is not an isolated entity, its design and performance are dependent upon the means selected for joining or coupling its output terminals to a load and coupling its input terminals to a signal source. The choice and design of coupling networks has a strong influence upon operating-point stability, standby-power requirements, frequency response, and efficiency of amplification.

Seldom is the amplification provided by a single stage sufficient to meet practical specifications. But the importance of the single transistor stage lies in its use as the building block for the cascade or multistage amplifier. Multistage amplifiers often provide sufficient gain to result in high signal levels. Because small-signal analysis does not apply to such "power" stages they require special treatment and will be discussed in the following chapter. Further consideration is given to the multistage circuit in Chapter 7.

A few additional words should be devoted to the subject of frequency response. Addition of collector capacitance and cognizance of the variation of alpha with frequency do not alone turn the low-frequency h-circuit into an all-band equivalent. Such circuit alterations may be used as a check on the higher-frequency performance capabilities of an audio-range circuit, but more accurate results are achieved from other equivalents (see Chapter 9), which among other refinements, take base-spreading resistance and the "Miller effect" into account.

PROBLEMS

5-1. Make a thorough comparison between a low-power silicon transistor and a germanium transistor of comparable ratings.

5-2. A signal source has an internal resistance of 10,000 ohms and is feeding a transistor stage that presents an input resistance of 2000 ohms (including biasing resistors). Determine the size of the coupling capacitor necessary for the lower half-power frequency to be 25 cps.

5-3. A transistor exhibits C_{ob} of 12 $\mu\mu f$, $f_{\alpha b}$ of 10 mc, and h_{fbo} of -0.985. Determine nominal C_{oe}, $f_{\alpha e}$ and h_{feo} and the magnitude of h_{fe} at 1 mc.

5-4. If h_{fe} at 2 mc has a value of 4, and $f_{\alpha e}$ is 100 kc, calculate h_{fbo} and the 2-mc value of h_{fb}.

5-5. Derive an expression for the power gain of a common-emitter connected transistor in terms of common-base h-parameters including C_{ob} and $f_{\alpha b}$.

5-6. From the formula derived in Problem 5-5, with $h_{ib} = 25$, $h_{rb} = 10^{-4}$, $h_{fbo} = -0.96$, $h_{ob} = 10^{-6}$, $C_{ob} = 10$ $\mu\mu f$, and $f_{\alpha b} = 1$ mc, plot G vs. f when the transistor is feeding a direct-coupled 10,000-ohm load.

5-7. A given interstage uses a coupling capacitor of 1.0 μf; the shunt elements are $R_o = 25,000$ ohms, $R_C = 10,000$ ohms, $R_i = 2000$ ohms and transistor and wiring capacity is 40 $\mu\mu f$. Determine

(a) The mid-frequency current attenuation of the coupling network alone.

(b) The lower half-power frequency.

(c) The upper half-power frequency.

5-8. The transistor of the circuit below has $\alpha = 0.99$, $f_{\alpha b} = 0.2$ mc, $C_{out} = 100$ $\mu\mu f$ and $R_o = 20,000$ ohms. Calculate the following:

(a) The mid-frequency current attenuation of the coupling network alone.

(b) The mid-frequency a-c load seen by the transistor.

(c) The upper half-power frequency of the overall circuit.

(d) The lower half-power frequency of the overall circuit.

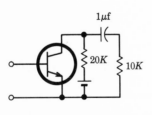

Problem 5-8.

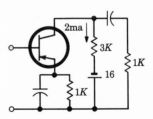

Problem 5-9.

5-9. For the accompanying circuit, draw the d-c and a-c load lines on a sketch of the collector characteristics of the 2N43 and locate the Q point. With a sinusoidal base current drive, what is the maximum amount of power that can be delivered to the load before clipping occurs?

5-10. Reverse the supply potential and repeat Problem 5-9 for a 2N475.

5-11. Draw the d-c and a-c load lines for the circuit of the figure on a sketch of the 2N344 transistor collector characteristics. Locate the Q point.

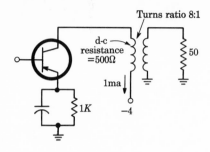

Problem 5-11.

How much can base current vary before clipping of the collector current will occur?

5-12. To the input resistance of a transistor common-emitter stage must be added the approximate term $(\beta + 1)Z_e$ to include the effects of impedance in the emitter branch. If Z_e is the equivalent of R_1 paralleling C_1, derive Eq. (5-17) for the lower half-power frequency of the network of Fig. 5-3 altered by inclusion of bypassed emitter-resistance. For simplicity, neglect the effects of the coupling capacitor. The transistor itself may be considered to have a resistive input impedance R_i.

5-13. Compare the current gain frequency response of a particular transistor operating common-emitter with the response of that same transistor operating common-base. Consider alpha reduction as the only source of gain falloff, and assume that the transistor is feeding a low-resistance load. Which orientation provides the greater gain at $f_{\alpha e}$ and at $f_{\alpha b}$?

5-14. A high-fidelity amplifier with a current gain bandwidth of 12 cps to 40,000 cps is to be incorporated into a measuring circuit. Find the frequency range over which the amplifier's current gain does not change by more than 1 db. If the specification were 10% rather than 1 db would it be tighter?

Design Problems. In the problems that follow perform the operations necessary in order to obtain a stage that will meet the listed requirements. Choose an appropriate biasing arrangement, and, for each solution, choose a transistor from those in Appendix I, and correct the nominal parameters for operating point and temperature. Itemize any assumptions made and clearly indicate the steps leading to your choice of each component.

5–15. Requirements:

1. Carrier frequency: 400 cps
2. Load resistance: 10 ohms
3. Input resistance: 500 ohms (minimum)
4. Power gain: 30 db (minimum)
5. Source impedance: 50 ohms (resistive)
6. Temperature: $25 \pm 5°$ C
7. Supplies available: designer's choice

5–16. If the design of Problem 5–15 is subjected to ambient temperature excursions of from $0°$ C to $50°$ C will the gain requirement still be satisfied?

5–17. Requirements:

1. Frequency response: 30 to 20,000 cps (minimum)
2. Load resistance: 5000 ohms
3. Input impedance: no requirements
4. Voltage gain: 10 (minimum load-voltage to source-voltage ratio)
5. Source characteristics: impedance—100 ohms (resistive) in series with generator of 0 to 20 mv.
6. Temperature: $20°$ C
7. Power supply available: -8 volts

5–18. Requirements:

1. Carrier frequency: 120 cps
2. Load resistance: 10,000 ohms
3. Input impedance: $50,000 \pm 10\%$ ohms
4. Power gain: 10 (minimum)
5. Source characteristics: impedance—50,000 ohms (resistive); 1 mv maximum
6. Temperature: $25 \pm 3°$ C
7. Power supply available: -12 volts

REFERENCES

1. Lo, A. W., *et al.*, *Transistor Electronics*, Prentice-Hall, Inc., Englewood Cliffs, New Jersey, 1955.
2. Riddle, R. L., and Ristenbatt, M. P., *Transistor Physics and Circuits*, Prentice-Hall, Inc., Englewood Cliffs, New Jersey, 1958.
3. Ryder, J. M., *Electronic Fundamentals and Applications*, 2nd Ed., Prentice-Hall, Inc., Englewood Cliffs, New Jersey, 1959.
4. Shea, R. F., *Transistor Circuit Engineering*, John Wiley & Sons, Inc., New York, 1957.

Chapter 6

LARGE-SIGNAL AMPLIFIERS

Devices that perform the function of amplifying large signals are commonly called *power amplifiers*. Since it has been shown previously that all transistors are power amplifiers, this chapter will be devoted to those applications where the assumptions of linear operation are not valid, and where variations in collector voltage and current are a significant fraction of the total allowable range of operation.

The power stage is the final unit of a cascade amplifier and serves to drive the energy-conversion device that transforms electrical energy into some other form, such as sound or mechanical energy. The power stage is, in turn, dependent upon the "driver stage" for its signal.

The equations for circuit gains and impedances developed in Chapter 4 are not directly applicable to power stages because those relations were derived from equivalent circuits valid for small-signal excursions, and include small-signal parameters. When transistor operation swings over a large region of its characteristics, more accurate analysis is made using graphical prodecures. The Chapter 4 equations may be useful in approximating actual operation provided the parameters are available (they are not normally published for power transistors), and the input and output signals are generally sinusoidal (no clipping of the waveforms).

We have previously discussed the drawing of both a-c and d-c load lines. Graphical techniques, when applied to small-signal amplifiers, permit study of the suitability of the operating point, determination of maximum allowable current and voltage swings, and calculation of overload capacity. In this chapter we shall rely upon graphical methods to determine gains and impedance levels, output power and overload capacity, and the distortion content of the output waveform. Large-signal analysis is often necessary for the driver stage of a multistage amplifier.

6–1. Limitations. One of the general problems associated with the design of power amplifiers is that of obtaining the maximum possible power output. Power output for a common-emitter stage is limited by the following:

1. The maximum allowable collector-to-emitter operating potential
2. The maximum allowable collector current
3. The maximum allowable power dissipation
4. The saturation region
5. The cutoff region

Fig. 6–1 depicts the limiting regions. The maximum power dissipation line is a hyperbolic curve having the equation

$$V_C I_C = K \tag{6-1}$$

for a given junction temperature. If, in actual operation, the voltage-current product exceeds the design constant K, damage to the transistor will result.

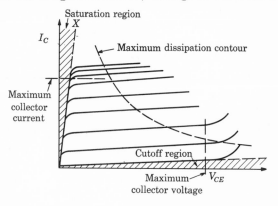

Fig. 6–1. Operation limits.

The resistive parameters of the device will cause internal power conversion. The heat generated, if unable to completely escape from the device, will raise the operating temperature, and with internal temperature rise comes breaking of covalent bonds. Transistor operation ceases when sufficient covalent bonds are broken.

A collector-current limit is set in part by the decrease in α (or β) at high current densities; the amount of reduction in current amplification can be used as a criterion to place a limit on maximum allowable current.

Breakdown of the collector junction is shown in Fig. 6–1 by the upswing of the lines of constant base current. The Zener theory, that under the influence of a strong electric field, electrons are pulled from their valence bonds to become mobile carriers, may account for this increased current; more likely the cause is avalanche breakdown, a secondary emission phenomenon. A high voltage may also widen the collector-depletion layer so that it contacts the emitter-depletion layer, resulting in a form of short-circuit. (A depletion

layer, it is recalled, is the region near a semiconductor junction where a reduced number of mobile carriers are to be found.)   A collector-voltage limit
is also set by thermal runaway characteristics as discussed in the next section.

The region of saturation is of little consequence in germanium transistors,
but must be taken into account when silicon units are used because of their
high R_{CS}. R_{CS} is the inverse of the slope of line O–X in Fig. 6–1 and can be
thought of as the collector-to-emitter resistance of a transistor in the full ON
condition.

The cutoff region, often erroneously considered to be below the $I_B = 0$
line, in reality lies below the I_{CO} line, because it is possible to operate with
small positive values of base current (p-n-p).   Because of nonlinearities at
such levels, particularly in the input characteristics, some distortion may
result just prior to complete cutoff.

6–2. Thermal Considerations.   The removal of heat from the collector-base
junction must be considered when employing all types of transistors, but it
warrants considerable attention in
high-power types.   The cooling of
low-power transistors (below 200 mw)
is generally accomplished by radiation to the surroundings.   For power
transistors (500 mw and up) cooling
fins are sometimes used, but more
often the units are firmly attached
to metallic heat sinks (chassis or
separate plate).   Mounting for the
2N539A is shown in Fig. 6–2. When
feasible, the transistor case can make
direct contact with the heat sink;
more often a mica washer is employed for electrical insulation, as shown in
the diagram, since the collector, in most power transistors, is directly attached to the case.

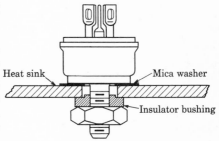

Fig. 6–2.   Typical mounting of a power
transistor.

A maximum allowable collector-junction temperature is specified for all
transistors.   For germanium units this maximum temperature is between
85° C and 100° C.   A similar figure for silicon is 175° C.   The temperature at
which the junction is operating (T_j) depends upon the ambient temperature
(T_a), the thermal resistance of the heat path from the junction to surroundings
(θ_T), and the electrical power being converted into heat (P_T), according to
the relation

$$T_j = T_a + \theta_T P_T \qquad °\text{ C.} \qquad (6\text{–}2)$$

Thermal resistance is measured in degrees Centigrade per watt (° C/w).

Internal power dissipation almost entirely occurs at the collector junction
so

$$P_T = V_C I_C. \tag{6-3}$$

The maximum dissipation is

$$P_{T\max} = (V_C I_C)_{\max} = \frac{1}{\theta_T}(T_{j\max} - T_a), \tag{6-4}$$

which is the hyperbola of Eq. (6-1).

The overall thermal resistance, θ_T, is determined by solving a thermal network, analogous to an electrical circuit. The network for a power transistor is shown in Fig. 6-3. A current source symbolizing the heat-power generating properties of the transistor is in series with three electrical resistances, each representing the thermal resistance of a portion of the thermal circuit. θ_{jc} is the resistance from junction to transistor case, θ_{cs} represents resistance from case to heat sink, and θ_{sa} stands for sink-to-ambient resistance.

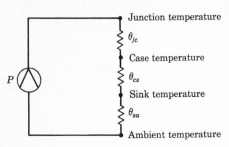

Fig. 6-3. Transistor thermal network.

Solution of the thermal network by electrical series circuit theory gives

$$\theta_T = \theta_{jc} + \theta_{cs} + \theta_{sa} = \theta_{ja}. \tag{6-5}$$

For low-power transistors a single resistance from junction to ambient (θ_{ja}) is often specified, because heat sinks are generally not employed; a typical value for θ_{ja} is 250° C/w. For the larger power transistors, thermal resistances are smaller, and conduction is the primary method of heat transfer, so values of θ_{jc} are made available and range from 0.5 to 2.5° C/w. If the transistor case and the heat sink are separated by an electrical insulator such as a mica washer, θ_{cs} takes on values of 0.2 to 0.5° C/w.

Removal of heat from a power transistor is accomplished mainly by conduction to the heat sink and convection from the sink to the cooler surrounding air. Forced-air cooling reduces the size requirement for the sink, but most applications depend upon natural convection from both sides of an aluminum or copper plate. Vertical mounting of the sink is preferable, to make use of natural air movement.

To estimate the total surface area required for a sink to adequately dissipate the heat developed in a power transistor, use can be made of Figs. 6-4 and 6-5, which give the thermal resistance of flat aluminum and copper plates for various surface areas and plate thicknesses. A numerical example may prove of assistance in understanding the cooling problem. Consider 10 watts being converted to heat at a collector junction and a junction-to-case thermal resistance of 2.0° C/w, with mounting hardware accounting for an additional resistance of 0.5° C/w. The problem is to predict the dimensions of a mounting plate so junction temperature will not exceed 80° C in a 40° C ambient. Eq. (6–2) limits θ_T to 4.0° C/w, and since the transistor and the insulator represent 2.5° C/w, 1.5° C/w remains for the plate. In Fig. 6–5 this requirement corresponds to a $\frac{3}{16}$-inch copper plate of approximately fifty square inches per side mounted horizontally; the dimensions could be 7.1 by 7.1

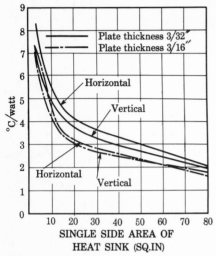

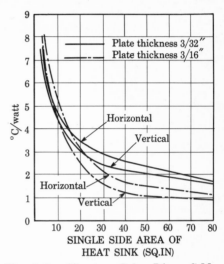

Fig. 6–4. (*Courtesy Delco Divn., G.M. Corp.*) Heat transfer characteristics of square aluminum heat sinks.

Fig. 6–5. (*Courtesy Delco Divn., G.M. Corp.*) Heat transfer characteristics of square copper heat sinks.

inches if both sides are utilized. An aluminum sink to do the same job must be $\frac{3}{16}$ inch or thicker and nearly 10 by 10 inches. It is normal to include a safety factor.

A thermocouple fastened to the transistor case may be used to measure the temperature at that point, although it must be remembered that the temperature of importance is at the inaccessible junction.

Because the heat sink represents resistance in the thermal path, at first thought one may suggest doing away with the sink, and thereby removing a limitation upon allowable power-handling capacity. But after removing the sink from the circuit diagram, we should have to place in its stead another resistance, namely that of the case-to-ambient convection and radiation. Such a resistance is considerably larger than that contributed by a flat metallic plate.

Associated with each thermal resistance of Fig. 6–3, but not shown on the diagram, is a parallel capacitance that is necessary to explain transient behavior. The thermal time constant, the product of thermal resistance and capacitance, is long for the external elements in the diagram (capacitance very large), but relatively short for the transistor itself (30 milliseconds for the 2N539A). With a short time constant, junction temperature may consequently be governed by the peak, instantaneous power dissipation rather than by the average collector dissipation. The circuit designer is concerned with thermal time constants when the transistor is operated *across* the maximum-dissipation hyperbola.

A condition known as *thermal runaway* can result if the rate of increase in collector dissipation with junction temperature exceeds the ability of the thermal circuit to remove heat. After differentiation of Eq. (6–2), thermal runaway may be expressed symbolically by

$$\frac{\partial(V_C I_C)}{\partial T_j} > \frac{1}{\theta_T}. \tag{6–6a}$$

For a constant V_C, instability results when

$$V_C \left(\frac{\partial I_C}{\partial T_j}\right) > \frac{1}{\theta_T}. \tag{6–6b}$$

The change in collector current due to temperature change chiefly is the result of increased leakage current, I_{CO}, and depends upon the biasing circuitry employed. This can be seen by writing Eq. (6–6b) in the form

$$V_C \left(\frac{\partial I_C}{\partial I_{CO}}\right)\left(\frac{\partial I_{CO}}{\partial T_j}\right) > \frac{1}{\theta_T}. \tag{6–7}$$

We shall make use of the stability factor as defined in Chapter 3.

$$S = \frac{\partial I_C}{\partial I_{CO}}. \tag{6–8}$$

For a germanium transistor, a doubling of I_{CO} every 9° C is apparent from examination of Fig. 3–5; this represents an 11% change per °C. Mathematically,

$$I_{CO} = I_{CO}'(1.11)^{\Delta T_j} \tag{6–9}$$

I_{CO}' is the leakage current at the reference temperature, usually 25° C. The derivative of interest is

$$\frac{\partial I_{CO}}{\partial T_j} = I_{CO}'(0.104)(1.11)^{\Delta T_j}. \tag{6–10}$$

At $\Delta T_j = 0$, an assumption that is not always valid, this derivative becomes

$$\frac{\partial I_{CO}}{\partial T_j} = I_{CO}'(0.104). \tag{6–11}$$

For a stable circuit, Eq. (6–7) requires that

$$V_C S I_{CO}'(0.104) < \frac{1}{\theta_T}.$$ (6–12a)

The collector-voltage limit is

$$V_C < 10/S I_{CO}' \theta_T.$$ (6–12b)

Leakage current is limited to

$$I_{CO}' < 10/S V_C \theta_T.$$ (6–12c)

Eqs. (6–12b) and (6–12c) set an upper limit on collector voltage and leakage current. The foregoing analysis applies to either the common-emitter or the common-base stage since leakage current for the former is proportional to I_{CO} and thus will exhibit essentially the same amount of change due to temperature.

6–3. Large-signal Parameters. Information supplied by manufacturers of power transistors differs from that made available concerning low-power devices. In most applications, the load resistance on a power stage will be low, to make use of the allowable collector current swing, and thus h_{22} and h_{12} will be of little consequence. The parameters of importance will thus be h_{11} and h_{21}. Occasionally the small-signal values of these parameters will be given, more often large-signal or d-c values are available. The variations in large-signal values of h_{11} and h_{21} are normally obtainable.

D-c beta, the static value of the common-emitter short-circuit forward current transfer ratio, is defined by the ratio of direct currents according to

$$H_{FE} \text{ or } h_{FE} = \left. \frac{I_C}{I_B} \right|_{V_{CE}=\text{constant}}.$$ (6–13)

Since, when dealing with direct quantities, leakage current may be a considerable fraction of the total, Eq. (6–13) is often modified to

$$H_{FE} \text{ or } h_{FE} = \left. \frac{I_C - I_{CEO}}{I_B} \right|_{V_{CE}=\text{constant}}.$$ (6–14)

The d-c or large-signal value of input resistance is

$$H_{IE} \text{ or } h_{IE} = \left. \frac{V_{BE}}{I_B} \right|_{V_{CE}=\text{constant}}.$$ (6–15)

Of course the values of these parameters are very dependent upon the operating point chosen.

Other systems of large-signal parameters are employed. Transconductance

$$G_M = \frac{I_C}{V_{BE}} \qquad (6\text{--}16)$$

and power conductance

$$G_P = \frac{I_C{}^2}{V_{BE}I_B} \qquad (6\text{--}17)$$

are used by some (Appendix I).

6–4. Modes and Configurations. The operational modes originally defined for vacuum-tube circuits apply to transistor work. Basically, in Class-A operation, the device conducts over the entire cycle, and the output waveform reasonably duplicates the input waveform. This is the mode of operation assumed in all preceding and succeeding discussions unless specified to the contrary. To satisfy the definition, no appreciable clipping is allowable, but distortion in the output waveshape due to nonlinearities of characteristics is tolerable.

In Class-B operation the device conducts over one half of the entire input-signal cycle, so in order to successfully amplify a sinusoidal signal two transistors are necessary, each working on successive alternations. Class-B operation is achieved by biasing transistors near cutoff. The use of a relatively small amount of forward biasing for the emitter-base diode is common and necessary to eliminate crossover distortion (described later). This type of operation has been referred to as Class-AB, but generally the simpler nomenclature (Class-B) is used.

Class-C performance results when the device conducts over less than one half of the cycle. Because relatively few applications for Class-C transistor circuits are available, no detailed discussion of this mode will be presented. The reader who desires more information is referred to the literature.[10]

Because the common-emitter configuration provides the highest power gain, the use of other configurations is limited to applications where they exhibit a distinct advantage over the common-emitter. Occasionally such an advantage arises. It may be that a very low input resistance is necessary, or the requirement may be for better frequency response; in either case a common-base circuit may be the solution to the problem. When one is concerned with distortion as in large-signal amplifiers, the extreme linearity of the common-base output characteristics may, for some applications, justify its use. Since the input circuit is a prime contributor to distortion, the following general rule may be helpful in providing grounds for the determination of the proper configuration for a particular job: *To minimize distortion, a common-emitter power stage should be fed from a low source resistance compared with its input resistance, while a common-base stage should be fed from a high source resistance compared with its input resistance.* From this statement we may conclude that the nonlinearities of the common-emitter input circuit are useful to compensate for those of the output; for common-base stages, since the output circuit is very linear, we wish to swamp the input circuit resistance with a high source resistance. Exceptions to this rule exist.

Our concern, in this chapter, is with the common-emitter large-signal amplifier. Study, analysis, and design of circuits in the other configurations will be left to the reader. Sufficient information is available in the literature.[2, 5, 6]

6–5. Distortion. When the transistor is operated over a significant range of its characteristics, the nonlinearities inherent in semiconducting devices

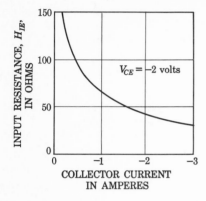

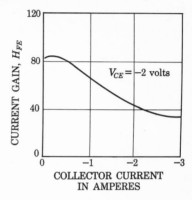

Fig. 6–6. Variation of input resistance with collector current for a typical power transistor.

Fig. 6–7. Variation of current gain with collector current for a typical power transistor.

present sources of distortion to signal waveforms. The input characteristics, which relate base-to-emitter voltage to base current, are exponential and therefore the input resistance of the device is not constant, but varies with signal amplitude. While the effect of this variation can be minimized by driving the transistor from a current source, it must be remembered that current sources are inefficient and cannot always be designed into a particular circuit. A typical variation to be expected in input resistance is shown in Fig. 6–6.

The current gain of a transistor is dependent upon collector current as shown in Fig. 6–7. If we imagine a stage biased at one ampere and handling a signal that ranges both positively and negatively from that

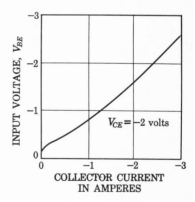

Fig. 6–8. Transfer characteristic for a typical power transistor.

point, the figure shows that the positive excursion would get considerably more amplification than the negative excursion.

The two sources of distortion described above tend somewhat to cancel each other and will result, when combined, in an overall transfer characteristic such as that shown in Fig. 6–8. It can be noted that while this curve is a plot of base voltage versus resulting collector current, a curve of base current versus collector current could also be described as a transfer characteristic for this device.

Let us assume that, for any particular situation, the collector current will contain harmonics, and can thus be represented by a Fourier Series

$$i_c = I_Q + A_0 + A_1 \cos \omega t + A_2 \cos 2\omega t + A_3 \cos 3\omega t + \cdots \qquad (6\text{–}18)$$

where the fourth and higher order harmonics may be omitted with negligible error. We shall further assume that the signal voltage applied to the transistor input is a pure sinusoid and shall sample both input and output wave-

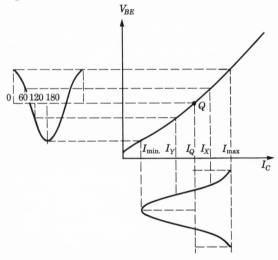

Fig. 6–9. Graphical determination of distortion content in output current.

forms at several time intervals to obtain the coefficients of the terms of Eq. (6–18). Let us take our samples at $\omega t = 0°$, $60°$, $120°$, and $180°$ with corresponding collector currents designated as $I_{\max}$, I_x, I_y, and $I_{\min}$. Graphically, this operation is shown in Fig. 6–9.

Substitution in Eq. (6–18) yields:

$$\left.\begin{array}{rl}
\omega t = 0° & I_{\max} = I_Q + A_0 + A_1 + A_2 + A_3, \\[4pt]
\omega t = 60° & I_x = I_Q + A_0 + A_1/2 - A_2/2 - A_3, \\[4pt]
\omega t = 120° & I_y = I_Q + A_0 - A_1/2 - A_2/2 + A_3, \\[4pt]
\omega t = 180° & I_{\min} = I_Q + A_0 - A_1 + A_2 - A_3.
\end{array}\right\} \qquad (6\text{–}19)$$

The solution of these four simultaneous equations results in expressions for the harmonic amplitudes:

$$A_0 = (\tfrac{1}{6})(I_{\max} + I_{\min}) + (\tfrac{1}{3})(I_x + I_y) - I_Q,$$
$$A_1 = (\tfrac{1}{3})(I_{\max} - I_{\min}) + (\tfrac{1}{3})(I_x - I_y),$$
$$A_2 = (\tfrac{1}{4})(I_{\max} + I_{\min}) - (\tfrac{1}{2})I_Q,$$
$$A_3 = (\tfrac{1}{6})(I_{\max} - I_{\min}) - (\tfrac{1}{3})(I_x - I_y).$$
$$\text{(6-20)}$$

The total harmonic content in a wave can be expressed as the ratio of the rms value of all harmonics to the effective value of the fundamental.

$$D = \frac{\sqrt{A_2{}^2 + A_3{}^2 + \cdots}}{A_1} \times 100\%. \qquad (6\text{-}21)$$

Usually the ratio of harmonic amplitude to fundamental amplitude is of concern.

$$D_2 = \frac{A_2}{A_1} \times 100\%, \qquad (6\text{-}22)$$

and

$$D_3 = \frac{A_3}{A_1} \times 100\%. \qquad (6\text{-}23)$$

6-6. Class-A Amplification. A single transistor, biased by the methods of Chapter 3 and capable of handling the required load power, may be used as the output stage of an amplifier. The transistor may be $R\text{-}C$ or transformer-coupled to its load and to its driver.

Fig. 6-10 symbolizes the output characteristics of a transistor. It is desirable to provide an operating point (such as Q) that is equidistant from each axis. The Q point and load are often selected so that the maximum collector-dissipation hyperbola is tangent or nearly tangent to the load line at Q; these conditions are easily achieved with a transformer-coupled load, because a turns ratio may be chosen to reflect almost any load value into the collector circuit.

To achieve an operating point such as Q of Fig. 6-10, a large standby collector current must be supplied to a high-power stage. This quiescent current for a Class-A power amplifier stage may be as much as six or eight amperes, and consequently it

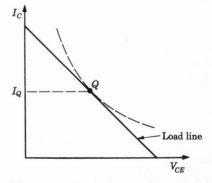

Fig. 6-10. Typical operating point for Class-A power stage requires high quiescent current.

is easy to understand why Class-B amplifiers, which require almost zero quiescent current, are widely employed as output stages.

Two transistors may be connected in Class-A push-pull if more output power is required than can be supplied by a single transistor. Two such circuits are shown in Fig. 6–11. In Fig. 6–11a, the transistors are both *p-n-p* and two input signals are required; these signals must differ in phase by 180°. The required phase inversion may be supplied by a transformer or by one of the active phase-inversion circuits described in a later section.

In Class-A push-pull operation both devices operate at all times, and each

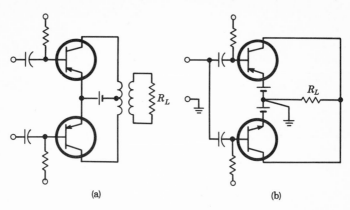

Fig. 6–11.   Class-A push-pull output circuits.

supplies one half of the total load power. If the transistors are matched, the addition of the two signals in the load will result in the elimination of all even harmonic distortion, and d-c magnetomotive force in the output transformer will be minimized.[7]

A Class-A push-pull stage utilizing complementary symmetry is depicted in Fig. 6–11b. No phase inversion is required; instead each transistor receives the same input signal. The use of opposite conductivity types, while simplifying some circuit designs, creates additional problems for the designer. In the diagram two power supplies are used, and this in itself is undesirable in many applications. The matching problems may be difficult to overcome.

Power-Amplifier Design Example—Class-A. The design of a Class-A output stage by graphical methods is considered in this example.

Object. Design a transistor amplifying stage to meet the following requirements:

1. Load resistance: 2000 ohms
2. Power output: 1 watt (maximum)

3. Temperature: 40° C

4. Supply potential available: 12 volts

5. Frequency: 400 cps

Solution. It may be assumed from the power-output specification that the stage output should enter the saturation and cutoff regions of the characteristics for any power delivery in excess of one watt of full-load power (P_{FL}). A specification of this type is encountered when feeding a load that may be damaged by excessive signal. Since here we shall transformer-couple to the load, let us assume an output-transformer efficiency of 67%. The stage must supply

$$P_{\max} = \frac{P_{FL}}{\eta} = \frac{1.0}{0.67} = 1.5 \text{ watts.}$$

The type 2N539A power transistor is available and will be used. It is capable of handling the required power.

If we assume no d-c resistance in the transformer primary, then, as can be seen in Fig. 6–12, the d-c load line is vertical from 12 volts. Since saturation

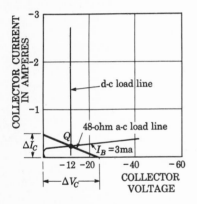
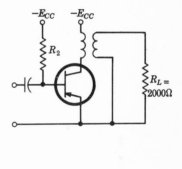

Fig. 6–12.   Load lines for Class-A stage design example.

and cutoff should exist concurrently, the collector-voltage swing will be 2(12), or 24 volts. We must find the corresponding collector-current excursion.

$$P_{\max} = 1.5 = \left(\frac{\Delta V_C}{2\sqrt{2}}\right)\left(\frac{\Delta I_C}{2\sqrt{2}}\right),$$

(ΔV_C and ΔI_C are peak-to-peak values and division by $2\sqrt{2}$ yields rms.)

$$\Delta I_C = \tfrac{1}{2}\tfrac{2}{4} = 0.5 \text{ ampere.}$$

The load seen by the transistor is

$$R_L = \frac{\Delta V_C}{\Delta I_C} = \frac{24}{0.5} = 48 \text{ ohms.}$$

The impedance ratio of the output transformer must be 48:2000.

The quiescent point is

$$V_{CE} = 12 \text{ volts,}$$

$$I_C = 0.25 \text{ ampere,}$$

and results in a 3-watt standby dissipation.

The base-circuit characteristic is defined by the plot of H_{IE} vs. I_C in Appendix I. If it is assumed that the curve applies at $V_{CE} = 12$ volts, then at $I_C = 0.25$ ampere,

$$R_i \cong H_{IE} = 135 \text{ ohms}$$

H_{FE}, from the manufacturer's curve at $I_C = 0.25$ ampere, is

$$H_{FE} = \frac{I_C}{I_B} \cong \frac{I_c}{I_b} = 85.$$

Power gain is given by,

$$G = \frac{P_o}{P_i} \cong \frac{I_c^2 R_L}{I_b^2 H_{IE}} \cong \frac{(H_{FE} I_b)^2 R_L}{I_b^2 H_{IE}} = 2570.$$

A rough calculation may be made to determine base-bias resistance R_2. The Q point is located at $I_B \cong 3$ ma.

$$R_2 \cong \frac{E_{CC}}{I_B} = \frac{12}{3 \times 10^{-3}}$$

$$= 4000 \text{ ohms.}$$

This should be checked in the laboratory.

The design discussed here contains no stabilization or feedback. Further investigation must be directed along those lines.

6–7. Shifting of the Operating Point. The A_0 term in the distortion discussion is necessary in the event that the performance of the transistor differs on the positive and negative half cycles of the input signal, and the resulting output waveform contains a constant or d-c term in addition to the quiescent current I_Q. Because of characteristics nonlinearities, the operating point of many Class-A amplifiers will shift slightly during the presence of a signal to be amplified.

Again refer to Fig. 6–10. The Q point is assumed equidistant from the two limiting regions. In the presence of a sinusoidal base-current signal that drives the stage to both extremes, the resulting collector current will be squared (the peaks will be clipped). The operating point will remain at Q and not change from its no-signal value, because Q is equidistant. A pronounced shift in the operating point will occur, however, when the stage is driven into only one of the limiting regions (saturation or cutoff). Fig. 6–13 illustrates this. The stage has a no-signal bias that determines Q. When the base-current variation is of such a magnitude as to cause the stage to saturate, clipping occurs and the quiescent point must shift because of the new average or d-c value of the distorted wave. In this instance, the point shifts away from the saturation region, I_Q is re-duced, and because of this the clip-ping is softened.

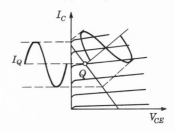

It must be remembered that when the operating point shifts, it moves up or down the *d-c load line;* the a-c load line always passes through Q.

Should input variations result in collector-current excursions that tend to exceed the allowable drive, and should a stage originally be biased at a point closer to cutoff, a harder form of clipping will occur. However, it

Fig. 6–13. Clipping occurs when the operating point is not in the center of the allowable range and the input signal is large.

too will be somewhat softened by a shifting of the Q point, because of distor-tion of the current waveform. This case is characterized by a noticeable in-crease in I_C.

6–8. Class-B Amplification. Since Class-B operation results in conduction over one half of the input-signal cycle, it is necessary to employ two transistors in a push-pull arrangement in order to amplify an entire sinusoidal waveform. The two halves of the waveform are added at the load to re-establish the com-plete wave.

Class-B circuits are widely accepted because of their low standby-current requirements. It has been noted that Class-A circuits require an operating point that is characterized by a high value of collector current; for a Class-B stage or push-pull pair little or no standby collector current is necessary, for biasing is at or near cutoff. A single-sided stage is seldom used because of its inability to reproduce the input-signal waveform.

In analyzing a push-pull arrangement, it is customary to treat only one of the transistors, since each is operating at identical levels into an identical load. Transformer load-coupling as shown in Fig. 6–14a is widely used, with the collector supply fed to the center tap of the output transformer. The d-c load per stage consists of one half of the d-c resistance of the transformer primary; this can often be assumed to be negligible when high-quality trans-formers are used. In each collector circuit only one half of the primary turns are applicable. Consequently the total primary resistance (R_{cc}) to alternating

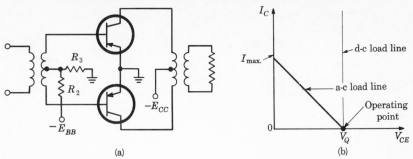

Fig. 6–14.   Class B push-pull pair: (a) circuit diagram; (b) output characteristic.

signals is given by

$$R_{cc} = 4R_L, \tag{6-24}$$

where R_L is the load per transistor, and is the secondary load resistance referred to one half of the primary.

The diagram of Fig. 6–14b indicates an operating point set at

$$I_C = 0,$$

$$V_{CE} = V_Q.$$

A load line joins this Q point with

$$I_C = I_{\max},$$

$$V_{CE} = 0.$$

This diagram assumes that cutoff is at zero current instead of I_{CO} and saturation is at zero collector voltage.   Then

$$R_L = \frac{V_Q}{I_{\max}}.$$

The power delivered by a stage that is driven through its total range (cutoff to saturation) is given by

$$P_o = \frac{1}{2}\left(\frac{V_Q}{\sqrt{2}}\right)\left(\frac{I_{\max}}{\sqrt{2}}\right) = \frac{V_Q I_{\max}}{4}. \tag{6-25}$$

The $\frac{1}{2}$ factor is used because we are dealing with half-wave pulses.   For a push-pull pair

$$P_o = \frac{V_Q I_{\max}}{2}. \tag{6-26}$$

D-c drawn from the collector supply is negligible during standby operation.

During signal-amplification periods the d-c source must supply, during each half cycle of maximum swing,

$$I_{\text{d-c}} = \frac{I_{\max}}{\pi}. \tag{6-27}$$

The power from the d-c supply is

$$P_{\text{d-c}} = \frac{V_Q I_{\max}}{\pi}. \tag{6-28}$$

Therefore the maximum efficiency of each transistor is

$$\eta = \frac{P_o}{P_{\text{d-c}}} = \frac{V_Q I_{\max}/4}{V_Q I_{\max}/\pi} = 78\%.$$

It is important to know the power being dissipated at the collector junction.

$$P_{\text{diss}} = P_{\text{d-c}} - P_o = \frac{V_Q I_{\max}}{\pi} - \frac{V_Q I_{\max}}{4}$$

$$= 0.068 V_Q I_{\max}$$

$$= 0.27 P_o. \tag{6-29}$$

Should a Class-B stage be driven to a fraction (k) of its total allowable swing,

$$\Delta V_C = k V_Q,$$

$$\Delta I_C = k I_{\max}.$$

Therefore,

$$P_o = \frac{k^2 V_Q I_{\max}}{4}. \tag{6-30}$$

Power-Amplifier Design Example—Class-B. An example of the design of a Class-B output stage is not presented at this point. In the next chapter such a design is illustrated in conjunction with a complete ten-watt amplifier.

Distortion in Class-B Stages. The two transistors employed in any push-pull arrangement should be operationally matched, the degree of such matching depending upon the extent to which distortion must be minimized. In addition to the sources of distortion discussed under Class-A amplification, Class-B circuits are subject to "crossover distortion."

Crossover distortion is best understood by study of a diagram. Fig. 6–15a shows the nonlinearity of the input characteristic of a common-emitter connected transistor. The exponential nature of the curve signifies high input resistance at low-voltage levels; thus little base current will flow until input voltage exceeds some value such as M. Because collector current is almost directly proportional to base current, resulting collector current will be small until the input voltage is sufficiently high. The collector current for a push-pull pair is shown in Fig. 6–15b; distortion at the "crossover" point is obvious.

To overcome this type of distortion, a base potential or current bias can be supplied that will permit operation at a more desirable point on the input characteristic, such as N. The summation of the alternate half-cycle signals at the load will consequently be free from a major distortion contribution and the output waveform will approximate a pure sine wave. The input biasing

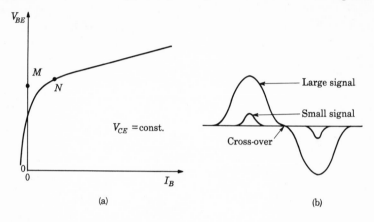

Fig. 6–15. Crossover distortion: (a) input characteristic; (b) collector-current waveforms.

network composed of R_2, R_3 and E_{BB} in the circuit of Fig. 6–14a compensates for this type of distortion by providing the required slight forward bias. R_3 must be kept small, for signal power will be lost in that element. Often, because of temperature effects upon the transistor emitter-base characteristics, the biasing network will contain temperature-compensating elements such as thermistors or junction diodes. The addition of a bypass capacitor across R_3 is not recommended, for its discharge through that resistance will develop a potential that tends to reverse bias both transistor input junctions and, therefore, contribute to distortion.

Unbypassed emitter resistance is often used with the Class-B push-pull pair in order to improve bias stability and to reduce distortion by providing some signal degeneration.

6–9. Phase Inverters. To drive a push-pull output stage when complementary symmetry is not employed, two signals differing in phase by 180° must be supplied to the high-power pair. A transformer, with its secondary center tap grounded, is often used, the phasing of the voltage from CT to each end of the winding differing by 180°. When the cost, weight, or frequency requirements so dictate, a transistor phase inverter may provide the required signals. The transistor phase inverter must be capable of supplying two identical outputs of opposite polarities, and output impedances must be equal in order to satisfy the needs of each of the power transistors.

The "split-load phase inverter" is shown in Fig. 6–16a. The input impedance of this stage will be fairly high, because of the unbypassed emitter resistance R_E. The circuit has two sources of unbalance: if R_E is made equal to R_c as would seem natural, load #2 would receive slightly more signal, because i_e is always greater than i_c ($i_c = \alpha i_e$); also, load #2 is fed from a common-collector type of generator, whereas load #1 is fed from a common-

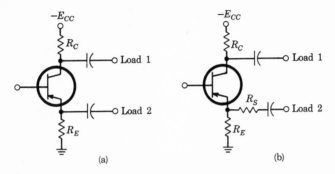

Fig. 6–16. Split-load phase inverter: (a) basic circuit; (b) circuit modified to adjust for output impedances. Biasing not shown.

emitter type of output resistance.

For the common-emitter configuration

$$R_o \cong \frac{h_{ib} + R_g(1 + h_{fb})}{h_{ob}(h_{ib} + R_g) - h_{rb}h_{fb}}, \tag{4–56A}$$

where h_{ib} includes all resistance in series with the emitter terminal; in this case h_{ib} plus R_E in parallel with load #2. The output resistance of a common-collector circuit is

$$R_o \cong \frac{h_{ib}(1 + R_g h_{ob}) + R_g(1 + h_{fb})}{1 + R_g h_{ob}}.$$

For this circuit, h_{ib} does not include the resistance of the parallel combination of R_E and load #2, but h_{ob} will include R_c and load #1. These resistances, however, will not materially affect h_{ob} (see Problem 4–12). The insertion of numbers into the formulas may simplify the analysis. Consider $h_{ib} = 50$, $h_{fb} = -0.98$, $h_{rb} = 10^{-4}$, $h_{ob} = 10^{-6}$, $R_g = 5\,K$, $R_c = R_E = 2\,K$ and the loads each of 500 ohms. The output resistance of the common-emitter portion is 100,000 ohms and this in parallel with R_c yields 1960 ohms. For the common-collector portion of the circuit, $R_o = 150$ ohms, and this paralleled by R_E yields 139 ohms. To equalize the drive impedance a series resistor of 1821 ohms could be added as shown in Fig. 6–16b. The values of R_c and R_E must now be realigned because of the loss of power in the equalizing resistor R_s.

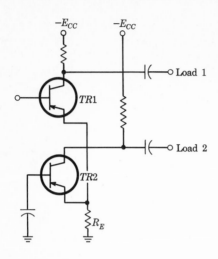

Fig. 6–17. Emitter-coupled phase inverter. Biasing not shown.

In the phase inverter of Fig. 6–17 the input signal is supplied to only one transistor; $TR1$ emitter current, flowing through the common R_E establishes a varying emitter-to-base potential for transistor $TR2$. The output of $TR2$ consequently differs from that of the directly supplied transistor by 180°. This circuit has been called the "emitter-coupled inverter." A mathematical analysis of operation is similar to that of the difference amplifier discussed in Chapter 8, and proceeds with the drawing of the equivalent circuit, followed by calculation of the collector voltages V_{c1} and V_{c2}. For perfect inversion

$$\frac{V_{c1}}{V_{c2}} = 1, \qquad (6\text{–}31)$$

and the output resistances of each transistor are identical. The emitter-coupled inverter does not quite satisfy Eq. (6–31).

Another two-transistor phase inverter circuit is shown in Fig. 6–18. The resistor R_s can equalize the gain of $TR2$ to make its output signal equivalent to that of $TR1$. The phase inversion due to $TR2$ is used for load #2; the re-

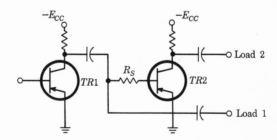

Fig. 6–18. Another type of phase inverter. Biasing not shown.

quirement, as previously stated, is a 180° difference between currents to the loads. Output resistances will tend to differ for this circuit.

6–10. Summary. An extremely important consideration in the design of large-signal stages is junction temperature and its effects upon circuit operation. Changing transistor parameters with temperature cause variations in gain and resistance levels, but of even greater importance is the possibility of thermal runaway. Such runaway is not always destructive because there is usually external resistance in the collector-emitter circuit to limit the quiescent current to a finite and sometimes seemingly satisfactory value; investigation of the standby collector-to-emitter potential as well as the current is helpful in determining if runaway has occurred.

Because of the large standby current requirement, Class-A high-power stages have not gained wide acceptance. Class-B push-pull circuits are usually used and have been refined to a high degree by the addition of thermistors and other temperature-sensitive compensating devices.

PROBLEMS

6–1. On a sketch of the 2N344 output characteristics, show the maximum dissipation contour (20 mw at 40° C).

6–2. A particular transistor is dissipating 25 mw at its collector junction. The thermal resistance is given as 0.6° C/mw for operation in free air. At what temperature is the collector-base junction when the ambient is 40° C?

6–3. If the transistor in Problem 6–2 were attached to a clip-on sink of one square inch radiating surface, and θ_T was found to be 0.45° C/mw, at what temperature is the junction for the same ambient condition and dissipation?

6–4. The maximum allowable operating temperature for the transistor of Problems 6–2 and 6–3 is 90° C. In an ambient of 40° C, what is the permissible collector dissipation with and without the sink?

6–5. Consider a high-power transistor, mounted vertically and cooled by natural convection from a $\frac{1}{8}$-inch thick copper sheet. Eight watts are being dissipated in the transistor, the junction-to-case resistance is 1.0° C/w, and mounting hardware is 1.0° C /w. The ambient is 30° C and maximum allowable junction temperature is 90° C. Find the minimum dimensions of the sink.

6–6. Will a common-base stage with $S = 10$, $V_{CB} = 20$, $\theta_T = 0.25°$ C/mw, and $I_{CO}' = 20 \, \mu a$ exhibit thermal runaway? If the same transistor is operated common-emitter under the same voltage and bias conditions, and has a beta of 50, will it run away?

6–7. Now consider the transistor of Problem 6–6 to be made of silicon, and that $\partial I_{CO}/\partial T_j = 0.15 \, I_{CO}'$. Leakage current at 25° C (I_{CO}') is 0.1 μa. Will the circuit run away? Is it more stable with the silicon or with the germanium transistor?

6–8. For an output waveform, $I_Q = 1$ a, $I_x = 1.6$ a, $I_y = 0.5$ a, $I_{max} = 2$ a, $I_{min} = 0.3$ a.

(a) Write the Fourier series for this wave with numerical coefficients through the third harmonic.

(b) Obtain the percentage of each harmonic of the fundamental.

6–9. Operating Class-A, a power transistor is to deliver a maximum of 4 watts of audio power to a 4-ohm load. A 12-volt power supply is to be used. Assume ideal characteristics, ideal transformer coupling, and a quiescent point adjusted for symmetrical clipping. Determine the following:

(a) What transformer impedance ratio is required?

(b) What is the operating point of the stage?

(c) What is the standby-power requirement?

(d) What is the peak collector current?

6–10. Draw each of the following circuits and state which of the arrangements require phase inversion:

(a) Push-pull Class-B pair (p-n-p and p-n-p).

(b) Push-pull Class-A pair (p-n-p and n-p-n).

(c) Push-pull Class-A pair (n-p-n and n-p-n).

(d) Push-pull Class-B pair (n-p-n and p-n-p).

6–11. Consider a Class-A stage being driven from saturation to cutoff. If the operating point is at $(V_{CE})_O$ and the collector current swing is from zero to twice $(I_C)_O$, determine the efficiency of the stage as the ratio of output or load power to standby power. This is the maximum efficiency possible. What type of coupling must be employed? What is the a-c load resistance in terms of operating point coordinates?

6–12. Prove that the collector efficiency of a Class-A stage is given by

$$\eta = k^2(50) \qquad \%,$$

where k is the fraction of total allowable swing and is unity when the stage is operating between ideal cutoff and saturation.

6–13. Show how a reactive load on a Class-A stage can result in an elliptical load line. How can this affect the maximum signal handling capabilities of the stage?

6–14. For a Class-B push-pull transformer-coupled circuit, find the collector potential on the OFF transistor in terms of the direct supply potential, E_{CC}, when the pair is operating with full signal.

6–15. A d-c meter in the E_{CC} branch of an ideal Class-B amplifier reads 0.75 ampere. If each transistor is working into 10-ohm load, how much power is being delivered to that load? The circuit is that of Fig. 6–14a.

6–16. Specify the area, thickness, material, and mounting position of a flat metallic plate that can adequately serve as a heat sink for a power transistor, biased at cutoff and feeding a transformer-coupled load. The supply potential is 30 volts, and the transistor is half of a Class-B pair delivering 30 watts to the load when swinging from cutoff to saturation. Consider $1.5°$ C/w for the transistor, $0.5°$ C/w for the mounting washer. The transformer has an efficiency of 75% and negligible winding resistances. Choose a heat sink that will just enable the junction to operate at $75°$ C in a $35°$ C ambient; do not include a safety factor.

6–17. A push-pull Class-B pair is wired as shown in the diagram. Crossover distortion is evident in the output waveform and it is desired to overcome

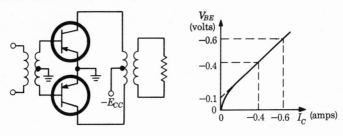

Problem 6–17.

this with a compensating network. Working with a knowledge of the transfer curve (above) and available supplies of $+20$ and -20 volts, design a resistive circuit to minimize crossover distortion and include your network in a sketch of the circuit above.

6–18. A two-transistor bridge circuit with a speaker load is shown in the accompanying diagram. The bridge is adjusted to have a zero direct voltage

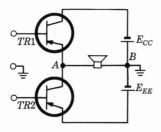

Problem 6–18.

from A to B, thus a conventional loudspeaker may be employed. Study the operation of this circuit and answer the following:

(a) $TR1$ and $TR2$ are operating in what configurations?

(b) What direct collector-emitter potentials exist across $TR1$ and $TR2$?

(c) If each transistor is operating Class-B, explain how the circuit will reproduce the entire signal at the speaker.

(d) If each transistor is operating Class-A, explain how the circuit will reproduce the entire signal at the speaker.

(e) Add biasing to the diagram for Class-A operation.

6–19. Design a Class-A power stage using a 2N539A to meet the following requirements:

1. Load resistance: 50 ohms
2. Power output: 2 watts (maximum)
3. Temperature: 25° C
4. Supply potential available: −16 volts
5. Frequency: 800 cps

Assume an output transformer efficiency of 75% and an input transformer efficiency of 50%, with negligible d-c resistances. Sketch the circuit and determine all component values, both transformer impedance ratios, circuit gains and the input resistance of the complete stage.

6–20. Design a push-pull Class-B stage to directly feed a center-tapped loudspeaker.

1. Load resistance: 4 ohms each side
2. Power output: 5 watts
3. Temperature: 25° C
4. Potentials available: −20 and +20 volts
5. Frequency response: 60 to 6000 cps.

Itemize any assumptions made in the design.

REFERENCES

1. Bevitt, W. D., *Transistors Handbook*, Prentice-Hall, Inc., Englewood Cliffs, New Jersey, 1956.
2. DeWitt, D., and Rossoff, A. L., *Transistor Electronics*, McGraw-Hill Book Co., Inc., New York, 1957.
3. Hunter, L. P., *Handbook of Semiconductor Electronics*, McGraw-Hill Book Co., Inc., New York, 1956.
4. Hurley, R. B., *Junction Transistor Electronics*, John Wiley & Sons, Inc., New York, 1958.
5. Lo, *et al.*, *Transistor Electronics*, Prentice-Hall, Inc., Englewood Cliffs, New Jersey, 1955.
6. Riddle, R. L., and Ristenbatt, M. P., *Transistor Physics and Circuits*, Prentice-Hall, Inc., Englewood Cliffs, New Jersey, 1958.
7. Ryder, J. D., *Electronic Fundamentals and Applications*, 2nd Ed., Prentice-Hall, Inc., Englewood Cliffs, New Jersey, 1959.
8. Shea, R. F., *Principles of Transistor Circuits*, John Wiley & Sons, Inc., New York, 1953.
9. Shea, R. F., *Transistor Circuit Engineering*, John Wiley & Sons, Inc., New York, 1957.
10. Wolfendale, E., *The Junction Transistor and Its Applications*, The Macmillan Company, New York, 1958.

Chapter 7

MULTISTAGE AMPLIFIERS

When more amplification is required than can be supplied by a single stage, additional stages are joined to form a *composite* or *cascade* or *multistage* amplifier. Vacuum-tube stages can easily be connected in cascade because of their isolating properties; transistors, on the other hand, because of their finite input resistance, present a considerable load to preceding circuitry, and therefore warrant special attention.

The performance of a single stage can be obtained by using the equations derived in Chapter 4; coupling networks and their effects upon gain, frequency response and impedance levels were discussed in Chapter 5; and the high-power stage was described in Chapter 6. The problem at hand is to combine this information in order to analyze and synthesize the multistage amplifier. From the point of view of overall requirements, the multistage amplifier must join a particular source to a particular load and provide the required amplification over the desired frequency range; it must be capable of supplying the proper power to the load, of presenting the required input resistance to the source, and of working under the environmental conditions to be expected with the power supplies available.

7–1. Analysis by Blocks. The amplifier designer can make use of systems concepts because a multistage circuit is a system of different circuits, some

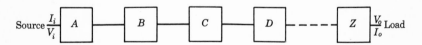

Fig. 7–1.   Block diagram of multistage circuit.

capable of supplying gain, as for example the active elements, and some providing attenuation; coupling networks and feedback paths are examples of this latter type. A cascade amplifier can be depicted as in Fig. 7–1, a series of blocks each representing significant circuitry. Each block is capable of voltage and current gain, although the gain of some of the blocks may be less than unity and they therefore serve to attenuate. The block designated "A" may, in reality, be the coupling circuit between the source and the first amplifying stage marked "B."   The "C" block may represent a coupling network, an equalizing network, or some other group of passive or active elements.

Since overall operation is to be considered, the load power may be written as

$$P_o = I_o{}^2 R_L, \tag{7-1}$$

and the input power as

$$P_i = I_i{}^2 R_{iA}. \tag{7-2}$$

The power gain is

$$G = \frac{P_o}{P_i} = \frac{I_o{}^2 R_L}{I_i{}^2 R_{iA}}. \tag{7-3}$$

But

$$I_o = I_i(A_{iA}A_{iB} \cdots A_{iZ}). \tag{7-4}$$

Therefore

$$G = \frac{R_L}{R_{iA}}(A_{iA}A_{iB} \cdots A_{iZ})^2. \tag{7-5}$$

The operation of a multistage amplifier can be specified in terms of the individual voltage gains, because, at the load, power can be expressed by

$$P_o = \frac{V_o{}^2}{R_L}, \tag{7-6}$$

and at the input by

$$P_i = \frac{V_i{}^2}{R_{iA}}. \tag{7-7}$$

Then power gain is

$$G = \frac{P_o}{P_i} = \frac{V_o{}^2/R_L}{V_i{}^2/R_{iA}}. \tag{7-8}$$

But

$$V_o = V_i(A_{vA}A_{vB} \cdots A_{vZ}). \tag{7-9}$$

Therefore

$$G = \frac{R_{iA}}{R_L}(A_{vA}A_{vB} \cdots A_{vZ})^2. \tag{7-10}$$

Another approach is to use the power gains of each stage

$$G = G_A G_B \cdots G_Z. \tag{7-11}$$

Eq. (7-11) requires all gain factors to be numerical ratios. Should gains be given in logarithmic units (decibels), the overall amplification is the sum of the individual gains.

To analyze the overall performance of a multistage amplifier, it is necessary only to determine the numbers to use in an equation such as (7-5). R_L will undoubtedly be known, but the determination of R_{iA} is not as simple as might be desired. R_{iA} depends upon the load on block A, and the load on block A is the input resistance of block B, and so on. Similarly, in order to calculate any of the A_i terms, the input resistance of the following block must be known. Therefore, it may be concluded that *in order to predict the operation of a multistage transistor amplifier, it is necessary to proceed from the last element (or block) and work forward toward the initial block.*

In order to determine the output resistance of a cascaded circuit, an exception must be made to the rule quoted in the preceding paragraph, namely that analysis must proceed from the final element toward the initial element. Output resistance depends upon the properties of the driving source, and therefore its calculation is not possible until all preceding elements are adequately specified.

The frequency response of composite circuits may be considerably poorer than that of an individual stage. As a chain is no stronger than its weakest link, so a cascade amplifier is no wider than its narrowest stage (in the absence of external feedback). If the stages are more-or-less identical, overall performance may be entirely unsatisfactory, even if the response of each individual stage contains a safety factor.

The upper half-power frequency for n identical stages is to be investigated. It is defined by reduction in voltage (or current) gain to $1/\sqrt{2}$ of the mid-band value. The gain of each stage ideally declines with increasing frequency according to the relation

$$A = \frac{A_{\mathrm{mid}}}{\sqrt{1 + (f/f_h)^2}}. \qquad (7\text{--}12)$$

f_h represents the upper cutoff frequency of a single stage. Now if the overall performance of the cascade amplifier (A_T) is equated to that of the composite stages, at the frequency of interest we have

$$\frac{A_T}{\sqrt{2}} = A^n = \left(\frac{A_{\mathrm{mid}}}{\sqrt{1 + (f/f_h)^2}}\right)^n.$$

Note that the gains A_T and $(A_{\mathrm{mid}})^n$ at the mid-frequency reference are identical.

Mathematical manipulations give

$$2^{1/n} = 1 + (f/f_h)^2,$$

from which

$$f = f_h\sqrt{2^{1/n} - 1}. \qquad (7\text{--}13)$$

Eq. (7–13) is an expression for the upper "cutoff" frequency (response 3-db down) for a multistage circuit consisting of n identical stages.

At the low-frequency end of the spectrum circuit gain can be approximated by

$$A = \frac{A_{\text{mid}}}{\sqrt{1 + (f_l/f)^2}}. \tag{7-14}$$

f_l represents the lower half-power frequency of a single stage. Hence, low-frequency cutoff is at

$$f = \frac{f_l}{\sqrt{2^{1/n} - 1}}. \tag{7-15}$$

A numerical example is illuminating. Consider three stages in cascade, each with $f_l = 20$ cps and $f_h = 20{,}000$ cps. From Eqs. (7–13) and (7–15), the overall bandwidth is found to be 39 cps to 10,200 cps. It is obvious, therefore, that the bandwidth reduction resulting from the cascading of stages is an important design factor; it may be overcome by designing all stages to have broad response, or by the use of feedback (treated in Chapter 8).

7–2. Analysis by Kirchhoff's Laws. An alternate method of obtaining performance information for a multistage amplifier is by solution of the composite equivalent circuit. When a large number of stages are included, or when feedback loops are evident, the solution of the simultaneous circuit equations becomes a laborious task, and often the results of such a study are not worth the time devoted to it. The procedure is identical with that used in Chapter 4 to analyze single-stage circuits; the equivalent circuit must be drawn, loop or nodal equations written, the equations solved to determine the unknown voltages and currents, and finally, the ratios of the important quantities determined.

Fig. 7–2 gives the equivalent circuit, in terms of T-parameters, for two common-emitter stages in cascade. The literature contains other examples.[1]

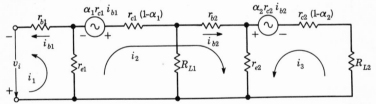

Fig. 7–2.   Equivalent circuit for two common-emitter stages in cascade.

Examination of the figure will disclose an R_{L1}, the purpose of which is to lump any collector-return resistance for stage one and base-bias resistance for stage two into one element. Often this is not necessary, for the input resistance of the second stage may be small enough so that it will be the only significant load upon stage one. Notice that the equivalent circuit excludes other biasing resistances.

Let us write loop equations for the circuit, excluding R_{L1}:

$$v_i = i_1(r_{b1} + r_{e1}) + i_2 r_{e1},$$
$$0 = -i_1(\alpha_1 r_{c1} - r_{e1}) + i_2[r_{c1}(1 - \alpha_1) + r_{b2} + r_{e2} + r_{e1}] + i_3 r_{e2}, \quad (7\text{-}16)$$
$$0 = -i_2(\alpha_2 r_{c2} - r_{e2}) + i_3[r_{c2}(1 - \alpha_2) + r_{e2} + R_{L2}].$$

Solution of these equations for the ratio of i_3 to i_1 gives

$$A_i = \frac{(\alpha_1 r_{c1} - r_{e1})(\alpha_2 r_{c2} - r_{e2})}{\begin{Bmatrix} [r_{c1}(1 - \alpha_1) + r_{b2} + r_{e2} + r_{e1}][r_{c2}(1 - \alpha_2) + r_{e2} + R_{L2}] \\ + r_{e2}(\alpha_2 r_{c2} - r_{e2}) \end{Bmatrix}}. \quad (7\text{-}17)$$

The complete expressions for A_v, G, R_i, and R_o are unwieldy and will not be offered here.

If both transistors are operating at the same point and can be considered to have the same parameter values the gain equations can be simplified. Thus

$$A_i = \frac{(\alpha r_c - r_e)^2}{[r_c(1 - \alpha) + r_b + 2r_e][r_c(1 - \alpha) + r_e + R_{L2}] + r_e(\alpha r_c - r_e)}, \quad (7\text{-}18)$$

and voltage gain, $i_3 R_{L2}/v_i$, is

$$A_v = \frac{(\alpha r_c - r_e)^2 R_{L2}}{\begin{Bmatrix} (r_e + r_b)\{[r_c(1 - \alpha) + r_b + 2r_e][r_c(1 - \alpha) + r_e + R_{L2}] \\ + r_e(\alpha r_c - r_e)\} + (\alpha r_c - r_e)r_e[r_c(1 - \alpha) + r_e + R_{L2}] \end{Bmatrix}}. \quad (7\text{-}19)$$

These equations may be further simplified by assuming that $r_c \gg r_b$, $r_c \gg r_e$, and $R_{L2} \gg r_e$. Then

$$A_i \cong \frac{\alpha^2 r_c{}^2}{[r_c(1 - \alpha)][r_c(1 - \alpha) + R_{L2}] + r_e \alpha r_c}, \quad (7\text{-}20)$$

and

$$A_v \cong \frac{\alpha^2 r_c{}^2 R_{L2}}{\begin{Bmatrix} (r_e + r_b)\{[r_c(1 - \alpha)][r_c(1 - \alpha) + R_{L2}] + \alpha r_e r_c\} \\ + \alpha r_c r_e[r_c(1 - \alpha) + R_{L2}] \end{Bmatrix}}. \quad (7\text{-}21)$$

To include R_{L1}, we may write four loop equations. The complete gain expressions are very lengthy. If the simplifying assumptions are again employed,

$$A_i \cong \frac{\alpha^2 r_c{}^2 R_{L1}}{\begin{Bmatrix} [R_{L1} + r_c(1 - \alpha)][R_{L1} + r_b + r_e][r_c(1 - \alpha) + R_{L2}] \\ + \alpha r_e r_c[r_c(1 - \alpha) + R_{L1}] - R_{L1}{}^2[r_c(1 - \alpha) + R_{L2}] \end{Bmatrix}}. \quad (7\text{-}22)$$

Derivations of other performance relationships are left to the reader.

7-3. Analysis by h-Parameters. The h-matrix parameters offer a means for determining circuit performance that is somewhat more general than the conventional method described in the preceding section. Consider the two-stage equivalent circuit of Fig. 7–3. The parameters are simply h_i, h_r, h_f, and h_o, without designation of the configuration employed, and the single prime represents the first stage whereas the double prime stands for the second stage parameters of the cascaded pair.

If a load is attached at the output terminals and a source at the input pair, equations can be written for A_i, A_v, G, R_i, and R_o in terms of the general

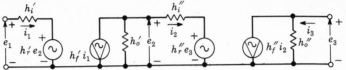

Fig. 7–3.   General h-parameter equivalent for two stages.

parameters. Should stage one be common-base and stage two be common-emitter, then $h_i' = h_{ib}$, etc., and $h_i'' = h_{ie}$, etc. Therefore, one set of performance equations can suffice for the nine possible combinations of the three configurations connected as a pair. Such equations will not be offered here.

A somewhat simpler means of finding the operation of the cascaded pair is to find the *h-parameters of the entire circuit*, not just for individual transistors. It must be remembered that a complete circuit such as that of Fig. 7–3 may have an h_i, which is defined as the "input impedance with output a-c short-circuited," and likewise an h_r, h_f, and h_o. To determine these h-

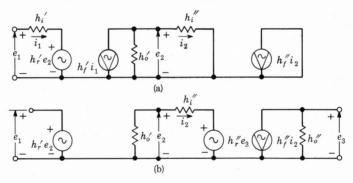

Fig. 7–4.   Simplifications of Fig. 7–3: (a) circuit for determination of h_{11} and h_{21}; (b) circuit for determination of h_{12} and h_{22}.

parameters for the composite circuit, Fig. 7–3 may be simplified to that of Fig. 7–4a for the calculation of h_i and h_f, both of which require that the a-c output be short-circuited. Fig. 7–4b may be used to calculate h_r and h_o, for each require that the a-c input circuit be opened. The results of such an analysis follow:

$$h_i = \frac{e_1}{i_1} = h_i' - \frac{h_i''h_r'h_f'}{h_i''h_o' + 1}, \tag{7-23}$$

$$h_f = \frac{i_3}{i_1} = -\frac{h_f'h_f''}{h_i''h_o' + 1}, \tag{7-24}$$

$$h_r = \frac{e_1}{e_3} = \frac{h_r'h_r''}{h_i''h_o' + 1}, \tag{7-25}$$

$$h_o = \frac{i_3}{e_3} = h_o'' - \frac{h_f''h_r''h_o'}{h_i''h_o' + 1}. \tag{7-26}$$

After determination of the composite parameters, they can be used in the general equations of Table 4–4. Those equations are listed here for convenience:

$$A_v = \frac{h_f R_L}{h_i + R_L \Delta^h}, \tag{7-27}$$

$$A_i = \frac{h_f}{1 + R_L h_o}, \tag{7-28}$$

$$R_i = \frac{h_i + R_L \Delta^h}{1 + R_L h_o}, \tag{7-29}$$

$$R_o = \frac{h_i + R_g}{\Delta^h + R_g h_o}. \tag{7-30}$$

Note that biasing resistances have been assumed to be of no consequence in the preceding derivations.

7–4. Design of Multistage Amplifiers. The remainder of this Chapter is devoted to two multistage amplifier design examples. The purpose in presenting these designs is to familiarize the reader with complete circuits and the complexities involved in the design of cascaded amplifiers.

The designs presented here are incomplete in the sense that further investigations may be warranted to simplify the circuitry, improve efficiency, provide more adequate feedback, design power supplies, and investigate interchangeability and temperature limitations.

Design of a 10-Watt Servo Amplifier

Object. Design an amplifier to meet the following specifications:

1. Rated load power: 10 watts
2. Load: 500 ohms (resistive)
3. Overload capacity: 25%

4. Input signal to give rated output = 0.25 volts into 10,000 ohms (or greater)
5. Carrier frequency: 60 cps
6. Ambient temperature: 25° C
7. Supply potentials available: 28 and 6 volts

Solution.

General

The minimum power gain required is

$$G = \frac{P_o}{P_i} = \frac{10}{(0.25)^2/10\,K} = 1{,}600{,}000 \text{ or } 62 \text{ db.}$$

A Class-B push-pull output stage can handle the required load power and provide a gain of 25–30 db. A stabilized (local feedback) driver stage can provide 20–25 db, so a low-power amplifying stage will also be necessary. Type 2N43 and type 2N539A transistors are available. Transformer coupling will be used where applicable.

The design will proceed according to the block approach, commencing with the final stages and working toward the low-level stages.

Push-pull Class-B Power Stage

To supply 10 watts (P_{FL}) to the load in Fig. 7–5,

$$\text{Transformer primary power} = \frac{P_{FL}}{\eta} = \frac{10}{0.75} = 13.33 \text{ watts}$$

where η represents the efficiency of the output transformer (assumed to be 75%). The stage must be capable of handling

$$(125\%)\,(13.33) = 16.7 \text{ watts}$$

Each power transistor is required to supply a maximum of 8.35 watts.

The symbols I_C' and V_C' are explained by Fig. 7–6, and represent maximum swings in output quantities. For each transistor, under overload conditions,

$$P_{\max} = \frac{V_C' I_C'}{4}.$$

Since this is Class-B

$$V_C' \cong E_{CC} = 28 \text{ volts,}$$

so

$$I_C' = \frac{4(8.35)}{28} = 1.2 \text{ amps.}$$

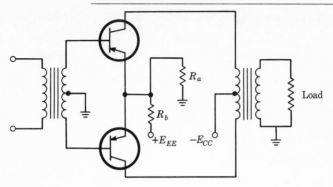

Fig. 7–5. Conventional Class-B push-pull output stage with biasing network to compensate for crossover distortion.

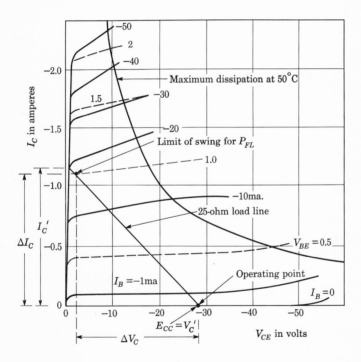

Fig. 7–6. Output and input characteristics for the 2N539A, shown on one set of axes. (This curve is not included in the section of Appendix I devoted to the 2N539A.)

Therefore the load to be supplied by each transistor is

$$R_L = \frac{V_{C'}}{I_{C'}} = \frac{28}{1.2} \cong 25 \text{ ohms.}$$

For the entire primary, the reflected load resistance is

$$R_{cc} = 4(25) = 100 \text{ ohms.}$$

(If the factor of 4 is not clearly understood, a proof based upon turns ratios is suggested.)

Full load for each transistor is

$$P_{FL} = \frac{13.33}{2} = 6.67 \text{ watts.}$$

Refer again to Fig. 7–6. To find the actual swings for rated full load, ΔI_C and ΔV_C, make use of the laws of similar triangles

$$P_{FL} = \frac{(\Delta I_C)(\Delta V_C)}{4}$$

$$= \frac{(kI_C')(kV_C')}{4}.$$

Thus $k^2 = 0.795$ and $k = 0.891$. Therefore

$$\Delta I_C = kI_C' = 1.1 \text{ amps,}$$

$$\Delta V_C = kV_C' = 25 \text{ volts.}$$

To drive an 2N539A to 1.1 amps and through a 25-volt swing requires (from Fig. 7–6)

$$\Delta I_B = 18 \text{ ma,}$$

$$\Delta V_{BE} = 1.1 \text{ volts.}$$

Therefore the required input power is

$$P_i = \frac{(\Delta I_B)(\Delta V_{BE})}{4} = \frac{(18 \times 10^{-3})(1.1)}{4} = 4.95 \text{ mw.}$$

Nominal power gain per stage is

$$G = \frac{P_{FL}}{P_i} = \frac{6.67}{4.95 \times 10^{-3}} = 1350 \text{ or } 31.3 \text{ db.}$$

The gain, including output transformer losses, is

$$G = (0.75)(1350) = 1012 \text{ or } 30.0 \text{ db.}$$

Total power to be supplied from the preceding stage $= (2)(4.95) = 9.9$ mw.

A bias circuit to prevent crossover distortion is necessary. Figure 7–7 shows input-circuit characteristics (replotted from the information of Fig. 7–6). When $I_B = 0$, approximately 0.2 volts is required from base to emitter. To eliminate this type of distortion, a circuit composed of E_{EE}, R_a, and R_b

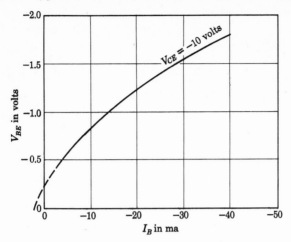

Fig. 7–7.   Input characteristics for the 2N539A (obtained from Fig. 7–6).

will be designed to put $+0.2$ volt on the emitter.   Assume

$$R_a = 1 \text{ ohm.}$$

Since

$$E_{EE} = 6 \text{ volts,}$$

then

$$\frac{E_{EE}R_a}{R_a + R_b} = 0.2.$$

Therefore

$$R_b = 29 \text{ ohms.}$$

The bias-power dissipation in these resistors is

$$P = (0.2)^2/1 = 0.04 \text{ watts in } R_a,$$

$$P = (5.8)^2/29 = 1.16 \text{ watts in } R_b.$$

The values obtained for R_a and R_b are approximate and must be checked by laboratory methods.

Input resistance is to be determined,

$$H_{IE} \text{ (published)} \cong 60 \text{ ohms (at peak of input signal).}$$

The one-ohm emitter resistor affects input resistance according to

$$R_i \cong \beta R_E + H_{IE} = \left(\frac{1.1}{18 \times 10^{-3}}\right)(1) + 60 = 121 \text{ ohms.}$$

Total secondary impedance of the input transformer = $4(R_i) = 484 \cong 500$ ohms. The bias circuit will cause degeneration of signal and therefore a loss in amplification. Since the one-ohm resistor doubles input resistance, it will cause a loss of 50% in stage gain (3 db), but because the biasing circuit is not positively defined until laboratory correlation is made, this loss will not be figured into the calculations.

Although this design used the information displayed in Fig. 7–6, calculations based upon the 2N539A curves of Appendix I, namely those involving H_{FE} and H_{IE}, could have been used along with

$$G = \frac{(H_{FE})^2 R_L}{H_{IE}}.$$

Driver Stage

To supply 9.9 mw to the output stage with an assumed interstage transformer efficiency of 60%, the driver must be capable of handling

$$P_{FL} = \frac{9.9}{0.60} = 16.5 \text{ mw},$$

and, with overload capacity included,

$$P_{\max} = 16.5(125\%) = 20.6 \text{ mw}.$$

A 2N43 is capable of this loading and will be used for $TR1$ and $TR2$. Examine the diagram of Fig. 7–8. Single-battery bias is employed, with operating-point stability offered by R_{12} and R_{e2}, and gain stabilization by R_{e2}. Since E_{CC} is fixed, the d-c load line will have a slope of $-1/3500$ from 28 volts; this can be seen on the characteristics of Fig. 7–9 (200 ohms for the transformer resistance, 3000 ohms for R_{12} and 330 ohms for R_{e2}). An a-c line of 4000 ohms drawn through the Q point will allow generally undistorted output power of

$$P = \frac{(\Delta I_C)(\Delta V_{CE})}{8} = \frac{(7.4 \times 10^{-3})(30)}{8} = 28 \text{ mw}.$$

The operating point chosen is

$$I_C \cong I_E = 3.75 \text{ ma} \quad \text{and} \quad V_{CE} = 15 \text{ volts},$$

and the circuit elements are as shown in Fig. 7–8. R_{22} will be determined experimentally.

The nominal values of the parameters of a 2N43 are

$$h_{fb} = -0.977 \qquad h_{ib} = 29 \text{ ohms},$$

$$h_{rb} = 5 \times 10^{-4} \qquad h_{ob} = 0.8 \times 10^{-6} \text{ mho}.$$

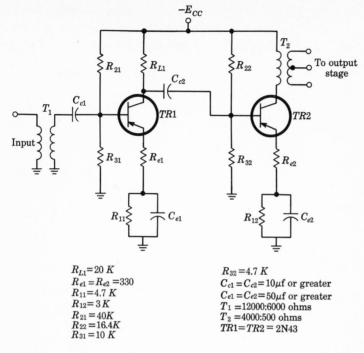

$R_{L1} = 20\ K$
$R_{e1} = R_{e2} = 330$
$R_{11} = 4.7\ K$
$R_{12} = 3\ K$
$R_{21} = 40K$
$R_{22} = 16.4K$
$R_{31} = 10\ K$

$R_{32} = 4.7\ K$
$C_{c1} = C_{c2} = 10\mu f$ or greater
$C_{e1} = C_{e2} = 50\mu f$ or greater
$T_1 = 12000{:}6000$ ohms
$T_2 = 4000{:}500$ ohms
$TR1 = TR2 = 2N43$

Fig. 7–8. Circuit diagram for low-power stages of design example.

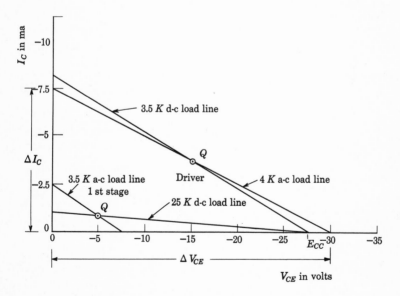

Fig. 7–9. Load lines on the collector characteristics of the 2N43.

Corrections must be made because the chosen operating point differs from the recommended point,

for $h_{fe} = (1.3)(1.3) = 1.7$,   for $h_{ib} = (0.3)(1.1) = 0.3$,

for $h_{rb} = (1.3)(0.6) = 0.8$,   for $h_{ob} = (3.0)(0.6) = 1.8$.

Therefore the corrected parameters are

$$h_{fb} = -0.986,$$ $$h_{ib} = 8.7 \text{ ohms},$$

$$h_{rb} = 4.0 \times 10^{-4},$$ $$h_{ob} = 1.4 \times 10^{-6} \text{ mho}.$$

Power gain:

$$G = \frac{h_{fb}{}^2 R_L}{(h_{ib} + R_e)(1 + R_L h_{ob})[R_L h_{ob} + (1 + h_{fb})]}$$

$$= \frac{(-0.986)^2 4000}{(8.7 + 330)(1 + 4000 \times 1.4 \times 10^{-6})(0.0056 + 0.014)}$$

$$= 580 \text{ or } 27.6 \text{ db}.$$

Input resistance:

$$R_i = \frac{(h_{ib} + R_e)(1 + R_L h_{ob})}{R_L h_{ob} + (1 + h_{fb})}$$

$$= 17{,}500 \text{ ohms for the transistor}.$$

The required power at the base is

$$\frac{P_{FL}}{G} = \frac{16.5 \times 10^{-3}}{580} = 28.5 \ \mu\text{w},$$

and

$$\frac{P_{max}}{G} = \frac{20.8 \times 10^{-3}}{580} = 35.9 \ \mu\text{w}.$$

R_i of this stage is paralleled by R_{22} and R_{32}. If R_{22} is large, then the input resistance of the complete stage is 3700 ohms.

1st Amplifying Stage

Refer to the d-c load line of Fig. 7–9, which starts at 28 volts and has a slope dictated by approximately 25,000 ohms; 20 K for a load and 5 K for R_{11}. An operating point is chosen at

$$I_C \cong I_E = 1 \text{ ma}, \quad \text{and} \quad V_{CE} = 5 \text{ volts}.$$

The a-c load on this stage is 20 K paralleled by 3.7 K in series with 330; thus 3450 ohms.

The coupling network, R_{22} and R_{32} and R_{L1}, results in only 18% of the first-stage output power being delivered to the second transistor base. This is rather severe, and should be corrected in a later design.

The first stage must be capable of supplying

$$P_{FL} = \frac{28.5 \times 10^{-3}}{0.18} = 158 \ \mu\text{w},$$

and

$$P_{\max} = \frac{35.9 \times 10^{-3}}{0.18} = 200 \ \mu\text{w}.$$

Parameters need not be corrected because of the Q chosen. With a feedback resistor of 330 ohms, calculation of power gain yields

$$G = 355 \text{ or } 25.5 \text{ db}.$$

Calculation of input resistance gives

$$R_i = 14{,}100 \text{ ohms}.$$

If R_{31} is chosen to be 10,000 ohms, then the input resistance of the entire first stage is 6000 ohms. Since the specifications require a 10 K input resistance, the input transformer impedance ratio should be 2:1 or greater.

TRANSFORMER SPECIFICATIONS

	Output	Driver	Input
Maximum primary power	16.7 w	25 mw	μw
Impedance ratio	100CT:500	4000:500CT	12,000:6000
Turns ratio—$N_1:N_2$	0.447	2.83	1.41
Unbalanced d-c in primary	none	5 ma	none
Maximum primary 60 $\sim$ voltage	20 (rms)	11 (rms)	2 (rms)
Minimum primary inductance	0.5	tune	tune

PERFORMANCE SUMMARY

	Power Out	Gain	Power In
Output transformer	10 w	0.75	13.33 w
Output stage	13.33 w	1350	9.9 mw
Driver transformer	9.9 mw	0.60	16.5 mw
Driver stage	16.5 mw	580	28.5 μw
Coupling	28.5 μw	0.18	158 μw
1st stage	158 μw	355	0.45 μw
Coupling including input transformer	0.45 μw	0.25	1.8 μw

$$\text{Overall power gain} = \frac{P_o}{P_i} = \frac{10}{1.8 \times 10^{-6}} = 5.5 \times 10^6 = 67 \text{ db}$$

Results and Conclusions. The amplifier designed here was built and tested and the following notes pertain to its performance:

(a) Overall gain 66 db vs. 67 db calculated.

(b) $R_{21} = 40,000$ ohms and $R_{22} = 16,400$ ohms. The best value of R_b to eliminate crossover distortion was found to be 85 ohms.

(c) Input resistance was found to vary from 9700 to 11,500 ohms, depending upon input signal level and the frequency of that signal.

(d) In order to meet the requirement that 10 watts be delivered to the load, the 28-volt power supply must be well regulated for the amplifier draws nearly an ampere from the supply.

Because this design is inefficient in some aspects, and represents a "first design," it is recommended that the reader consult Problem 7–9, and discuss or study the design in order to use the information already derived to suggest improvements and establish goals for a second, or improved amplifier design.

Design of a Three-Stage Transistor Amplifier

Object. Design a three-stage R-C coupled, low-power, high-gain transistor amplifier to serve as a basis for laboratory investigation of multistage feedback. The specifications to be met are:

1. Load: 50 ohms (resistive)
2. Nominal frequency: 400 cps
3. Ambient temperature: 25° C
4. Supply potential available: +14 volts
5. Open-loop power gain: 10^8, or 80 db

Solution.

General

No local feedback will be utilized. Three common-emitter stages are necessary and will be designed using available 2N475 silicon transistors.

The circuit of Fig. 7–10 depicts the three amplifying stages in cascade. Fixed biasing will provide a fairly stable operating point because the 2N475, being silicon, has a low leakage current.

PARAMETERS FOR DESIGN EXAMPLE

Values Corrected for Operating Point

Parameters	Nominal Value	Output Stage	2nd Stage	Input Stage
h_{ib} (ohms)	60	21	60	120
h_{rb}	4×10^{-4}	3.4×10^{-4}	4×10^{-4}	4×10^{-4}
h_{fb}	-0.97	-0.97	-0.97	-0.97
h_{ob} (mho)	0.5×10^{-6}	1.4×10^{-6}	0.5×10^{-6}	0.35×10^{-6}

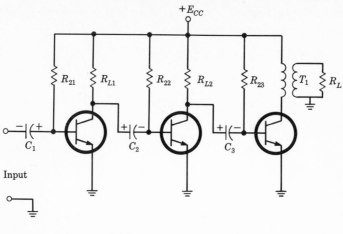

$$C_1 = C_2 = C_3 = 5\mu f \qquad R_{21} = 540{,}000 \text{ ohms}$$
$$R_{L1} = 15{,}000 \text{ ohms} \qquad R_{22} = 335{,}000 \text{ ohms}$$
$$R_{L2} = 8{,}000 \text{ ohms} \qquad R_{23} = 85{,}000 \text{ ohms}$$
$$R_L = 50 \text{ ohms} \qquad T_1 = 1500{:}50 \; CT \text{ ohms}$$
$$E_{CC} = +14 \text{ volts}$$

Fig. 7–10. Three-stage high-gain amplifier.

Output Stage

The 50-ohm load will be transformer-coupled to the 3rd or output stage for insufficient power gain may result with capacitive coupling to such a low-resistance load. An impedance ratio of 1500:50 is achieved with the particular transformer available. 2000 ohms is the reciprocal of the slope of the a-c load line because the transformer is assumed to have a primary d-c resistance of 500 ohms. This fact dictates the d-c load line. The operating point has been chosen at

$$I_C \cong 5 \text{ ma} \quad \text{and} \quad V_{CE} = 11.5 \text{ volts,}$$

and thus, from the curve of Fig. 7–11, $I_B = 160 \ \mu a$. The 2000-ohm a-c line is shown in the figure as passing through this Q point.

A rough calculation can be made to determine R_{23}. From the manufacturer's literature, the voltage drop $V_{BE} = 0.7$ volt. Therefore

$$R_{23} \cong \frac{14 - 0.7}{160 \times 10^{-6}} = 85{,}000 \text{ ohms,}$$

but must be checked by laboratory methods.

The maximum power delivered by this stage before clipping occurs is

$$\frac{(\Delta V_3)(\Delta I_3)}{8} = \frac{(19)(9.2 \times 10^{-3})}{8} = 21.9 \text{ mw.}$$

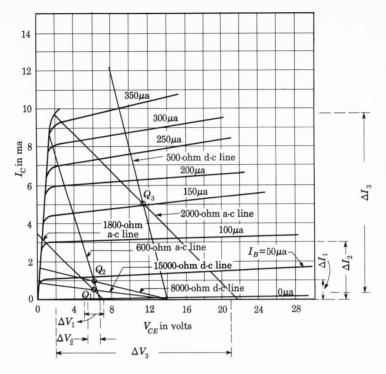

Fig. 7–11.   Output characteristics, sample amplifier design.

If we assume an efficiency of 60% in the output transformer, then corresponding load power is approximately 13 mw.

The stage gain can now be calculated.   Refer to the listing of parameter values.   As in the preceding amplifier design examples, Eq. (4–54A) will again be used to determine power gain.

$$G = 2700, \text{ or } 34.3 \text{ db.}$$

Input resistance is determined by substitution of values into Eq. (4–55A)

$$R_i = 660 \text{ ohms.}$$

Second Stage

The load on the 2nd stage consists of the input resistance of the 3rd stage in parallel with R_{L2} and R_{23}.   The maximum signal power that must be passed on to the 3rd stage is $21.9 \times 10^{-3}/2700$, or 8.1 μw.   Because this is such a low number, it is possible to choose a fairly large value of R_{L2}.   Selection of 8000 ohms for R_{L2} permits the operating point coordinates to be

$$I_C = 1 \text{ ma} \quad \text{and} \quad V_{CE} = 6 \text{ volts.}$$

Thus

$$I_B = 40 \ \mu\text{a.}$$

This is the manufacturer's specified typical operating point so no correction need be made to the parameters.

The resulting a-c load on the stage is

$$\frac{(8000)(660)}{8000 + 660} = 610 \text{ ohms,}$$

which dictates the a-c load line. The signal loss in R_{L2} is

$$\frac{660}{8660} \times 100\% = 7.6\%.$$

The power gain formula, Eq. (4–54A), is again used and yields

$$G = 315, \text{ or 25 db.}$$

Input resistance, from Eq. (4–55A) is

$$R_i = 2000 \text{ ohms.}$$

This stage is capable of a maximum (unclipped) output power of

$$\frac{(\Delta V_2)(\Delta I_2)}{8} = \frac{(1.2)(2 \times 10^{-3})}{8} = 300 \ \mu\text{w.}$$

Stage #3 requires only 8.1 μw. A 7.6% signal loss in R_{L2} means that the 2nd stage output should be $8.1 + (0.076)(8.1) = 8.7 \ \mu$w. Since 300 μw is available, the design is satisfactory.

$$R_{22} \cong \frac{14 - 0.6}{40 \times 10^{-6}} = 335,000 \text{ ohms.}$$

This must be checked experimentally.

The power supplied to the second stage must be less than

$$\frac{300 \times 10^{-6}}{315} = 0.95 \ \mu\text{w}$$

in order for that stage not to be driven into cutoff.

Input Stage

Selection of 15,000 ohms for R_{L1} permits us to choose an operating point at

$$I_C = 0.5 \text{ ma} \quad \text{and} \quad V_{CE} = 6 \text{ volts.}$$

Thus

$$I_B \cong 25 \ \mu\text{a}.$$

Corrections must therefore be made to the parameters.

The load on the input stage is the 2nd stage input resistance paralleled by R_{L1} and R_{22}. R_{22} will be very large, so essentially the load is

$$\frac{(15 \ K)(2 \ K)}{15 \ K + 2 \ K} = 1770 \text{ ohms},$$

which dictates the a-c load line. Loss of signal in R_{L1} amounts to 2000/17,000 or 11.8%.

The stage power gain is

$$G = 450 \text{ or } 26.5 \text{ db},$$

and

$$R_i = 3900 \text{ ohms}.$$

Also

$$R_{21} \cong \frac{14 - 0.55}{25 \times 10^{-6}} = 540,000 \text{ ohms}.$$

This must be checked.

Summary

Calculated power gains are summarized:

1st stage	450
R_{L1}	0.78
2nd stage	315
R_{L2}	0.76
3rd stage	2700
Output transformer	0.60

Overall calculated power gain $= 1.4 \times 10^8$, or 81 db.

The amplifier was constructed and measurements indicated a power gain of 86 db. With the power supply and transistors used, R_{21}, R_{22}, and R_{23} were 820 K, 470 K, and 82 K ohms respectively.

PROBLEMS

7-1. Confirm Eqs. (7–16) through (7–22).

7-2. Two transistors are connected in cascade to supply a 2000-ohm load. Each has the following parameters: $h_{ib} = 50$ ohms, $h_{rb} = 10^{-4}$, $h_{fe} = 60$ and $h_{ob} = 10^{-6}$ mho.

(a) Calculate the power gain of the pair if the first is connected common-base and the second common-emitter.

(b) Calculate the current gain of the pair if both transistors are being operated common-emitter.

To arrive at answers to parts a and b, utilize the composite h-parameter method.

7–3. Consider the circuit shown in the accompanying figure. Base-biasing resistances are very large and may be neglected. Bypassed resistances are

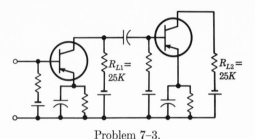

Problem 7–3.

assumed to have no effect upon circuit gains and impedances. Each transistor has $r_e = 25$ ohms, $r_b = 130$ ohms, $r_c = 10^6$ ohms and $\alpha = 0.975$. You are asked to calculate the following by using any convenient method:

(a) The current gain of the composite amplifier.

(b) The input resistance of the composite amplifier.

7–4. For the two-stage circuit of Problem 7–3, calculate the following:

(a) The overall voltage gain.

(b) The amplifier output resistance when the first stage is connected to a source of 4000-ohms internal resistance.

7–5. Three non-identical stages are cascaded. From the data given below, determine the overall bandwidth.

	f_l (cps)	f_h (cps)
Stage one	30	42,000
Stage two	44	50,000
Stage three	60	80,000

7–6. Show that an iterative (repeating) arrangement of common-base stages with direct or capacitive coupling provides no usable power amplification.

7–7. A particular coupling transformer is designated as 4000 CT:1000 CT, the numbers represent the nominal impedance ratio, and CT indicates that the center tap of each winding is brought out. For this transformer, calculate the following.

(a) The resistance reflected into the entire primary if the entire secondary is connected to 400 ohms.

(b) The reflected resistance if each half of the secondary is joined to 400 ohms.

(c) The resistance reflected to one half of the primary if the entire secondary is connected to 900 ohms.

7–8. For the servo-amplifier design example, calculate the following, using 2N539A information available in Appendix I:

(a) The power being dissipated at the collector junction of each Class-B transistor at maximum overload.

(b) The minimum size of a vertical, square, $\frac{3}{32}$ inch, aluminum heat sink necessary to keep junction temperature below 60° C in a 40° C ambient. Allow 1.0° C/w for the washer.

7–9. Study the low-power stages of the servo-amplifier design example.

(a) Comment upon the possibility of voltage breakdown.

(b) Calculate the stability factor (S) of each stage.

(c) Discuss the inefficiency of the biasing and coupling circuits. Suggest a biasing arrangement making use of the +6 volt supply.

7–10. The frequency response requirements for the second design example dictate a bandwidth (3-db points) of from 100 cps to 800 cps (minimum). Allow 0.5 db for each of the coupling circuits.

(a) Calculate the size of the coupling capacitor needed between a source of 600 ohms and stage number one.

(b) Calculate the size of the coupling capacitor needed between stage number one and stage number two.

7–11. "Decoupling" is usually necessary in high-gain multistage circuits.

(a) What is decoupling?

(b) How can decoupling be incorporated into the second design example? Sketch.

Design Problems. In the problems that follow perform the operations necessary in order to obtain a circuit that will meet the listed requirements. For each solution, select transistor types from Appendix I, and choose a biasing arrangement. Correct the design-center parameters for operating point and temperature, and in each solution itemize any assumptions made and clearly indicate the steps leading to your choice of each component.

7–12. Requirements:

1. Carrier frequency: 800 cps
2. Load resistance: 100 ohms
3. Input resistance: 2000 ± 200 ohms
4. Load power: up to 5 watts
5. Power gain: 45 db (minimum)
6. Temperature: 0 to 50° C
7. Supplies available: designer's choice

7–13. Requirements:

1. Frequency response: 10,000 to 30,000 cps

2. Load resistance: 1000 ohms

3. Input resistance: 10,000 ± 1000 ohms

4. Voltage gain: 100 minimum (ratio of load voltage to amplifier input voltage)

5. Source characteristics: resistance of 10,000 ohms in series with a generator of 0 to 10 mv

6. Temperature: 25° C

7. Power supply available: +10 volts

REFERENCES

1. Coblenz, A., and Owens, H. L., *Transistors: Theory and Applications*, McGraw-Hill Book Company, Inc., New York, 1955.
2. DeWitt, D., and Rossoff, A. L., *Transistor Electronics*, McGraw-Hill Book Company, Inc., New York, 1957.
3. Shea, R. F., *Transistor Circuit Engineering*, John Wiley & Sons, Inc., New York, 1957.

Chapter 8

FEEDBACK

The discussion of transistor equivalent circuits and parameters presented in Chapter 4 led to the conclusion that circuit gain is "at the mercy" of parameter variations. It is also true that input and output resistance, frequency response, and phase shift are highly dependent upon transistor parameters. Parameter variations are due to many causes: manufacturing tolerances cause units of the same type to differ; aging of semiconducting materials results in parameter changes; operating-point shift, frequency, and climatic conditions also have a strong effect upon the resistances and capacitances of the transistor.

To overcome the expected variations, feedback, the addition of a portion of the output signal to the input signal, is employed. Reduction of the magnitude of the input signal by addition of a feedback signal is called *inverse, degenerative,* or *negative* feedback, while an increase in total input due to this summation is termed *direct, regenerative,* or *positive* feedback. The use of negative feedback is widespread and will be the only type considered here, although positive feedback certainly is employed in oscillator circuits and occasionally in radio-receiver circuits.

8–1. Feedback—General Theory. The block diagram of Fig. 8-1 can be used to illustrate feedback in an elementary way. The output voltage v_o of an amplifier with a voltage gain of A supplies a load; v_o is also available to the feedback network, and Bv_o, a fraction of v_o, is added to the input circuit. (B, as used here should not be confused with beta, the common-emitter short-circuit current-amplification factor.) The nominal amplifier gain is

$$A = \frac{v_o}{v_i}. \tag{8–1}$$

If we take polarities into account A will normally be negative and may be complex. B normally will be positive, and also may be complex. In the presence of a feedback signal a summation at the input yields

$$v_i = e_i + Bv_o. \tag{8–2}$$

The voltage amplification of the composite network is

$$A_f = \frac{v_o}{e_i} = \frac{v_o}{v_i - Bv_o} = \frac{A}{1 - BA}. \qquad (8\text{-}3)$$

Eq. (8-3) will now be interpreted. In the absence of feedback $(B = 0)$, the amplifier exhibits a gain of A. If the magnitude of the denominator is greater than unity, the overall amplification will be less than A and the feedback is degenerative; the converse of this statement also applies. If the entire output voltage is supplied to the input $(B = 1)$, the composite gain is less than unity. When

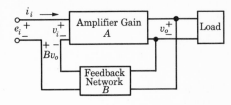

Fig. 8-1. General feedback diagram.

$BA = 1$, the resultant gain is infinite, and the circuit has an output independent of any external input voltage.

If $|BA| \gg 1$, then the amplification approaches

$$A_f \rightarrow \frac{1}{B}. \qquad (8\text{-}4)$$

Eq. (8-4) signifies that gain is independent of elements in the forward path. Because B is usually a passive network, A must be very large to satisfy the condition specified by Eq. (8-4). Since B is usually a fraction, A_f can be a large number. Aging, tolerances, and temperature would certainly have negligible effect upon an amplifier that behaves according to Eq. (8-4).

The price to be paid for the advantages of feedback (they will be considered in detail in the following sections) is reduction in overall gain. A given amplifier having an open-loop gain of A, will have a closed-loop gain of less than A because of incorporation of any negative feedback circuitry. But the advantages of feedback are so numerous that it generally pays to design our original amplifier with sufficient gain so that added feedback will not reduce gain below the desired value. The inclusion of additional gain to offset feedback losses is a small price to pay when compared with the advantages as indicated in the sections to follow.

Stabilization of Gain. The performance of a feedback amplifier of gain A_f is to be compared with that of an unstabilized amplifier having open-loop gain A. Of course, for A, when a change in amplification is experienced,

$$\frac{dA}{dA} = 1. \qquad (8\text{-}5)$$

By Eq. (8-3), for the amplifier with feedback,

$$\frac{dA_f}{dA} = \frac{1}{1 - BA}\left(\frac{A_f}{A}\right). \tag{8-6}$$

We may conclude that the feedback amplifier will show a much greater stability with respect to the internal factors that cause gain changes.

Consider an amplifier with a gain of -10^4. The fraction B is to be $\frac{1}{100}$. Then, from Eq. (8–3), feedback will reduce the gain to approximately -100. For a 10% variation in forward gain, the overall gain of the feedback amplifier will suffer less than a 0.1% change. Variations in gain will be reduced by the same amount as forward gain.

Reduction in Distortion. In earlier discussions it was evident that nonlinear distortion increases with the swing or level of the output signal, and hence may be some function of v_o:

$$D = f(v_o). \tag{8-7}$$

Consider that D is being generated in the final stage of an amplifier. The output voltage including distortion (v_o') is given by

$$v_o' = v_o + D, \tag{8-8a}$$

and

$$v_o' = Av_i + D. \tag{8-8b}$$

The new equation at the summation point is

$$v_i = e_i + Bv_o + BD. \tag{8-9}$$

So

$$v_o = Ae_i + ABv_o + ABD, \tag{8-10a}$$

and

$$v_o = \frac{Ae_i}{1 - BA} + \frac{ABD}{1 - BA}. \tag{8-10b}$$

Therefore

$$v_o' = v_o + D = \frac{Ae_i}{1 - BA} + \frac{D}{1 - BA}. \tag{8-11}$$

The distortion factor for a closed loop system is

$$D_f = \frac{D}{1 - BA}. \tag{8-12}$$

Since $|1 - BA|$ is usually much greater than one, nonlinear distortion will be reduced by a factor equivalent to the amount of gain reduction.

It may seem reasonable that if one is reducing amplifier gain by the addition of feedback, signal swings will be proportionally reduced and therefore nonlinearities will be less evident in the output of the feedback circuit. This reasoning is true, but reduction in signal amplitude was not of concern in the above analysis, distortion having been handled by using a lumped term D, rather than $f(v_o)$. The reduction in the harmonic content of the output voltage can be visualized if we consider that we are sampling the distortion and adding the amplified, out-of-phase sample to the original distorted waveform in order to cancel a portion of it. It is important to realize that output-signal swing can be the same with or without feedback.

Reduction in Noise Content of Output. Noise or extraneous signals may be reduced by the addition of feedback, but, under certain practical conditions, the overall noise level may be increased because of the requirement for higher forward gain and thus more stages of amplification.

Consider the diagram of Fig. 8–1 with another input signal e_n, which can be assumed to be a noise voltage introduced in the first stage. Eq. (8–2) becomes

$$v_i' = e_i + Bv_o + e_n. \tag{8–13}$$

Since this equation tells us that the noise signal will be treated in the same manner as e_i, e_n will be reduced by the same amount as e_i, namely

$$e_n' = \frac{e_n}{1 - BA}. \tag{8–14}$$

Feedback has no effect on the signal-to-noise ratio.

Change in Input Impedance. Input impedance of a multistage amplifier without feedback was given in Chapter 4 as a function of R_L, h_{ib}, h_{fb}, and h_{ob}. From Fig. 8–1, in the absence of feedback, the corresponding relationship is

$$Z_i = \frac{e_i}{i_i} = \frac{v_i}{i_i}. \tag{8–15}$$

With the feedback loop closed, Eq. (8–15) becomes

$$Z_{if} = \frac{v_i - Bv_o}{i_i}. \tag{8–16}$$

Since

$$v_o = Av_i, \tag{8–17}$$

then Eq. (8–16) becomes

$$Z_{if} = \frac{v_i(1 - BA)}{i_i}. \tag{8–18}$$

Therefore

$$Z_{if} = Z_i(1 - BA). \tag{8–19}$$

The presence of the $(1 - BA)$ term indicates an increase in input impedance due to closing of the loop.

Change in Output Impedance. The method used previously for determining output impedance is to connect a hypothetical generator of voltage e_o across the output terminals of a circuit or device and measure or calculate the current i_o with the input short-circuited. Then, for the amplifier without feedback,

$$Z_o = \frac{e_o}{i_o}.$$
(8–20)

With the feedback loop closed, as in Fig. 8–2,

$$v_i = Be_o.$$
(8–21)

The output loop current is

$$i_o = \frac{e_o - BAe_o}{Z_o}.$$
(8–22)

Therefore, the effective output impedance is

$$Z_{of} = \frac{e_o}{i_o} = \frac{Z_o}{1 - BA}.$$
(8–23)

The conclusion that can be drawn is that output impedance is reduced by the addition of inverse feedback. This reduction is not caused, in this case, by the paralleling of Z_o by the feedback network, because in the treatment given here it was assumed that no current was drawn from e_o by the feedback network.

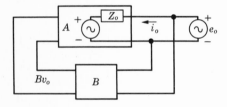

Fig. 8–2. Feedback diagram for calculation of output impedance.

Increase in Bandwidth. To investigate the effects of feedback upon the bandwidth of a circuit, we must assign frequency dependence to the forward amplifier gain. A good assumption may be that

$$A = \frac{A_o}{1 + jf/f_{3\,db}}$$
(8–24)

where $f_{3\,db}$, as used in Chapter 5, is the upper cutoff frequency, and A_o is the mid-frequency reference gain. Substitution of Eq. (8–24) into Eq. (8–3) yields

$$A_f = \frac{A_o}{1 - BA_o + jf/f_{3\,db}}.$$
(8–25)

Now the denominator will be of the form $K + jK$ when

$$f/f_{3\,db} = 1 - BA_o.$$
(8–26)

Eq. (8–26) indicates that the new cutoff or half-power frequency (f_f) occurs at

$$f_f = f_{3\,\mathrm{db}}(1 - BA_o).\qquad(8\text{--}27)$$

In conclusion, the upper cutoff frequency has been increased, and the bandwidth extended by an appreciable amount. For analysis of low-frequency performance, see Problem 8–2.

Conclusions to General Feedback Theory. The preceding discussion of operational properties serves to provide a basic understanding of the reasons why negative feedback is so frequently employed in electronic circuits. The discussion was limited to what is usually called "voltage" or "shunt" feedback; the output voltage is sampled, operated upon by the feedback circuit, and fed into the input circuit. It is also possible to employ "current" or "series" feedback in which the load current is sampled (usually by using the potential drop across a small resistor in series with the load), and this signal fed through appropriate circuitry to the amplifier input. The conclusions to an equivalent analysis of the current-feedback amplifier would be similar except for the changes in circuit impedances. Analysis of current feedback is left for a student exercise (Problems 8–3 and 8–4) or can be obtained from the literature.[10, 11]

Instability in Feedback Circuits. The benefits derived from the use of negative feedback are great, but are achieved at the expense of gain. Additional low-level stages may usually be added to compensate for the loss of gain. Another drawback to be contended with is the possibility of self-oscillation because forward and feedback elements are frequency sensitive. At low and also at high frequencies the output voltage may be shifted in phase and changed in magnitude relative to the mid-frequency value. The summation of output and input voltages in a feedback circuit may, because of this additional phase shift, result in regeneration and possibly oscillation.

Self-oscillation can be visualized with the help of Eq. (8–3), which is repeated here:

$$A_f = \frac{A}{1 - BA}.\qquad(8\text{--}3)$$

When $BA \rightarrow +1$, $A_f \rightarrow \infty$, a condition intolerable in amplifiers, and represents an output limited only by the saturation and cutoff regions of the characteristics. Should BA approach some positive value lower than unity, regenerative operation results.

For BA to be positive either B or A or the combination must contribute the 360° phase shift required to cause a summation of in-phase signals at the amplifier input. Although B is often a mere resistive network, wiring capacitances may cause unwanted phase shift. 180° of shift is normally supplied by an active circuit consisting of an odd number of common-emitter stages. Each stage is frequency sensitive, and with three in cascade, each only need shift an additional 60° in order for one oscillation requirement to be satisfied—

namely for BA to be positive. The other requirement is that $BA = 1 + j0$. In the mid-frequency range $|BA| > 1$ is the accepted condition. However, as was apparent in Chapter 5, A decreases in magnitude because of coupling capacitances at low frequencies, and because of alpha reduction and collector capacitance at high frequencies—it would be expected that, at some frequency, $|BA| = 1$.

To avoid oscillations,

$$1 - BA \neq 0, \tag{8-28a}$$

or

$$BA \neq +1. \tag{8-28b}$$

This condition can be slightly altered by including the fact that A is normally negative in inverse feedback amplifiers. Thus Eq. (8–28b) can be written

$$BA \neq -1. \tag{8-29}$$

To test the stability of a circuit we may plot BA on polar coordinates and examine the length of the phasor when 180° of additional phase shift is apparent. According to the Nyquist criterion, oscillations will exist if the locus of BA encloses the $(-1,0)$ point.[8]

A measure of the amount of feedback employed in an amplifier is given by the "number of db of feedback." This term can be defined as the ratio of the gain of an amplifier without feedback to the gain of that same amplifier including feedback, the ratio being expressed in decibels.

Example. A three-stage transistor amplifier with the feedback loop open was found to have a frequency response that could be approximated by the relation

$$BA = \frac{5}{(1 + jf10^{-4})^3}.$$

The ratio of measured values of voltages Bv_o and e_i gives this equation. It is desired to investigate the stability of this amplifier.

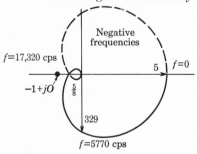

$f=17,320$ cps

$-1+j0$

$\frac{5}{8}$

329

$f=5770$ cps

Fig. 8–3. Nyquist diagram for text example.

A polar plot of this function is the curve of Fig. 8–3. From the equation, the intersection of the plot with the negative real axis will occur when the imaginary part of BA is zero. Therefore

$$f^2 10^{-8} = 3$$

or $f = 17,320$ cps. The magnitude of BA at this frequency is $5/(1 - 3f^2 10^{-8}) = -\frac{5}{8}$. This is less than -1, and as seen from the curve, no encirclement of the $-1 + j0$ point is apparent at this value of gain. In fact, for this example the gain could be increased by $\frac{8}{5}$ before $-1 + j0$ is intersected (the total gain could become $(\frac{8}{5})(5)$ or 8). A condition for absolute stability for networks having this form of open-loop transfer function is

$$BA < 8$$

at the reference frequency.

8–2. Local Feedback. The term "local feedback" as used here, pertains to feedback that is applied to a single amplifying stage. Two examples of local feedback were given in Chapter 4: the unbypassed emitter resistor, and the resistor from collector to base. At that point in the text complete formulas were given for the performance of these simple circuits, and in the first design example of Chapter 7 emitter resistance was used to stabilize the gain of a multistage amplifier. The use of local feedback is widespread, owing in part to the simplicity of calculating the effects of the feedback elements upon operation.

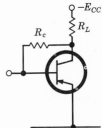

Fig. 8–4. Single stage with collector-to-base feedback.

Feedback from Collector-to-Base. As shown in Fig. 8–4, it is only necessary to connect a resistor such as R_c in order to provide the circuit input with a signal proportional to the output of the stage. The 180° phase shift inherent in the common-emitter stage provides the necessary subtraction of signals at the base terminal. At first glance this circuit appears to provide "voltage" feedback, because the output voltage is being sampled and a function of that voltage made available at the input. Indeed, such is the case, the ratio of signal voltage fed back to voltage at the load is

$$B_v = \frac{R_i}{R_c}. \tag{8–30}$$

However, in the circuit under consideration, collector current can be thought of as splitting; the major portion flowing to R_L, and the remainder back to the input circuit through R_c. Another B can be defined as the ratio of current fed back to load current

$$B_i = \frac{Y_c}{Y_L} = \frac{R_L}{R_c}. \tag{8–31}$$

It is assumed that $R_i \ll R_c$.

In order to predict the operation of this stage it can be assumed that voltage gain will not be affected nearly as much by the presence of R_c as will current gain, particularly when one considers a low value of R_L, possibly several thousand ohms, and a fairly high value of R_c, possibly 100,000 ohms. If we modify Eq. (8–3) it becomes

$$A_{if} = \frac{A_i}{1 - B_i A_i}. \tag{8-32}$$

The approximate expression for A_i of a normal stage is, from Table 4–6,

$$A_i \cong \frac{h_{fb}}{h_{ob}R_L + (1 + h_{fb})}. \tag{8-33}$$

Insertion of Eqs. (8–31) and (8–33) into Eq. (8–32) gives

$$A_{if} = \frac{h_{fb}}{R_L(h_{ob} - Y_c h_{fb}) + (1 + h_{fb})}, \tag{8-34a}$$

or, for $h_{fb} \cong -1$,

$$A_{if} \cong \frac{h_{fb}}{R_L(h_{ob} + Y_c) + (1 + h_{fb})}. \tag{8-34b}$$

This result should agree with the derived equation in Chapter 4 for the case

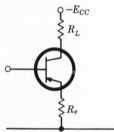

Fig. 8–5. Single stage with emitter feedback.

of Y_c paralleling h_{ob}. It is only necessary to add Y_c to h_{ob} in Eq. (8–33) to modify that equation for the feedback element. The obvious agreement between Eq. (8–34b) and modified Eq. (8–33) provides a basis for examination of more complex circuitry by the methods of this chapter.

Feedback in Emitter Circuit. The circuit of Fig. 8–5 contains local feedback because it is obvious that load current flowing through R_e causes a potential drop which is "felt" by the input circuit. Although this scheme is often called "current feedback," the presence of R_e will not materially affect current amplification since R_L will usually be many times larger than R_e. The voltage gain of such a stage, will, however, be severely altered. Voltage gain is given by the following approximate formula from Table 4–6:

$$A_v \cong \frac{h_{fb}R_L}{h_{ib}(1 + R_L h_{ob})}. \tag{8-35}$$

It is to be remembered that the equivalent circuit used for derivation of this formula would place R_e in series with h_{ib}. The equation, including feedback, is

$$A_{vf} \cong \frac{h_{fb}R_L}{(h_{ib} + R_e)(1 + R_L h_{ob})}. \tag{8-36}$$

The method of this chapter requires the definition of a feedback fraction, in this case

$$B_v = \frac{R_e}{R_L}. \tag{8-37}$$

We recall that

$$A_{vf} = \frac{A_v}{1 - B_v A_v}. \tag{8-38}$$

A_v is given by Eq. (8–35) and B by Eq. (8–37); substitution into Eq. (8–38) yields

$$A_{vf} \cong \frac{h_{fb} R_L}{h_{ib}(1 + R_L h_{ob}) - R_e h_{fb}}. \tag{8-39}$$

Eq. (8–39) agrees with Eq. (8–36) since h_{fb} is negative and approximately of unit magnitude, and $R_L h_{ob} \ll 1$.

Designing for a Specified Gainspread. The common-emitter power gain expression for a single stage of amplification is

$$G \cong \frac{h_{fb}{}^2 R_L}{h_{ib}(1 + R_L h_{ob})[R_L h_{ob} + (1 + h_{fb})]}, \tag{8-40}$$

where h_{fb}, h_{ib}, and h_{ob} are subject to variation because of temperature, etc. Of the three parameters, h_{ib} and h_{ob} may change by several hundred percent, while h_{fb} is fairly constant and its variations may be of only a few percent. However, $(1 + h_{fb})$ may account for considerable variation in the gain of a single-stage amplifier.

Examination of Eq. (8–40) indicates that for values of $R_L h_{ob}$ such that

$$(1 + h_{fb}) \ll R_L h_{ob} \ll 1, \tag{8-41}$$

the gain formula may be simplified to

$$G \cong \frac{h_{fb}{}^2}{h_{ib} h_{ob}}. \tag{8-42}$$

Eq. (8–42) describes a stage whose gain is independent of the $(1 + h_{fb})$ factor and also R_L. If we incorporate feedback resistors (both R_c and R_e) into the circuit, the condition expressed by Eq. (8–41) becomes

$$(1 + h_{fb}) \ll R_L(h_{ob} + Y_c) \ll 1. \tag{8-43}$$

The simplified gain expression is now

$$G \cong \frac{h_{fb}{}^2}{(h_{ib} + R_e)(h_{ob} + Y_c)}. \tag{8-44}$$

The numerator of this expression will cause no great amount of difficulty when designing for a specific gain; however, the denominator is greatly dependent upon h_{ib} and h_{ob}, unless they can be swamped by R_e and Y_c. Such swamping would result in considerable loss of gain and we can conclude that we can expect very little gain from a highly stable single-stage amplifier.

If we analyze the "sensitivity of gain" to these parameters, an incremental change in gain is given by

$$dG = \frac{\partial G}{\partial h_{ib}} \, dh_{ib} + \frac{\partial G}{\partial h_{ob}} \, dh_{ob}. \tag{8-45}$$

Thus

$$\Delta G = -h_{fb}^2 \left[\frac{\Delta h_{ib}(h_{ob} + Y_c) + \Delta h_{ob}(h_{ib} + R_e)}{(h_{ib} + R_e)^2(h_{ob} + Y_c)^2} \right]. \tag{8-46}$$

The ratio of gainspread to gain is

$$\frac{\Delta G}{G} = -\left[\frac{\Delta h_{ib}}{h_{ib} + R_e} + \frac{\Delta h_{ob}}{h_{ob} + Y_c} \right]. \tag{8-47}$$

The minus sign indicates that positive excursions of h_{ib} and h_{ob} actually reduce the magnitude of G. Now with Eqs. (8–43) and (8–47) we may design a stage to a specific value of gainspread required.

Example. Consider a 2N475 transistor with the following parameters feeding a resistive load of 10,000 ohms:

	Min.	Design Center	Max.	
h_{ib}	30	60	90	ohms
h_{rb}	—	4	—	$\times 10^{-4}$
h_{fe}	20	30	50	
h_{ob}	0.1	0.5	1.5	$\times 10^{-6}$ mho

We may encounter some units for which $h_{ib} = 30$ and $h_{ob} = 1.5 \times 10^{-6}$ and also some units for which $h_{ib} = 30$ and $h_{ob} = 0.1 \times 10^{-6}$. h_{fb} is likely to change from -0.969 to -0.980 or down to -0.953.

For design-center values of parameters, Eq. (8–40) gives the following value of gain for a stage without feedback:

$$G = 4200, \text{ or } 36.2 \text{ db.}$$

For a unit with all parameters at their maximum values,

$$G = 3000, \text{ or } 34.8 \text{ db.}$$

Therefore the ratio of gainspread to gain is

$$\frac{\Delta G}{G} = \frac{1200}{4200}, \text{ or } 28.6\%.$$

This rather low spread is caused by the compensating effect of the $(1 + h_{fb})$ factor in the denominator of the gain expression, $(1 + h_{fb})$ decreased when the $R_L h_{ob}$ term increased. If, however, h_{fb} had taken on its minimum value when h_{ob} and h_{ib} were at their maximums, then

$$G = 1600, \text{ or } 32.0 \text{ db},$$

and the gainspread-to-gain ratio is

$$\frac{\Delta G}{G} = \frac{2600}{4200}, \text{ or } 62\%.$$

This analysis is limited to reduction in overall gain. An analysis of increase in gain due to parameter tolerances in the other direction is, of course, possible.

To satisfy the requirement posed by Eq. (8–43), we must make

$$(h_{ob} + Y_c)R_L \cong 0.2,$$

so

$$Y_c = \frac{0.2}{R_L} - h_{ob} = 19.5 \times 10^{-6} \text{ mho}.$$

Let it be determined that a gainspread of 10% is tolerable. From Eq. (8–47)

$$0.10 = \left[\frac{30}{60 + R_e} + \frac{10^{-6}}{0.5 \times 10^{-6} + 19.5 \times 10^{-6}} \right].$$

Hence

$$R_e = 540 \text{ ohms}.$$

The nominal gain of the stage, now stabilized to 10%, is

$$G = \frac{0.938}{600(20 \times 10^{-6})} = 78, \text{ or } 18.9 \text{ db}.$$

Therefore it is obvious that to stabilize the gain of a single stage of amplification, a large reduction in gain is the price to be paid.

8–3. Multistage Feedback. Consider a multistage amplifier composed of m identical stages each capable of providing a gain of A. The total amplification will be

$$A_t = A^m, \tag{8–48}$$

and

$$dA_t = mA^{m-1}dA. \tag{8–49}$$

Eq. (8–49) tells us that a 0.1 change in stage gain (dA) will result in a change in overall amplifier gain of twenty times that amount (for two stages each with an A of 10).

Let us now design a multistage feedback amplifier having n identical stages each providing a gain of A. Thus

$$A_f = \frac{A^n}{1 - BA^n}. \tag{8–50}$$

This feedback amplifier should do the same job as the one employing no feedback, so

$$A_t = A_f. \tag{8-51}$$

It follows that

$$A^m = \frac{A^n}{1 - BA^n}. \tag{8-52}$$

The feedback fraction may be derived from Eq. (8-52)

$$B = \frac{A^m - A^n}{A^{m+n}}. \tag{8-53}$$

If Eq. (8-50) is differentiated, and the value of B from Eq. (8-53) substituted,

$$\frac{dA_f}{dA} = nA^{2m-n-1}. \tag{8-54}$$

Insertion of Eq. (8-49) into Eq. (8-54) yields

$$\frac{dA_f}{dA} = \frac{nA^{2m-n-1}}{mA^{m-1}} \frac{dA_t}{dA}. \tag{8-55a}$$

This may be simplified to

$$\frac{dA_f}{dA} = \left(\frac{n}{m}\right) \frac{1}{A^{n-m}} \frac{dA_t}{dA}. \tag{8-55b}$$

Eq. (8-55) can most easily be interpreted with the aid of numbers. If the amplifier without feedback has one stage ($m = 1$) with a gain of 50, the feedback amplifier with three stages ($n = 3$) requires a B of approximately A^{-1} or $\frac{1}{50}$ according to Eq. (8-53). The relative drift in the feedback amplifier due to changes in A compared with the drift in the nonfeedback circuit due to the same cause is $\frac{1}{833}$.

The predication or analysis of operation of a multistage feedback amplifier by solution of the Kirchhoff equations is a lengthy procedure. In Chapter 7 we found analysis of a two-stage amplifier without feedback to be time-consuming; the additional loops or nodes with feedback require an even greater effort to derive the equations that will predict operation. However, once such equations are derived, they may prove useful on a number of occasions, for the possible methods of feedback are limited.

Here we shall treat four multistage circuits, two comprising three stages of amplification, and two comprising two stages of amplification. In our investigations we shall be limited to cascaded common-emitter stages. By doing so, and also being concerned with negative feedback exclusively, we shall find only a few possible circuits that will supply the required 180° phase differential. Each stage will be considered to have a voltage gain A_v, and a current gain A_i. Of course it is not always true that each stage of a cascade amplifier has the same gain, so the first-stage voltage gain will be symbolized by A_{v1}, the second by A_{v2}, etc. Current gain will be treated in a similar manner.

Since a number of amplifying stages are involved in each composite amplifier, the circuit diagrams may be somewhat simplified if a symbol is assigned to depict an entire stage. This will be done; the symbol to be employed is shown in Fig. 8–6. The letter A stands for a device capable of amplification of either voltage or current. In a particular arrangement we may wish to make use of only the voltage-amplification properties, or only the current-amplification properties of the device.

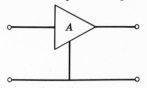

Fig. 8–6. Symbol used for amplifying stage.

When the feedback is around the outside of an overall amplifier as will be true for the three-stage amplifier which follows, Eq. (8–3) will be used. All that is necessary is knowledge of the open-loop gains and B. For two-stage amplifiers where, because of phasing, the feedback signal is not around the composite circuit, an approach based upon Kirchhoff's Laws using the symbolic form for complete amplifying stages yields satisfactory performance information.

Three-Stage Amplifiers. A widely accepted feedback scheme is shown in Fig. 8–7: multistage shunt feedback from the collector of the third stage to the base of the first stage. If it is assumed that here we are dealing with normal circuits having appropriate amplifications (for a three-stage amplifier,

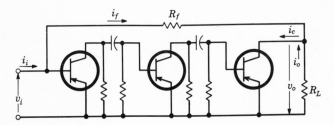

Fig. 8–7. Three-stage amplifier with overall shunt feedback.

A_{vT} may be 1000 to 100,000, and A_{iT} may be 1000 to 100,000) then the feedback resistor R_f will be a great deal larger than R_L. The overall voltage gain will be essentially unaffected by R_f, and therefore

$$A_{vf} = A_{v1}A_{v2}A_{v3} = A_{vT}. \tag{8–56}$$

Let us investigate overall current amplification. Collector current of the

third stage, i_c, is the sum of the two currents i_f and i_o, and the ratio of these currents is B_i. Consider that the input resistance of the first stage is small compared with R_f. Then

$$B_i = \frac{i_f}{i_o} = \frac{R_L}{R_f}. \tag{8-57}$$

The overall current amplification, by Eq. (8–3), is

$$A_{if} = \frac{A_{iT}}{1 - A_{iT}(R_L/R_f)}. \tag{8-58}$$

A_{iT} is the total forward current gain and equals $A_{i1}A_{i2}A_{i3}$.

The voltage gain has not been materially affected by feedback of this type, but since current gain is reduced, input resistance must be reduced by a like amount, hence

$$R_{if} = \frac{R_i}{1 - A_{iT}(R_L/R_f)}. \tag{8-59}$$

The minus sign in the denominator of Eq. (8–59) does not mean that the circuit exhibits a negative input resistance. A_{iT} must provide phase reversal; therefore a negative sign is associated with that term but not included in the equation.

A series type of feedback may be applied to the three-stage amplifier. Such a connection is depicted in Fig. 8–8. The emitter R_e is common to all stages,

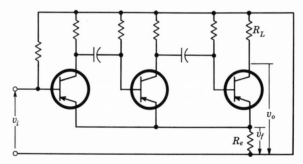

Fig. 8–8.   Three-stage amplifier with overall series feedback.

and will be of a small value because the large signal current in the final stage passes through it. As can be noted from current-gain expressions previously derived for single stages, emitter resistance in general has little effect upon current amplification. Thus

$$A_{if} = A_{iT}. \tag{8-60}$$

The ratio of feedback voltage to load voltage is

$$B_v = \frac{v_f}{v_o} = \frac{R_e}{R_L}. \tag{8-61}$$

This value of B assumes that the current through R_e is equal to that through R_L, which is very nearly the case. To solve for overall voltage gain we again make use of Eq. (8–3)

$$A_{vf} = \frac{A_{vT}}{1 - A_{vT}(R_e/R_L)}. \tag{8-62}$$

Current gain has not been altered; however, the reduction in voltage gain evidenced by Eq. (8–62) means that an incoming signal will find a higher input resistance.

$$R_{if} = R_i\left(1 - A_{vT}\frac{R_e}{R_L}\right). \tag{8-63}$$

Two-Stage Amplifiers. Two common-emitter stages, joined by an appropriate coupling network, could employ neither the overall shunt feedback nor the overall series feedback of the preceding section, on account of phasing. If, however, an "interior" signal is fed to an "exterior" point, or an "exterior" signal is fed to an "interior" point, the phasing will be correct for the degenerative form of feedback.

One such arrangement is shown in Fig. 8–9. A signal, taken from the emitter resistor of stage two is made available to the input circuit through

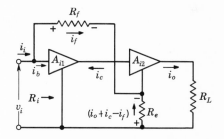

Fig. 8–9. Two stages with feedback; current gain calculations.

R_f. Our analysis of this circuit will be separated into two parts: determination of the overall current-gain expression, and derivation of the overall voltage-gain expression.

To find the ratio of i_o to i_i, we may write loop and nodal equations thus:

$$\left.\begin{aligned} i_i &= i_b + i_f \\ i_c &= A_{i1}i_b \\ i_o &= A_{i2}i_c \\ (i_o + i_c - i_f)R_e &= i_fR_f - i_bR_i. \end{aligned}\right\} \tag{8-64}$$

Solution of these simultaneous equations for current gain yields

$$A_{if} = \frac{A_{i1}A_{i2}(R_f + R_e)}{(A_{i1}A_{i2} + A_{i1} + 1)R_e + R_f + R_i}. \tag{8-65}$$

Letting $R_f \to \infty$ results in $A_{if} \to A_{i1}A_{i2}$. Should $R_e \to 0$, then

$$A_{if} \to \frac{A_{i1}A_{i2}R_f}{R_f + R_i}. \tag{8-66}$$

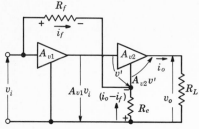

Fig. 8-10. Two stages with feedback; voltage gain calculations.

Eq. (8-66) clearly shows the current division at the input terminal.

Voltage gain for this circuit is not a simple expression, but depends upon the individual stage gains, and the external resistances. Let us write circuit equations, and make the additional assumption that collector current of stage number two is much greater than its base current. This generally will be true. From Fig. 8-10 we are able to determine that

$$\left.\begin{aligned}
v_i &= i_f R_f - (i_o - i_f)R_e \\
A_{v1}v_i &= v' + (i_o - i_f)R_e \\
v_o &= A_{v2}v' - (i_o - i_f)R_e \\
i_o &= v_o/R_L.
\end{aligned}\right\} \tag{8-67}$$

The solution of these simultaneous equations for the ratio of v_o to v_i yields

$$A_{vf} = \frac{R_L[(A_{v1}A_{v2} + A_{v2} + 1)R_e + R_f A_{v1}A_{v2}]}{R_L(R_e + R_f) + R_e R_f(A_{v2} + 1)}. \tag{8-68}$$

If feedback is removed by letting $R_e = 0$, then the above equation reverts to $A_{v1}A_{v2}$.

An alternate method for incorporating feedback in a two-stage amplifier is shown in Fig. 8-11, with the second-stage collector signal fed to the emitter of the first stage. Let us again separate our calculations, and investigate the overall circuit current amplification. The defining equations are

$$\left.\begin{aligned}
i_x &= i_f + i_o, \\
i_x &= A_{i2}i_c, \\
i_c &= A_{i1}i_i, \\
(i_c + i_f + i_i)R_e &= i_o R_L - i_f R_f.
\end{aligned}\right\} \tag{8-69}$$

The solution of these equations for the ratio of i_o to i_i is

$$A_{if} = \frac{A_{i1}A_{i2}(R_e + R_f) + A_{i1}R_e + R_e}{R_e + R_f + R_L}. \tag{8-70}$$

If we use Fig. 8–12 to derive an expression for the voltage amplification for this circuit, then under the assumption that first-stage base current is

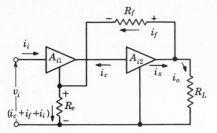 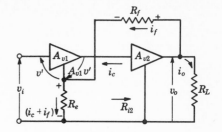

Fig. 8–11. Alternate two-stage feedback; current gain calculations.　　Fig. 8–12. Alternate two-stage feedback; voltage gain calculations.

negligible compared with collector current, the necessary relationships are

$$\left.\begin{aligned}
v_i &= v' + (i_c + i_f)R_e, \\
v_o &= (i_c + i_f)R_e + i_f R_f, \\
v_o &= A_{v2}[A_{v1}v' - (i_c + i_f)R_e], \\
v_o &= A_{v2}i_c R_{i2}.
\end{aligned}\right\} \tag{8-71}$$

Solution of Eqs. (8–71) for the ratio of terminal voltages gives

$$A_{vf} = \frac{A_{v1}A_{v2}R_{i2}(R_e + R_f)}{R_e[A_{v1}A_{v2}R_{i2} + A_{v2}R_{i2} + (A_{v1} + 1)R_f] + R_{i2}(R_e + R_f)}. \tag{8-72}$$

The method used here to analyze two- and three-stage amplifiers can be extended to a greater number of stages and also to circuits with multiple feedback loops.

To examine the effect of feedback upon input resistance, recall that

$$A_i = \frac{i_o}{i_i}, \tag{8-73}$$

and

$$A_v = \frac{v_o}{v_i} = \frac{i_o R_L}{v_i}. \tag{8-74}$$

Division of Eq. (8–73) by Eq. (8–74) yields

$$\frac{A_i}{A_v} = \frac{i_o/i_i}{i_o R_L/v_i} = \frac{v_i}{i_i R_L} = \frac{R_i}{R_L}. \tag{8-75}$$

Input resistance may be predicted from knowledge of A_i, A_v, and R_L.

8–4. Automatic Gain Control.   Closely allied with any discussion of feedback is the *automatic gain control* (AGC) system employed in communications receivers.   The function of such a system is to maintain a relatively constant signal at the *second detector* stage of a receiver regardless of the strength of the incoming signal, that is the signal at some previous section of the circuitry.   The detector, also called a *demodulator*, separates intelligence from a carrier frequency and discards the carrier.   In the prototype system it is normal to sample the detector output, which is intelligence superimposed upon d-c, and

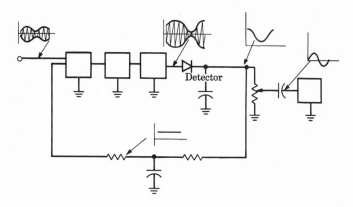

Fig. 8–13.   General AGC circuit showing waveforms at various points.

feed the average level of this signal back to a preceding stage to control the grid bias of a tube that is operating in a nonlinear region of its characteristics, and thereby control the gain of a stage by utilizing the magnitude of the output of a later stage.   Such a system actually controls the intelligence level by controlling the carrier magnitude, since both carrier and modulation are amplified equally.   The rectification and low-pass filtering accomplished by the detector stage leaves a d-c signal to be fed back whose amplitude is proportional to carrier amplitude.

Fig. 8–13 describes the operation of an AGC circuit by showing the important waveforms.   A simple demodulator is described by the diode, while the associated shunt capacitance helps eliminate high frequencies (the carrier) from the audio or video stages that follow.   In the feedback line further filtering is employed to smooth the waveform, since only the average value is of importance.

When working with transistor circuits, we must find a means of controlling gain by altering the quiescent or d-c conditions of an amplifier.   The variations of parameters with operating point were discussed in Chapter 4, and in Chapter 5 the results of an investigation of the relation of performance to operating point were presented.   Other investigations have been made and the results depicted in Figs. 8–14 and 8–15. A considerable variation in gain can be achieved if either emitter current or collector voltage is varied. In the case of AGC this operating point change is caused by the fedback signal.

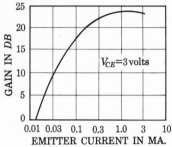

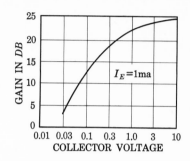

Fig. 8–14. Variation of gain due to emitter current for a typical common-emitter stage.

Fig. 8–15. Variation of gain due to collector voltage for a typical common-emitter stage.

To change either emitter current or collector voltage, power is required. Again we encounter the difference between vacuum-tube and transistor technologies. The output of the second detector must supply power to the controlled stage or stages. This control power requirement can be minimized if the d-c is made available to a base rather than an emitter. Fig. 8–16 illustrates an AGC that controls the emitter current of a transistor by altering base bias. Of course emitter current depends upon base current and this scheme can be studied by considering the controlled transistor to be a d-c amplifier that is amplifying the AGC signal. Emitter current variations cause variations in the potential drop across the bypassed emitter resistance and therefore changes in the available voltage across the transistor; one may reason that these two effects (I_E and V_{CE} control) tend to cancel, with no resulting gain variation. For this type of circuit,

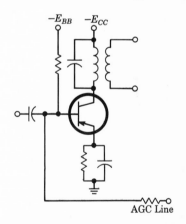

Fig. 8–16. Emitter current AGC.

the collector voltage must be fairly large, or, in other words, not in the sensitive region of operation.

It is possible, of course, to directly control emitter current by means of the AGC voltage, if sufficient power is available, or to include a separate AGC amplifier.

Maximum sensitivity of control is achieved at low values of emitter current, below 100 microamperes for the transistor whose operation is depicted in Fig. 8–14, and at low collector potentials, below 500 millivolts. These facts essentially limit the swing of applied signals to very small values, as are encountered in the radio-frequency (R.F.), converter, and first inter-mediate-frequency (I.F.) stages of a superheterodyne receiver. If a large collector resistor is added to the cir-cuit of Fig. 8–16 as shown in Fig. 8–17, and the emitter bias current made fairly large, then a small col-lector-to-emitter voltage is available. An AGC signal that alters base cur-rent will also change emitter current and thereby alter available collector voltage. The changing collector po-tential provides gain control. Quies-cent emitter current for this circuit should be fairly large and therefore not in the sensitive region of operation.

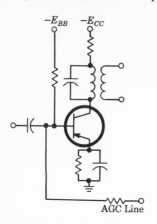

Fig. 8–17. Collector voltage AGC.

Fig. 8–18 and 8–19 show two practical circuits. In Fig. 8–18, the AGC is used to control the base bias of both the mixer and first I.F. amplifier stages of a receiver. Although resistors are in both collector circuits, they are of too low a value (1000 ohms) to provide collector-voltage control; the stages are I_E controlled. The variable resistance at the detector output provides manual volume control for the entire circuit. In the circuit of Fig. 8–19, the second detector is a Class-B-operated transistor, and the AGC voltage is obtained from the bypassed emitter resistance. The AGC signal controls the gain of both the R.F. amplifier and the first I.F. amplifier by addition of currents at the emitter of each of those stages.

Each of the aforementioned control systems must operate so that when the incoming signal is strong, the fedback voltage or current is of such a polarity as to reduce amplifier gain, and vice versa.

When changing the operating point of a transistor we might expect input and output impedances also to change. Since loads are normally tuned cir-cuits in receiver circuitry, the resonant frequency and bandwidth of such tuned circuits will be altered as a result of changing transistor impedances. Collector capacitance is a function of collector voltage, and thus a degree of detuning is almost certain to occur. It is desirable that the bandwidth of tuned circuits be wide when input signals are strong, and narrow when signals are weak. This is accomplished when using a collector-voltage AGC system, for the input impedance of the controlled stage is reduced when I_E increases, thereby detuning the input tuned circuit. On the other hand, when I_E is used for the direct control of gain, the input impedance of a stage will be increased and bandwidth narrowed when I_E decreases. Selectivity should be accomplished elsewhere in the receiver for such a system.

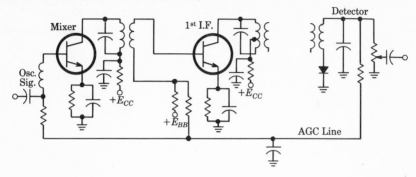

Fig. 8–18. Practical AGC system.

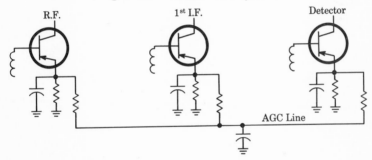

Fig. 8–19. Practical AGC system.

8–5. Direct-Coupled Amplifiers. Also called a direct-current or a direct-voltage amplifier, a direct-coupled (d-c) amplifier has, as its main application, the amplification of signals below several cps and down to zero cps, the d-c signal. It is to be realized that the circuits discussed thus far have used transformers and capacitors for coupling between stages; these elements are capable of passing time-varying signals exclusively, and severely attenuate the lower frequencies.

It is possible to remove the blocking capacitors from an R-C amplifier, thereby placing the direct potential at the second-stage base at the same level as the first-stage collector. This may be acceptable provided that the emitter and collector potentials of the second stage are adjusted to maintain the required operating voltages. Therefore, because of the need for adjusted potentials, we might expect to encounter numerous power supplies in any d-c amplifier. The amplifier will be sensitive to these supplies since a change in any supply voltage will be amplified just as a d-c input signal is amplified. When appearing at the load this amplified supply variation would be indistinguishable from signal.

The d-c amplifier supplies, to its load, a signal that is proportional to its input. As would be expected, the magnitude of the output quantity is dependent upon the amplification factors of the various circuits. However, since we are dealing with direct current, and usually desire that zero voltage exist at the load when zero input signal is impressed, then a change in gain may actually cause an output voltage even in the absence of input signal. This will be apparent from the circuit to be discussed directly. It is important

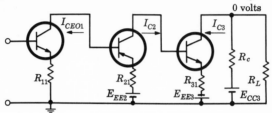

Fig. 8–20.   Simple d-c transistor amplifier.

to note that an output other than zero will result when the operating point of any stage changes, as a result, for example, of changes in temperature, because in the absence of isolation any operating-point variation will alter the operating points of the succeeding stages.

I_{CO} is a problem because of its extreme sensitivity to temperature, and, in general, must be compensated for. Compensation can be achieved by circuitry employing temperature-sensitive resistors and diodes. Both thermistors and diodes exhibit negative temperature coefficients of resistance, and, when used in conjunction with resistors having zero or positive temperature coefficients, networks may be designed having almost any desired temperature sensitivity.

These three causes of trouble for d-c amplifiers—power supply variations, parameter changes due to temperature and age, and changes in leakage current—are the prime contributors to *drift*. Drift can be defined as a variation in the amplifier output independent of the designated input. Methods for the reduction of drift in d-c vacuum-tube amplifiers are generally applicable to transistor circuits and will be subsequently considered.

Let us discuss the d-c amplifier of Fig. 8–20. This diagram is not a simplification, but actually represents all circuit elements necessary for a complete workable circuit. The first and third stages are *n-p-n* units, while the second stage is *p-n-p*. Reasoning behind the choice of different types will be clear after investigation of base and collector current directions.

Since the base circuit of the first stage has no driving voltage, no base current exists. A collector current, I_{CEO}, will be apparent and will be in the direction as shown on the diagram. I_{CEO} of the first stage *is* I_B of the second stage, and since transistor-conductivity types alternate, the current direction is correct for Class-A amplification. If stage two has a current gain of β_2, then its collector current is

$$I_{C2} \cong \beta_2 I_{CEO1}.$$

I_{C2} is in the proper direction, and serves as base current for stage three. The collector current of stage three is

$$I_{C3} \cong \beta_3 I_{C2} \cong \beta_2 \beta_3 I_{CEO1}.$$

Should a fourth stage be required, it must be *p-n-p*.

Examine collector-to-emitter voltages. The output stage collector is at ground potential, and the emitter is made negative by supply E_{EE3}; thus the collector is more positive than the emitter. Base potential is approximately that of emitter number three and is common to collector two. E_{EE2} is in series with E_{EE3} and together they supply the collector potential for stage two. Stage number one has a collector potential approximately equal to E_{EE2}. As shown, the base of the first stage is not at zero volts, but could be made so by additional circuitry. Actually, the circuit shown was fed from a differential amplifier and R_{11} was several thousand ohms to provide a high input impedance. R_{21} and R_{31} are low-valued resistors that provide degenerative feedback, and although they do not materially affect the current gain of any particular stage, they tend to increase the stability of collector current with respect to temperature variations.

In the amplifier as constructed, $I_{C1} = 6 \ \mu a$, $I_{C2} = 220 \ \mu a$ and $I_{C3} = 9 \ ma$, indicating that $\beta_2 \cong 37$ and $\beta_3 \cong 41$. The sensitivity of such a circuit to ambient temperature is apparent. The signal supplied to the load is based upon I_{CEO} of stage number one, and although silicon transistors were employed, we might expect a change of about 5% per degree Centigrade in that current. Even if I_{CEO} were not the quiescent current of the first stage, I_{CEO} would make up a sizable portion of it. Temperature compensation is a must for such an amplifier even if it is expected that the only temperature excursions will be those as encountered in a normal room.

The semiconductor diode is often used for temperature compensation because the temperature coefficient of resistance of the diode material is equivalent to the rate at which transistor leakage (I_{CO}) varies with temperature. For example, in the circuit of Fig. 8–21, it is desired to maintain I_{B2} constant although I_{C1} (which may

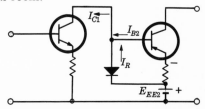

Fig. 8–21. Use of a semiconductor diode to temperature-compensate an amplifier.

be I_{CEO} of the first stage) is subject to vary because of climatic conditions. The diode is biased negatively, and we are concerned with the reverse current, I_R. Since E_{EE2} is the only circuit source,

$$I_{B2} = -I_R + I_{C1}. \qquad (8\text{--}76)$$

It is required that $dI_{B2}/dT = 0$. Therefore

$$\frac{dI_R}{dT} = \frac{dI_{C1}}{dT}. \qquad (8\text{--}77)$$

If I_{C1} is primarily leakage,

$$\frac{dI_R}{dT} = \frac{dI_{CEO1}}{dT} = \frac{dI_{CO}}{dT}. \qquad (8\text{--}78)$$

The diode should have leakage properties identical to those of the transistor.

An extremely interesting circuit is the *compound connection* shown in Fig. 8–22. The emitter terminal of $TR1$ is directly connected to the base of $TR2$; the collectors of both units share a common load. The two transistors present only three terminals to the external circuit (X, Y, and Z in the figure).

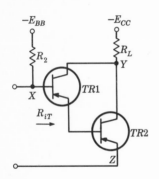

Fig. 8–22. Common-emitter compound connection.

Since $TR2$ is in the common leg of $TR1$, it will provide negative feedback that serves to gain-stabilize the composite circuit, and the resulting input resistance (R_{iT}) is much greater than that of a single common-emitter stage. For normal Class-A operation, resistance R_2 is chosen so that both stages are operating in the active region of their collector characteristics. It is of course easy to saturate $TR2$ by supplying too much base current to $TR1$, since the operating point of the second transistor depends upon

$$I_{B2} = I_{E1} \cong \beta_1 I_{B1},$$

and

$$I_{C2} \cong \beta_1 \beta_2 I_{B1}.$$

Since the collector currents of both transistors flow through the common load each will contribute to total load signal, but the extent of that contribution differs by the magnitude of the current amplification of $TR2$. Refinements can be made to the circuit shown. Bypassed emitter resistance for $TR2$ may be added, single-battery biasing (or other forms) may be used, or an additional stage added by connecting its base to the emitter of $TR2$, its collector to the common load, and its emitter to ground.

The results of building a compound-connected pair: $R_{iT} = 20,000$ ohms, $A_v = 90$, $A_i = 670$, for small, low-frequency, a-c signals when feeding a 2000-ohm load.

The Differential Amplifier. A popular circuit often employed in d-c amplifiers is the *differential amplifier,* so-called because its output voltage is proportional to the difference of two voltages supplied to its two separate inputs. Often one input terminal pair is used for the signal to be amplified, while the other input terminal pair is used as the termination of a feedback line. Two transistors are necessary to perform the subtraction operation, as can be seen in Fig. 8–23, and if they are matched, the output voltage, which can be taken from either collector, is independent of parameter changes and changes in the

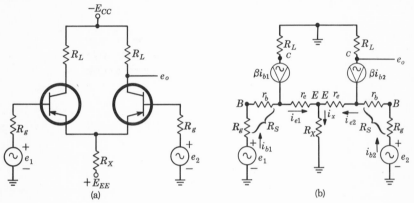

Fig. 8–23. Common-emitter differential amplifier: (a) circuit; (b) a-c equivalent.

value of I_{CO} of either transistor. In the figure, two inputs, e_1 and e_2 are shown. However, the circuit will amplify if but one input terminal is supplied, and the other grounded through an appropriate impedance.

An analysis of this circuit may be made on a d-c or an a-c basis. Here an a-c analysis is presented in order to prove the differential operation and the amplification constant of the circuit. In the analysis, r_c is assumed to be much larger than R_L, the channels are assumed identical and the transistor parameter r_b is lumped with generator resistance R_g to form a composite, which is termed R_s.

The Kirchhoff equations for Fig. 8–23b are:

$$\left.\begin{aligned}
e_1 &= i_{b1}R_s + i_{e1}r_e + i_xR_x, \\
e_2 &= i_{b2}R_s + i_{e2}r_e + i_xR_x, \\
i_x &= i_{e1} + i_{e2}, \\
i_{e1} &= (\beta + 1)i_{b1} \quad \text{and} \quad i_{e2} = (\beta + 1)i_{b2}.
\end{aligned}\right\} \quad (8\text{--}79)$$

For $R_x \gg r_e$ and $(\beta + 1)R_x \gg R_s$,

$$i_{b1} \cong \frac{e_1 - e_2}{2R_s} \quad \text{and} \quad i_{b2} \cong \frac{e_2 - e_1}{2R_s}. \qquad (8\text{-}80)$$

Since

$$e_o \cong -\beta R_L i_{b2} \qquad (8\text{-}81)$$

then

$$e_o \cong \frac{(e_1 - e_2)\beta R_L}{2[R_s + r_e(\beta + 1)]}. \qquad (8\text{-}82)$$

If the assumption of a large R_x or a small R_s is not valid, differential operation will still occur, but e_1 and e_2 will have differing coefficients in Eq. (8-82).

A similar analysis can be made of the common-base pair of Fig. 8-24.

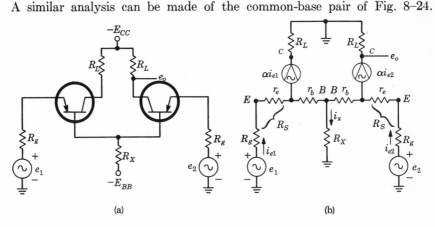

(a)   (b)

Fig. 8-24. Common-base differential amplifier: (a) circuit; (b) a-c equivalent.

The assumptions used to simplify analysis are again that $r_c \gg R_L$, the units are identical, and $i_x R_x \gg i_b r_b$. r_e will be lumped with R_g to form a composite R_s. The defining equations:

$$\left. \begin{array}{l} e_1 = i_{e1}R_s + i_x R_x, \\[4pt] e_2 = i_{e2}R_s + i_x R_x, \\[4pt] i_x = i_{e1}(1 - \alpha) + i_{e2}(1 - \alpha). \end{array} \right\} \qquad (8\text{-}83)$$

For $R_x(1 - \alpha) \gg R_s$

$$i_{e1} \cong \frac{e_1 - e_2}{2R_s} \quad \text{and} \quad i_{e2} \cong \frac{e_2 - e_1}{2R_s}. \qquad (8\text{-}84)$$

Since

$$e_o \cong \alpha R_L i_{e2}, \qquad (8\text{-}85)$$

then

$$e_o \cong \frac{(e_2 - e_1)\alpha R_L}{2R_s}. \qquad (8\text{-}86)$$

The input resistance of this circuit depends upon the signal level impressed upon the other input terminal pair, and under the condition that the signal level is identical at each input, the input resistance would be infinite according to Eq. (8–84).

Chopper Amplifiers. Because of the many problems associated with direct-coupled circuits, a widely accepted method of amplifying low frequencies and direct signals is to convert the signal to a-c, amplify this a-c and then rectify to re-establish the d-c. To change d-c to a-c a switching scheme may be used. The switch may be a circuit or device that will alternately pass and reject the d-c input as a function of time. The common name for this operation is "modulation." A modulator may be an electromechanical switch, such as a vibrator, or a circuit comprised of diodes, vacuum tubes or transistors, or it may be electromagnetic, such as a magnetic modulator. The vibrator has moving parts, and consequently a relatively short lifetime, and is limited to operation below 1000 cps. However, since it is practically drift free and exhibits a low noise level the vibrator is often used for this application.

A "demodulator" must be used when it is necessary to remove the alternating carrier and re-establish the d-c signal; its action is basically rectification and filtering. In a system using both a modulator and a demodulator, it is desired that the overall circuit be polarity conscious. For example, if +10 millivolts is to be amplified 1000 times, we normally expect the output to be +10 volts, and a negative load voltage to result from an input signal of negative polarity. It is therefore necessary that the demodulator be phase sensitive. Should modulator action result in an alternating current of a certain phase (with respect to any convenient reference) for a given polarity of d-c signal, then the demodulator will sample that phasing and supply the load with d-c of the correct polarity. The accepted names for this rectification circuit are "phase-sensitive demodulator," "phase-sensitive discriminator," or "phase-sensitive detector."

A complete d-c amplifier making use of the foregoing principle is shown in Fig. 8–25. The d-c input is shorted to ground (through resistances of low value) when the square wave modulator excitation is of the correct polarity for both diodes to conduct. On alternate half cycles neither diode can conduct and the d-c signal is passed through the modulator circuit to the amplifier. The resulting potential at A is a square wave with one half of its cycle at ground potential. This square wave, with a fundamental frequency of the chopper excitation, passes through C_{c1} to the base of $TR1$. Because of the large unbypassed emitter resistor, $TR1$ presents a high input impedance and therefore does not load down the chopper. $TR1$ is biased near cutoff because no direct base current is allowed. The square wave is amplified by three additional stages, each having a high degree of bias stability as well as some local feedback. The collector voltage of $TR4$ is made available to the bases of both $TR5$ and $TR6$.

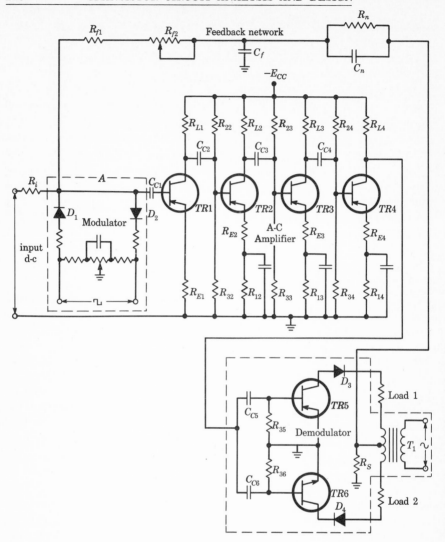

Fig. 8–25.   D-c chopper amplifier showing modulator and demodulator.

A four-terminal load is being supplied by the amplifier of this figure and could represent a hydraulic valve actuated by d-c, the motion of the valve dictated by the difference in the direct current flowing through its two windings.   The operation of the demodulator circuit will now be discussed. Consider the lower terminal of transformer T_1 to be instantaneously positive. Diodes D_3 and D_4 are connected so that each transistor has the proper collector-voltage polarity.   But since the transistors are of opposite conductivity types and are being operated Class-B, the transistor that will conduct and hence supply load current is the one being correctly stimulated by base signal. Each transistor is receiving the same base signal, and the detector is said to be phase sensitive because if the bases are instantaneously positive, only $TR6$ will conduct, causing current downward through load #2. However, if the bases were going negative during the half cycle when each collector is correctly excited, then only $TR5$ will conduct, resulting in a current downward through load #1. During the other alternation of supply to T_1, neither transistor can conduct.

All load currents flow through R_s, a small resistor, which supplies feedback voltage. In the feedback loop R_n and C_n help to shape the frequency response characteristic of the amplifier, and C_f is useful in filtering the feedback signal. The amount of feedback is dictated by R_{f1} and adjustable resistance R_{f2}, and is added to the amplifier input at A.

Chopper amplifiers have been found useful for many applications; the d-c output of thermocouples, thermopiles, strain gages and certain pressure sensors as well as many other process transducers must be amplified for indication and control of process variables, and chopper amplifiers have been widely accepted. The bandwidth of such circuits is narrow and a general rule of thumb is that a chopper amplifier can be used to amplify signals up to $\frac{1}{10}$ of the modulating frequency. The reader may verify the bandwidth limitation.

Operational Amplifiers. The term "operational amplifier" has been used to describe the circuit comprised of a d-c amplifier and associated external impedances that together "operate" upon a direct voltage or current in some mathematical way. Applications for such amplifiers in the measurement and computer fields are numerous.

Prior to the transistor, vacuum-tube operational amplifiers, characterized by their high input resistance and high voltage gain, took on certain standard forms. With transistor circuits, however, high or low input resistance is available. In the following circuits both resistance levels will be considered. The operations to be discussed are summation, integration and differentiation.

A d-c amplifier with no load and high input resistance is depicted in Fig. 8–26 with two input voltages, e_1

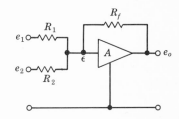

Fig. 8–26. Summing amplifier.

and e_2, available. More than two inputs are, of course, possible. It is desired that the output voltage, e_o, be proportional to the sum of e_1 and e_2. Thus

$$e_o = K(e_1 + e_2). \tag{8–87}$$

A summation of currents at the significant node yields

$$\frac{e_1 - \epsilon}{R_1} + \frac{e_2 - \epsilon}{R_2} = \frac{\epsilon - e_o}{R_f}. \tag{8-88}$$

For the amplifier alone, including phase reversal,

$$A = -\frac{e_o}{\epsilon}. \tag{8-89}$$

For a very large value of A, Eq. (8–88) becomes

$$e_o \cong -R_f \left(\frac{e_1}{R_1} + \frac{e_2}{R_2} \right). \tag{8-90}$$

Should all resistances be of equal magnitude,

$$e_o = -(e_1 + e_2). \tag{8-91}$$

It can be proved easily that if finite amplifier input resistance had been considered, input resistance would have acted as if it were parallel with R_1 and R_2. However a large A would result in an expression identical with Eq. (8–90).

For a single input to the circuit of Fig. 8–26 the expression for output voltage becomes

$$e_o = \frac{-e_1 A R_f}{R_f + (1 + A)R_1}. \tag{8-92}$$

Eq. (8–92) represents a standard feedback circuit that, for large values of A, exhibits a gain of

$$\frac{e_o}{e_1} \cong -\frac{R_f}{R_1}. \tag{8-93}$$

Consider the amplifier with single input channel shown in Fig. 8–27. Impedances Z_F and Z_I will determine the operation of the overall circuit. Because this circuit is very similar to the double-input case just discussed, the output voltage, for large A, is given by a modification of Eq. (8–93)

$$e_o \cong -e_i \frac{Z_F}{Z_I}. \tag{8-94}$$

Let Z_I be resistive and equal R, and let Z_F be capacitive. Using Laplace notation, $s = j\omega$, and thus $Z_F = 1/sC$. Eq. (8–94) can be written

$$E_o(s) = -\frac{E_i(s)}{RCs}. \tag{8-95}$$

In the time domain

$$e_o = -\frac{1}{RC}\int e_i dt. \qquad (8\text{–}96)$$

The circuit will integrate the input voltage.

If the positions of the capacitor and resistor are interchanged, that is if $Z_I = 1/sC$ and $Z_F = R$, then, from Eq. (8–94),

$$E_o(s) = -E_i(s)RCs. \qquad (8\text{–}97)$$

In the time domain, this corresponds to

$$e_o = -RC\frac{de_i}{dt}. \qquad (8\text{–}98)$$

The input voltage is differentiated if the amplifier gain is large.

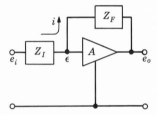

Fig. 8–27. Computing amplifier.

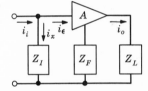

Fig. 8–28. Current analog of 8–27.

The possibility of using low input resistance transistor amplifiers has led to the so-called current-analog operational amplifier shown in Fig. 8–28. It is assumed that the input impedance of A is low compared with Z_F, and A is primarily a current amplifier, so

$$A = -\frac{i_o}{i_\epsilon}. \qquad (8\text{–}99)$$

Summing potential drops around the inner loop gives

$$i_x Z_I = (i_\epsilon - i_o)Z_F. \qquad (8\text{–}100)$$

It is obvious that

$$i_i = i_x + i_\epsilon.$$

A solution of these equations for load current yields

$$i_o \cong -i_i\frac{Z_I}{Z_F}, \qquad (8\text{–}101)$$

for large values of A. To integrate the input current, Z_I may be a capacitor and Z_F a resistor. To differentiate, the elements may be interchanged.

The operational amplifiers described above are subject to the drifts inherent in d-c amplifiers even though a large amount of feedback may be employed. Use could be made of chopper amplifiers, subject to their inherent high-frequency limitations. Automatic balancing circuits based upon chopper stabilization have proved very successful because the freedom of drift of the chopper amplifier and the superior high-frequency response of a conventional d-c amplifier are both realized.[3]

In the circuit of Fig. 8–29, D represents a d-c amplifier having a wide bandwidth, but drift, denoted by d, will be present and can be referred to the circuit input. D has a differential amplifier input stage of high input resistance. The amplifier A is a chopper circuit that will pass all low frequencies (often included with A is a low-pass filter while in the path to D a filter may be used to block d-c and pass the highs). Low-frequency amplification is the product

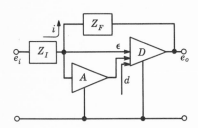
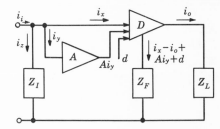

Fig. 8–29. D-c amplifier with automatic stabilization.

Fig. 8–30. Current analog of 8–29.

of A and D; high frequencies will exhibit a gain of D, modified by the appropriate networks.

It is desired to eliminate or at least greatly reduce the amount of d which is present at the output. By Kirchhoff's second law:

$$\epsilon = e_i - iZ_I = e_i - \frac{(e_i - e_o)}{Z_I + Z_F} Z_I. \qquad (8\text{–}102a)$$

Output voltage is

$$e_o = -AD\epsilon - Dd - D\epsilon. \qquad (8\text{–}102b)$$

Solution of these equations results in

$$e_o \cong -e_i\left(\frac{Z_F}{Z_I}\right) - \frac{d}{A}\frac{(Z_I + Z_F)}{Z_I}. \qquad (8\text{–}103)$$

It can be seen that the unwanted signal has been decreased by a factor close to $1/A$.

A current analog of the Goldberg d-c amplifier is shown in Fig. 8–30. Amplifier A is again a high-gain low-frequency d-c amplifier with modulating and demodulating circuits and D is a wideband d-c amplifier subject to drift d. Both amplifiers must have low input resistance for the following mathematical analysis to be correct. Let us consider that each amplifier primarily provides current gain and solve the circuit equations for overall amplification:

$$\left.\begin{aligned} i_i &= i_x + i_y + i_z \\ i_o &= -Di_x - ADi_y - Dd \\ i_z Z_I &\cong (i_x - i_o + Ai_y + d)Z_F \end{aligned}\right\} \tag{8-104}$$

At d-c and very low frequencies, i_x and Di_x may be negligible, particularly if a blocking capacitor is included in the i_x branch.

The resulting expression is

$$i_o \cong -i_i \left(\frac{Z_I}{Z_F}\right) - \frac{d}{A}\left(\frac{Z_I}{Z_F}\right) \tag{8-105}$$

Again, unwanted drift has been reduced by a significant amount.

The current analog chopper stabilized d-c amplifier has the disadvantage of requiring that the chopper amplifier (A) present a low input resistance. Other circuits are possible which circumvent this limitation.

PROBLEMS

8-1. The voltage gain of an amplifier is nominally -60 but varies $\pm 5\%$ from that value owing to changes in its power supplies. The addition of overall feedback with $B = 0.06$ will result in what nominal overall amplification? Determine the percentage variation in A_f.

8-2. If the response of an amplifier at low frequencies can be approximated by

$$A = \frac{A_o}{1 - jf_{3\,\mathrm{db}}/f}$$

with A_o the mid-frequency gain and $f_{3\,\mathrm{db}}$ the lower half-power frequency, derive an expression for f_f, the lower cutoff or half-power frequency for a feedback amplifier in terms of A_o, B, and $f_{3\,\mathrm{db}}$.

8-3. The feedback scheme shown in the above diagram has been labeled "current feedback" because the load current is being sampled. By making use of a method similar to that given in Section 8-1, derive an expression for A_{vf} in terms of A_v, R_f, and R_L. Consider $R_L \gg R_f$.

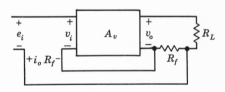

Problem 8-3.

8–4. Extend your analysis of Problem 8–3 to derive the expression for Z_{if} and Z_{of}.

8–5. Consult an information source such as Reference 7 to study phase-sensitive discriminators and draw three transistorized circuits of that type.

8–6. The network shown could be used in the feedback path of an amplifier.

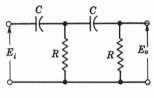

Problem 8–6.

(a) Derive an expression for the voltage transfer function (E_o/E_i).

(b) Is it possible for the network to provide a 180° phase shift? Explain.

(c) Derive an expression for the unloaded input impedance.

(d) Sketch the frequency response of this circuit.

8–7. Draw a feedback network that will result in increased amplifier voltage gain at high frequencies.

8–8. For a common-emitter connected transistor with $h_{ib} = 40$ ohms, $h_{rb} = 10^{-4}$, $h_{fb} = -0.972$ and $h_{ob} = 10^{-6}$ mho, make a plot of voltage gain *vs.* R_e for five values of feedback resistance from 0 to infinity.

8–9. For the transistor whose parameters are specified in Problem 8–8, show the variation in input resistance caused by emitter feedback.

8–10. For the transistor of Problem 8–8, plot current gain *vs.* R_c for five values from 0 to infinity.

8–11. Again using the transistor of Problem 8–8, show the variation of input resistance caused by collector-to-base feedback.

8–12. Amplifiers with open-loop voltage gains of 10,000, 5000, 700 and 300 have their gains reduced to 100 by feedback. Express the amount of feedback in db for each amplifier.

8–13. For a 2N43 feeding a 2000-ohm load and employing local feedback, determine the values of Y_c and R_e necessary to provide a $\Delta G/G$ ratio of 0.10 for units that tend to take on maximum parameters. Set $(h_{ob} + Y_c)R_L = 0.2$.

8–14. Compare the sensitivity of overall amplification to internal stage gain variations of a three-stage amplifier without feedback to a five-stage amplifier with overall feedback. Both circuits have the same overall gain, and are composed of identical individual stages.

8–15. In the absence of feedback, the input resistance of a three-stage transistor amplifier is 1000 ohms when the amplifier is feeding a 1000-ohm load. Each stage amplifies voltage 10 times and current 100 times. If feedback is to be added to this amplifier from the collector of stage number three to the base of stage one, of what value must the feedback resistance be in order to reduce the overall power gain by 50%? What has happened to the input resistance?

8–16. For a two-stage amplifier employing the type of feedback shown in

Fig. 8–9, compute the value of the required feedback resistor R_f for $A_{if} = 200$. $A_{i1} = A_{i2} = 20$, $A_{v1} = A_{v2} = 30$, $R_L = R_i = 1000$ ohms and $R_e = 100$ ohms. What is the overall voltage gain and input resistance?

8–17. Derive the equation for the output voltage of a common-emitter differential amplifier driven from sources of high internal resistance. The assumption that $(\beta + 1)R_x \gg R_s$ is not to be used.

8–18. Derive an expression for the output voltage of a common-emitter differential amplifier with d-c input signals. Include a leakage current generator with each transistor.

8–19. To study the input resistance of a common-emitter differential amplifier stage, consider that the other transistor base is returned to ground through R_g, and R_x is a very large-valued resistance. Confirm that

$$R_i \cong 2[r_b + r_e/(1 - \alpha)]$$

for the circuit of Fig. 8–23. Note that the second transistor appears as a common-base stage in the emitter branch of the transistor under study. How will the magnitude of R_g affect this expression?

8–20. By sketching show the effect of chopping upon a low-frequency alternating waveform, and consequently attempt to confirm the statement that a chopper amplifier will successfully pass frequencies up to a fraction of the frequency of the chopping action.

8–21. It is desired to analyze the circuit diagram and answer questions concerning it. Knowledge of the transistor material thus far presented in

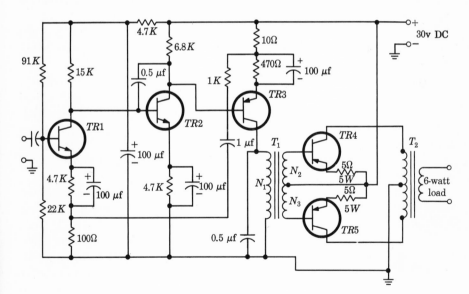

Problem 8–21.

the text plus a general electronic background (which is a prerequisite) and ability to extend these concepts to a new circuit is being tested.

(a) In what configuration is each transistor operating?

(b) Briefly discuss the methods of coupling employed between source, each transistor and load.

(c) In what mode (Class-A or B) is each transistor operating? Give a reason for your answers.

(d) Discuss the purpose of each of the following components.

    (1) 0.5 μf in $TR3$ collector

    (2) 5 ohms in $TR4$ and $TR5$ emitters

    (3) 10 ohms in $TR3$ emitter

    (4) 100 ohms in $TR1$

    (5) 4.7 K and 100 μf in $TR1$

(e) All the transistors are germanium. If $TR3$ has a quiescent collector current of 32 ma, calculate all direct potentials in the first three stages, and the collector currents of stages 1 and 2. Assume that the winding resistance of T_1 is negligible.

(f) Draw a complete small-signal low-frequency equivalent for the first two stages in terms of h-parameters with "e" subscripts. Include all pertinent R's and C's.

8–22. The two-stage feedback amplifier of Appendix III can be analyzed by the methods of this chapter. Consider that the transistor parameters are $h_{fe} = 30$, $h_{ib} = 53$, $h_{ob} = 0.2 \times 10^{-6}$ and $h_{rb} = 2 \times 10^{-4}$. Compare the published voltage gains of this amplifier with those calculated using Eq. (8–72). Consider all three values of feedback resistance and use $R_L = 10,000$ ohms.

8–23. Consider a current source I_o with parallel resistance R_o feeding R_L. Shunting the source and the load is a negative resistance device, $-R$. Show that this circuit may provide current amplification, and determine the condition for oscillation.

REFERENCES

1. Arguimbau, L. B., and Adler, R. B., *Vacuum-Tube Circuits and Transistors*, John Wiley & Sons, Inc., New York, 1956.
2. DeWitt, D., and Rossoff, A. L., *Transistor Electronics*, McGraw-Hill Book Company, Inc., New York, 1957.
3. Goldberg, E. A., "Stabilization of Wide-Band D-C Amplifier for Zero and Gain," *RCA Rev.*, vol. 11 (June, 1950).
4. Kiver, M. S., *Transistors in Radio and Television*, McGraw-Hill Book Company, Inc., New York, 1956.
5. Korn, G. A., and Korn, T. M., *Electronic Analog Computers*, McGraw-Hill Book Company, Inc., New York, 1956.

6. Lo, et al., *Transistor Electronics*, Prentice-Hall Inc., Englewood Cliffs, New Jersey, 1955.
7. Murphy, G. J., *Basic Automatic Control Theory*, D. Van Nostrand, Inc., Princeton, New Jersey, 1957.
8. Nyquist, H., "Regeneration Theory," *BSTJ*, vol. 11 (Jan., 1932).
9. Riddle, R. L., and Ristenbatt, M. P., *Transistor Physics and Circuits*, Prentice-Hall, Inc., Englewood Cliffs, New Jersey, 1958.
10. Ryder, J. D., *Electronic Fundamentals and Applications*, 2nd Ed., Prentice-Hall, Inc., Englewood Cliffs, New Jersey, 1959.
11. Seely, S., *Radio Electronics*, McGraw-Hill Book Company, Inc., New York, 1956.
12. Shea, R. F., *Transistor Circuit Engineering*, John Wiley & Sons, Inc., New York, 1957.

Chapter 9

COMMUNICATIONS AMPLIFIERS

The purpose of this chapter is twofold; first, to discuss several general topics heretofore unmentioned, and second, to take a look at the principles of transistor operation at high frequencies.

The preceding material was devoted to operation within the audio-frequency spectrum, but serves to provide general background for any transistor work. The subject of noise is presented here to extend that general background. The topics of gain control and shaping of the frequency response will also be briefly covered in the initial pages of this chapter.

Broad frequency band (video) amplifiers are important to television and radar applications for they serve to amplify a great deal of information in the form of the various frequencies, and consequently warrant our attention. The narrow-band or tuned amplifying stage has many uses in the radio, television, and military electronics fields and will also be discussed in this chapter.

9–1. Noise. Noise in electronic devices is any spurious signal, and is almost always unwanted. In radio and television receivers noise is apparent to the ear and the eye as "static" and "snow," respectively. Actually, noise has two general classifications: "external" noise caused by atmospheric disturbances, motor commutation, aircraft and auto ignition, and any sparking device; and "internal" noise generated in the receiver as a result of the physics of the materials and components used. External noise will not be discussed here because its existence bears no relation to the transistor; it can be eliminated or minimized by shielding, antenna location or design, and prayer.

Our concern with noise is at the load portion of a circuit, in the loudspeaker or cathode-ray tube or other terminating device, but the important sources of internal noise are in the low-signal portion of a circuit. The first stage of any receiver and the signal source are the areas that must be investigated to determine whether their operational sensitivity is too severely limited, for noise sets a limit on such sensitivity; any signal too weak when compared with the noise level will be covered up or masked by it. Often discussed is the output "signal-to-noise ratio" for any electronic circuit. This ratio, which is sometimes a specification to be met by the circuit designer, can be used as a performance yardstick. Typical S/N ratios, expressed in decibels, are in the 15 to 60 db range, and of course depend to a great extent upon the application.

Internal noise is generated in resistors, vacuum tubes, transistors, and, in fact, any conductor, and is due to many causes. It is said to be "random" in the sense that it is a completely unpredictable function of time, in contrast to normal electrical quantities whose future variations can be predicted from past performance or other information. A voltage such as $e = E_{max} \sin \omega t$ is obviously not random, for its past history is accurately known, and its future can be completely predicted. Random noise, on the other hand, contains terms of many frequencies with varying amplitudes.

It is possible by means of frequency analysis to classify noises. If the spectrum of frequencies in a wave is said to be "flat," then the wave contains equal magnitudes of all frequencies. Noise of this type is "white" noise or "thermal" noise; the latter name is derived from the fact that a familiar source of this type of noise is a function of temperature. Every electrical conductor, even if unconnected to a complete electrical circuit, generates noise by the random motions of current carriers; these motions are caused by thermal agitation. Thermally caused noise has been investigated and the rms magnitude of the voltage (E_n) is given by the *Nyquist relation*,

$$E_n{}^2 = 4kRT(BW) \tag{9-1}$$

where k = Boltzmann's constant = 1.38×10^{-23} watt-sec/per degree Kelvin
R = resistance of the conductor
T = temperature of the conductor in degrees Kelvin
(BW) = bandwidth of the measuring system in cps.

Eq. (9–1) provides us with a relationship for the thermal noise voltage across a given resistance. The value of noise voltage (and noise power) depends upon the bandwidth of the measuring device, for, since the spectrum is flat, a wider band contains more noise. When speaking of bandwidth in this application, the word technically refers to an ideal pass and rejection characteristic, although the frequency span between half-power points may be used as an approximation.

Eq. (9–1) informs us that to minimize thermal noise, the use of high-valued resistances must be limited. An additional noise source is found in carbon resistors because the passage of direct current forms minute arcs between carbon granules, resulting in high noise generation. This internal contact noise can be eliminated by the use of low-noise resistors in critical applications and should not be confused with thermal noise.

As an example of the amount of thermal noise generated, consider a one-megohm resistor at 20° C (293° K) and a four-megacycle bandwidth, as is used in television video amplifiers. From Eq. (9–1), we could expect 254 microvolts of thermal noise.

The transistor generates thermal noise primarily because of its base resistance. In any practical circuit the resistance of the signal source is a prime contributor of this type of noise. *Shot* noise, which has a uniform frequency spectrum, is also apparent and is due to the randomness of carrier diffusion from emitter to collector and subsequent collection, and of recombination, the meeting of electrons and holes and subsequent elimination of both as carriers. It is possible to specify an equivalent noise resistance for these sources of noise in the transistor. Information of this sort is not available from manufacturers and must be obtained by testing.

Another type of noise is present in transistors, the so-called *semiconductor* or $1/f$ noise. Noticeable particularly at low frequencies, the power density (watts per unit frequency) varies inversely with frequency and it is believed that this phenomenon arises from surface activity; it is dependent upon collector voltage, current and temperature.[2] Above a frequency of from several hundred to several thousand cycles per second, white noise predominates, below that range $1/f$ noise is important. The original transistor, the point-contact variety, was extremely noisy; $1/f$ noise predominated throughout the usable frequency spectrum.

Since with semiconductor noise, the noise power per unit frequency is inversely proportional to frequency, it is possible to dete·mine the noise content of a band by integration of $K_1 f^{-1}$ over the range of frequencies in which our interest lies. The resulting relationship is

$$\text{Noise power} = K_2 \ln \frac{f_h}{f_l} \qquad (9\text{–}2)$$

from which

$$E_n{}^2 = K \ln \frac{f_h}{f_l}. \qquad (9\text{–}3)$$

In the above equations, the K symbol always represents a constant term, f_h and f_l are the upper and lower frequency limits of the band being considered, and E_n is the rms value of noise voltage. The transistor manufacturer often specifies information to enable us to evaluate K in Eq. (9–3), and thus to calculate E_n due to $1/f$ noise.

The measure of the noise quality of an electronic device is the *noise figure;* it is customarily given for transistors that are to be employed in low-level circuits. Noise figure is defined in several ways, probably most widely accepted is "the ratio of total noise power at the load of the stage to the noise output power due to thermal noise in the source impedance." Noise figure is always expressed in decibels, is independent of load but is dependent upon source resistance. Commonly symbolized by F, noise figure can be expressed in terms of available S/N ratios as

$$F = \frac{S_i/N_i}{S_o/N_o}. \qquad (9\text{–}4a)$$

Subscripts i and o refer to input and output respectively. Since $S_o/S_i = G$, and available noise power, with matching, is $N_i = E_n{}^2/4R_g$, Eq. (9–4a) can be written as

$$F = \frac{N_o}{GkT(BW)}. \qquad (9\text{–}4b)$$

If no noise is added by the transistor, F equals unity, or zero db. A low value of noise figure is desirable.

Transistor manufacturers often specify a *spot noise figure*, F_o, which applies at a test frequency of 1000 cps, for a given source resistance (R_g) and a bandwidth of 1 cps. The 1000-cps frequency is taken to be within the $1/f$ noise region so this will be the predominant form of transistor noise. From the definition of noise figure, we may conclude that, in a region where $1/f$ noise predominates,

$$F = \frac{4kTR_g(BW) + K \ln (f_h/f_l)}{4kTR_g(BW)}. \qquad (9\text{–}5)$$

Eq. (9–5) approximates the ratio of total noise to source noise at the output.

Let us evaluate Eq. (9–5) when $(BW) = 1$ cps, $f_l = 1000$ cps and $f_h = 1001$ cps. The natural logarithm of f_h/f_l is 0.001. Then

$$F_o = 1 + \frac{K(0.001)}{4kTR_g} = 1 + \frac{6.25K(10^{16})}{R_g} \qquad \text{at } 20° \text{ C.} \qquad (9\text{–}6)$$

From this equation we may calculate K by knowing F_o and R_g, thus,

$$K = R_g(F_o - 1)(0.16 \times 10^{-16}). \qquad (9\text{–}7)$$

Substitution of this relationship into Eq. (9–5) and rearrangement gives

$$F = 1 + \frac{1000(F_o - 1) \ln (f_h/f_l)}{(BW)}. \qquad (9\text{–}8)$$

Eq. (9–8) enables us to find the noise figure for any bandwidth from the "1 cps (BW) at 1000 cps" figure provided that the source resistance encountered is of approximately the same magnitude as that used to determine F_o, and also provided that we are in the $1/f$ noise region.

Above the $1/f$ region, we must resort to measurements of noise. For a bandspread that encompasses both regions, measurement is also necessary. A common test for noise figure uses a *noise diode* operating in its temperature-limited emission mode; it is known to produce a noise current

$$I_n = \sqrt{3.2 \times 10^{-19} I_{\text{d-c}}(BW)} \qquad (9\text{–}9)$$

when the direct plate current ($I_{\text{d-c}}$) flows.[6] Noise voltage in R_g can be represented by

$$V_n = I_n R_g. \qquad (9\text{–}10)$$

The diode is connected as in Fig. 9–1 and a reading of amplifier output (V_o)

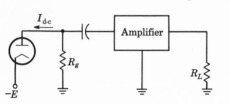

taken with noise diode current of zero. V_o is composed of amplified thermal noise from R_g, and transistor noise, but the amplification is not known. If the noise diode is then added to the system, and its direct current adjusted by filament voltage control until an amplifier output of twice the preceding power

Fig. 9–1. Noise diode test arrangement.

is attained, then

$$2\left(\frac{V_o^2}{R_L}\right) = \frac{(A_v V_n)^2}{R_L} + \frac{V_o^2}{R_L}. \qquad (9\text{–}11)$$

From Eq. (9–11) the unknown amplification can be obtained. Thus

$$A_v = \frac{V_o}{V_n}. \qquad (9\text{–}12)$$

From the definition, noise figure is the ratio of total output noise power (V_o^2/R_L) to noise power due to R_g as given by Eq. (9–1). This ratio is

$$F = \frac{V_o^2/R_L}{A_v^2 E_n^2/R_L} = \frac{V_n^2}{E_n^2}. \qquad (9\text{–}13)$$

Therefore, at room temperature,

$$F = \frac{3.2 \times 10^{-19} I_{\text{d-c}}(BW)R_g^2}{1.6 \times 10^{-20}(BW)R_g} = 20 I_{\text{d-c}} R_g. \qquad (9\text{–}14)$$

Noise figure can be determined from knowledge of the diode direct current and the source resistance after the measurements indicated above have been made.

The curve of Fig. 9–2, a plot of frequency versus noise factor, summarizes transistor noise. Semiconductor noise is responsible for a high value of F at frequencies below f_1, white noise predominates above f_1. Because noise figure can be defined as in Eq. (9–4b), a reduction in transistor gain and corresponding reduction in S_o/N_o causes an upswing of the curve at f_2. (There is no reduction in that portion of N_o due to the collector current.) Research is directed toward lowering f_1 and increasing f_2; for some transistor types f_1 is in the neighborhood of 100 cps, and advances in the design of high-frequency devices have made types available with f_2 equal to 150 mc.

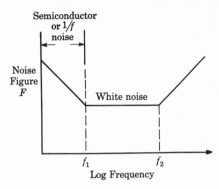

Fig. 9–2.   Noise output of a typical transistor.

Some additional thoughts concerning noise are appropriate: Terman and Pettit [17] have summarized noise testing; Lo [9] has concluded that the noisiness of a transistor is more or less independent of the configuration employed, whether common-base, common-emitter or common-collector; an extremely low noise figure is possible if collector voltage is very low or slightly negative according to Volkers and Pedersen; [21] and finally, it may be stated that noise figures of present-day low-noise transistors are comparable to those of vacuum tubes used for similar applications (2 to 4 db).

9–2. Volume Control.   It is often necessary to provide a manual means for setting or adjusting the gain of many types of circuits: audio amplifiers, servo amplifiers, radio and television receivers.   The placement of a variable resistance in a transistor circuit for this purpose is complicated by the absence of isolation between stages, and therefore the choice of a location for the control requires a great deal of study.   When deciding upon a location, attention must be paid to the following:

1. The volume control should usually provide for complete attenuation of the signal.
2. D-c biasing should not be upset by the adjustment of the control.
3. Overall frequency response should not suffer as a result of changed impedance levels.
4. The load on a stage should not be shifted by adjustment of the control because of distortion considerations.
5. If the control is located too near the circuit input, the S/N ratio may be adversely affected.
6. Location of the control too near the circuit output may allow overloading of prior stages.
7. Direct current through the control will contribute to circuit noise.
8. The taper specification for the potentiometer should not be unrealistic.

In nearly all installations, a compromise results, as circumvention of all the limitations posed by the items listed is impossible. Generally, the location of the control is near the circuit input, often items 3 and 4 cannot be completely satisfied, and consequently frequency response is dependent to some extent upon control setting.

Indiscriminate positioning of the volume control is liable to cause undesirable circuit operation; therefore, with the help of several illustrations, let us briefly investigate the problem. Consider the circuit of Fig. 9–3a. The

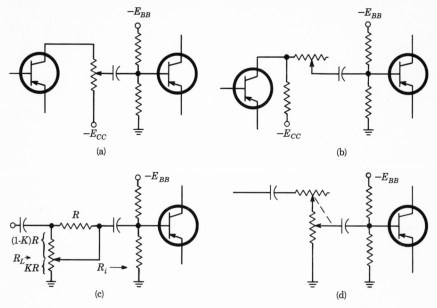

Fig. 9–3.   Volume control placement and arrangements.

volume-control setting will affect the a-c load line of the first stage and may or may not cause trouble. Circuit frequency response will change with setting and direct collector current in the potentiometer can result in noisy volume variation. The taper of the control must be tailored for the application. For the series control circuit of Fig. 9–3b, complete attenuation is not possible, however the control does not pass any d-c. The rheostat will be several hundred thousand ohms, but near its low end it may affect the load on stage number one. Frequency effects will be small.

In the circuit of Fig. 9–3c, consider all resistances including the control to be equal to the nominal input resistance of the following stage. Let us investigate the resistance (R_L) presented by this combination to the preceding stage. K designates the fraction of the variable control tuned in. The load is given by

$$R_L = \frac{R[(1 - K)R]}{R + (1 - K)R} + \frac{RKR}{R + KR}.$$

So

$$R_L = R \left[\frac{1 + 2K - 2K^2}{2 + K - K^2} \right]. \tag{9-15}$$

At each end of the setting, $R_L = 0.5R$, and at the center $R_L = 0.67R$. When we consider that this network will be paralleled by the collector resistor of the preceding stage, this variation in R_L is not too great for many applications.

An effective means of volume control is illustrated in Fig. 9–3d. This system makes use of two ganged potentiometers to maintain a constant load on the preceding stage. The taper of the pots can be chosen for the desired degree of constancy.

Many other arrangements are possible. In radio receivers, the control is almost always located at the output of the second detector (see Chapter 8). A feedback line oftentimes provides a convenient place for gain control; the amount of feedback is adjusted to determine overall amplifier gain.

9–3. Shaping of the Frequency Response. The designer of an audio amplifier is almost always required to provide frequency insensitive amplification throughout the audio range, usually considered as 20 to 20,000 cps. While oftentimes the cost of precision components alters this general specification, nevertheless the problem of adequate frequency response is always prevalent. For amplifiers used in control systems a flat response is generally required although the frequency range specification is narrower than for audio circuits.

In addition to the basic flat response requirement, the circuit designer usually must provide a network or series of networks for shaping the frequency response characteristic to equalize variations that may be due to other devices or circuits or requirements (such as the human ear). In audio amplifier circuits, it is desirable to provide for manual adjustment of the frequency response (such a circuit is generally termed a tone control). Placement of an adjustment of this type is a more complex problem in a transistor circuit than in a vacuum-tube circuit because the tone-control network is always loaded down by the input resistance of the transistor stage that follows.

One solution to the tone-control location problem is to incorporate a frequency selective network in a feedback loop. More often it will be

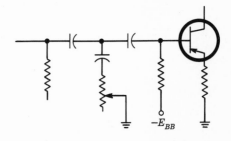

Fig. 9–4. Sample tone control circuit.

found preceding one of the early stages of a cascade amplifier. A satisfactory arrangement is shown in Fig. 9–4. A shunt circuit consisting of a capacitor and an adjustable resistance precedes a stage with emitter feedback. The input resistance of the transistor has been boosted to perhaps 25,000 to 50,000 ohms in order to minimize its loading effect upon the R-C leg. The operation of a circuit of this type may be analyzed by considering the signal current that reaches the transistor base at various frequencies. At low frequencies, the capacitor will present a large reactance to the signal, and so nearly all of the signal will reach the transistor base, but at high frequencies where the reactive effect of the capacitor is negligible, signal current will find an easier path to ground through the R-C network and thus a smaller proportion will reach the base. Such a circuit can be classified as "treble cut" because it serves to attenuate higher frequencies.

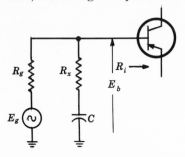

Fig. 9–5. Equalizing network.

Consider a transistor amplifier being fed from a signal source of voltage E_g and internal resistance R_g as shown in Fig. 9–5. It is our desire to investigate the transfer function E_b/E_g, which represents the ratio of voltage available at the base of the transistor (and consequently base current) to the transducer-voltage output. A solution of the circuit for the required transfer function yields

$$\frac{E_b}{E_g} = \frac{R_i(1 + j\omega C R_x)}{(R_g + R_i) + j\omega C(R_g R_x + R_g R_i + R_x R_i)}. \tag{9–16}$$

At very low frequencies (i.e., $\omega \to 0$)

$$\frac{E_b}{E_g} = \frac{R_i}{R_g + R_i}, \tag{9–17a}$$

and at very high frequencies (i.e., $\omega \to \infty$)

$$\frac{E_b}{E_g} = \frac{R_i R_x}{R_g R_x + R_g R_i + R_x R_i}. \tag{9–17b}$$

The denominator term of Eq. (9–16) will be frequency sensitive at lower values of ω than will the numerator; consequently the equation predicts an increasing attenuation throughout the frequency band from the first "break" that occurs at

$$\omega_{lo} = \frac{R_g + R_i}{C(R_g R_x + R_g R_i + R_x R_i)} \tag{9–18}$$

to the high-frequency "break" due to the numerator term that occurs at

$$\omega_{hi} = \frac{1}{CR_x}. \tag{9-19}$$

The frequency response of the transfer function E_b/E_g is plotted as Fig. 9–6.

A break frequency results when any term in an equation takes on the form $K \pm jK$. At frequencies below the break, the term is primarily real, above the break, the term is primarily imaginary. Analysis of frequency-variant expressions by means of break frequencies and straight-line diagrams is reserved for more advanced texts. The reader is referred to any book on feedback control systems for discussion of this method of analysis.

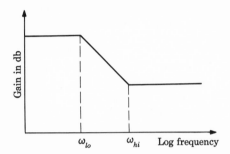

Fig. 9–6.   Performance of the network of Figure 9–5.

The range of adjustment afforded by variation in R_x can be seen from examination of the break-frequency expressions. If R_x approaches zero ohms, then ω_{lo} increases because the magnitude of the denominator of Eq. (9–18) has been reduced, and ω_{hi} is extended out to infinite frequency. An increase in R_x will have the opposite effects, the low-frequency break will occur at even lower frequencies and the high-frequency break will also occur at a lower ω.

Example.   It is desired to design a frequency selective network to precede the first stage of an audio amplifier; the input resistance of the transistor is 1000 ohms, and the source resistance is 1000 ohms. The network should attenuate frequencies above 1000 cps, and we are not interested in the range above 10,000 cycles.

We shall use the circuit of Fig. 9–5. The circuit elements to be determined are C and R_x. If we set $\omega_{lo} = 2\pi(1000)$ rad per sec and $\omega_{hi} = 2\pi(10,000)$ rad per sec, then R_x may be determined by noting that

$$\frac{\omega_{hi}}{\omega_{lo}} = \frac{2\pi(10,000)}{2\pi(1000)} = 10 = \frac{1/CR_x}{(R_g + R_i)/C(R_gR_x + R_gR_i + R_xR_i)}.$$

Therefore,

$$9R_x(R_g + R_i) = R_g R_i,$$

and

$$R_x = 55.6 \text{ ohms.}$$

Then we may determine C from the formula for ω_{hi}:

$$C = \frac{1}{\omega_{hi} R_x}$$

$$= \frac{1}{2\pi 10^4 (55.6)}$$

so

$$C = 0.286 \ \mu\text{f.}$$

It is interesting to note that the size of R_x is mainly dependent upon R_g and is fairly independent of the network load resistance R_i for small values of R_g. When driven from a current source, i.e., when R_g is large, R_x may take on higher values.

Equalization networks are useful in audio amplifiers to shape the frequency response in accordance with some predetermined specification. An example of a requirement of this type is furnished by the Record Industry Association of America (RIAA); phonograph records that have been cut according to their standards require, for flat frequency reproduction, an equalizing network within the amplifier whose operation should be as shown in Fig. 9–7. A net-

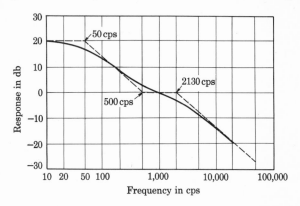

Fig. 9–7. RIAA playback (reproducing) characteristic.

work to achieve a response of this type will include a shunt leg consisting of R and C in series at the amplifier input.

In the field of automatic controls (servomechanisms, etc.) frequency-response shaping is commonplace, and numerous networks have been presented and analyzed by many authors.[5] The voltage-transfer function (ratio of output to input voltage) is usually given for such equalizing networks under the assumption of no loading of the network by the amplifier or circuit that follows. Because of the finite nature of transistor input resistance, transfer functions for unloaded networks must be modified when connected preceding a transistor. A common-collector or degenerative common-emitter stage is often employed to provide some degree of isolation.

9-4. High-Frequency Performance. Chapter 5 introduced the limitations on high-frequency performance imposed by the frequency dependence of alpha and the collector-junction capacitance, and it was concluded that in the upper audio range it is desirable to investigate these factors when calculating the expected performance of a transistor circuit. For bands above the audio, many small-signal equivalent circuits have been proposed; indeed, practically every manufacturer will present an equivalent circuit for his high-frequency types that most closely approximates the operation obtained from developmental units. Many of the specialized high-frequency equivalent circuits contain too many parameters to be useful for the calculation of circuit gains and impedance levels, and consequently the equivalent circuits serve principally to explain the limitations of the device. It is recommended that the circuit designer avail himself when possible of the manufacturer's equivalent circuit for the type or types he wishes to employ.

A mathematical treatment of the diffusion processes within the transistor has been given and will not be reproduced here. Such computations show that all transistor parameters are complex functions of frequency. In addition, so-called "parasitic" effects must be considered in order to arrive at a true equivalent circuit for high-frequency analysis. One such element is the "base-spreading resistance," for which we shall use the symbol $r_{bb'}$. (Although this parameter is often symbolized by $r_{b'}$, it should not be confused with the small-signal base resistance r_b of the current-generator equivalent tee network.) Base-spreading resistance is the electrical resistance of the base material and is proportional to the resistivity of the base material, and inversely proportional to the thickness of the base. It is not possible to reduce arbitrarily the resistivity of the base material, and consequently eliminate $r_{bb'}$, because collector capacitance, emitter efficiency, and junction breakdown would be adversely affected. Consequently a compromise must be made by the device designer. The emitter and collector materials also are resistive, but being more highly doped than the base material, their bulk resistances do not materially affect operation.

Other parasitic elements are barrier (transition or depletion-layer) capacitance, which shunts the collector-current generator of the transistor equivalent circuit; and leakage conductance, which parallels these elements. Interelectrode capacitances are also sometimes included in high-frequency studies.

The low-frequency current generator T-circuit is shown in Fig. 9-8a. The r_b parameter includes base-spreading resistance and additional (fictitious) resistance to provide for the known internal feedback within the device. To separate these two effects, the circuit of Fig. 9–8b has been devised, with collector circuit-emitter circuit feedback characterized by the behavior of the generator $\mu v_c'$. (μ is a new parameter introduced for this purpose.) This circuit bears a high degree of similarity to the hybrid equivalent described

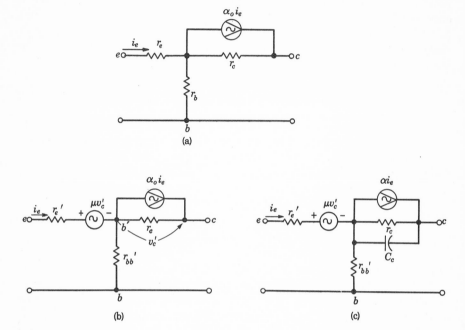

Fig. 9–8. T-circuits: (a) low-frequency equivalent; (b) modification of (a); (c) high-frequency equivalent.

previously, except that in Fig. 9–8b the base-spreading resistance is brought out from the internal base b' to the external base b. Actually $r_{bb'}$ is often 50 to 100 ohms; r_b is approximated by several hundred ohms.

Should high-frequency performance now be considered, the low-frequency current transfer ratio α_o must be altered to include the effects of frequency. Thus, from Eq. (5–18),

$$\alpha = \frac{\alpha_o}{1 + jf/f_{\alpha b}}. \qquad (9\text{–}20)$$

Collector-to-base barrier capacitance introduces a low reactance which parallels r_c. In most high-frequency studies, then, r_c is unimportant. The circuit of Fig. 9–8c includes collector-junction capacitance and α rather than α_o. This circuit is useful for high-frequency studies even with r_c and $\mu v_c'$ removed, for as the reactance of C_c decreases, the $\mu v_c'$ generator becomes of lesser importance, and the circuit is often approximated by only the r_e', $r_{bb'}$, C_c, and α parameters.

Under the condition that the transistor is matched to the circuit load, the common-emitter connected transistor T-circuit can be solved for its available power gain. Two conditions warrant study—when $r_{bb'}$ is constant and real and therefore independent of frequency, a condition approximated by the fused-junction variety, and the grown-junction behavior wherein base-spreading impedance is a complex quantity. Pritchard [12] has shown that for the former transistor type, available gain can be given by

$$G_{\mathrm{av}} \cong \frac{1}{25f^2}\left(\frac{f_{\alpha b}}{r_{bb'}C_c}\right) \tag{9–21}$$

for $0.05 - 0.1 < (f/f_{\alpha b}) < 2$

while for a grown transistor

$$G_{\mathrm{av}} \cong \frac{1}{10\pi f^{3/2}}\left[\frac{f_{\alpha b}^{1/2}}{(r_{bb'}r_e')^{1/2}C_c}\right] \tag{9–22}$$

for $0.05 - 0.1 < (f/f_{\alpha b}) < 2$ and $[r_{bb'}(f/f_{\alpha b})r_e']^{1/2} > 1$

r_e' is the Schockley, *et al.*, emitter resistance, and is equal to kT/eI_E. Van der Ziel [20] describes the above equations and concludes that the common-base operation for fused-junction units depends upon the same parameters. Hence it is not only necessary for a transistor to be characterized by a high alpha cutoff frequency, it must also exhibit a low $r_{bb'}C_c$ product for good performance in the radio-frequency spectrum. The 2N344, for example, has an $r_{bb'}C_c$ product of 1200 $\mu\mu$secs.

From an examination of Fig. 9–8c it can be concluded that $r_{bb'}$ will provide an unwanted feedback of output signal into the input circuit; this feedback will increase with frequency because the reactance of C_c decreases, and the net result is a deterioration in the gain magnitude, and a reduction in output impedance. $r_{bb'}$ effectively lowers the Q of the capacitive output impedance, requiring a low Q load for matching, and, as a consequence, power gain is severely limited at high frequencies.

The transit time for carrier diffusion through the base of a transistor can be specified in terms of the alpha cutoff frequency, and in the circuit of Fig. 9–8c the collector current gen-

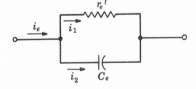

Fig. 9–9. Current division in a parallel R-C circuit.

erator is designated as αi_e. Either α or i_e can be thought of as frequency sensitive. Suppose that i_e were dependent upon frequency effects, for in reality the reduction in alpha is the result of the injected charge concentration in the base region varying with distance from the emitter junction, and it can be shown that this effect can be described by a capacitance which shall be called the emitter-diffusion capacitance.

If, to describe this effect, the transistor's emitter branch were to be of the form of Fig. 9–9, then, by current-division principles, the current through r_e' is

$$i_1 = i_e \frac{1/j\omega C_e}{r_e' + 1/j\omega C_e} = \frac{i_e}{1 + j\omega C_e r_e'} \tag{9-23}$$

Now the equivalent-circuit current generator could become

$$\alpha_0 i_1 = \frac{\alpha_0 i_e}{1 + j\omega C_e r_e'} = \frac{\alpha_0 i_e}{1 + j\omega/\omega_{\alpha b}}, \tag{9-24}$$

provided that

$$C_e r_e' = \frac{1}{\omega_{\alpha b}}.$$

Therefore emitter-diffusion capacitance is

$$C_e = \frac{1}{r_e' \omega_{\alpha b}}. \tag{9-25}$$

The high-frequency equivalent circuit of Fig. 9–10 includes emitter-diffusion capacitance, collector-barrier capacitance, and base-spreading resistance, and is generally satisfactory for describing the transistor in the common-base orientation at the higher frequencies. For common-emitter circuit studies the hybrid-π circuit of Fig. 9–11 has gained a substantial amount of accept-

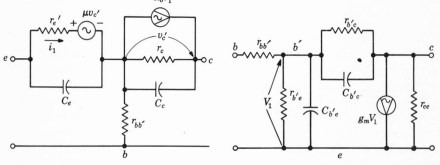

Fig. 9–10. Another form of the high-frequency T-circuit.

Fig. 9–11. The complete hybrid-π equivalent circuit.

ance, for it lends itself easily to the *entire* usable frequency spectrum, and contains a single generator.

The hybrid-π also has an external base terminal b, an intrinsic or true base b', and base-spreading resistance $r_{bb'}$ joining those points. Resistances $r_{b'e}$, $r_{b'c}$, and r_{ce}, and current generator $g_m v_{b'e}$ constitute the low-frequency parameters, with capacitances $C_{b'e}$ and $C_{b'c}$ of importance at higher frequencies. g_m is a conductance with ohms^{-1} its unit, but because a conductance may be thought of as the ratio of current to voltage, it is usually given in ma/volt and has been termed "intrinsic transconductance."

The conversion from the common-base T of Fig. 9–10 to the common-emitter hybrid-π circuit can be made with the following approximate results:

$$
\left.
\begin{aligned}
r_{b'e} &= \frac{r_e{}'}{1 - \alpha_o}, & g_m &= \frac{\alpha_o}{r_e{}'}; \\[2ex]
r_{b'c} &= \frac{r_c r_e{}'}{r_e{}' + \mu(1 - \alpha_o) r_c}, & C_{b'c} &= C_c, \\[2ex]
r_{ce} &= \frac{r_e{}'}{\mu}. & C_{b'e} &= C_e = \frac{1}{r_e{}' \omega_{\alpha b}}.
\end{aligned}
\right\}
\qquad (9\text{--}26)
$$

Notice that none of the hybrid parameters depend upon f. In an eloquent treatment, Middlebrook [10] has shown that all of the parameters of the hybrid-π are frequency sensitive, but some to a very slight degree. His admittance relationships, slightly modified, are

$$
\left.
\begin{aligned}
y_{b'e} &= K_1(1 - \alpha_o + j1.19 f/f_{\alpha b}), \\
y_{b'c} &= K_2(1 - \alpha_o + j1.19 f/f_{\alpha b}) + j\omega C_c, \\
y_{ce} &= K_3(1 - j0.214 f/f_{\alpha b}), \\
g_m &= K_4(1 - j0.214 f/f_{\alpha b}).
\end{aligned}
\right\}
\qquad (9\text{--}27)
$$

Eqs. (9–27) show that even to the alpha cutoff frequency the collector-to-emitter parameters are not seriously disturbed by frequency, but from base to emitter, as has been the case, emitter-diffusion capacitance can be employed to explain frequency effects. For the internal feedback path from base to collector, resistance and two parallel capacitances are obvious; one is the normal collector-base barrier capacitance, the other, a much smaller diffusion capacitance, can be neglected in many engineering studies.

Because the hybrid-π needs five low-frequency parameters, while only four are used in the T-circuit and the matrix h-circuit, it is necessary to know an additional parameter for the latter two networks in order to convert to the hybrid-π. This extra parameter is the base-spreading resistance. Using the normal tools of circuit theory, the relations may be derived; Table 9–1 lists some of the possible equalities.

TABLE 9–1. APPROXIMATE RELATIONS AMONG PARAMETERS

$$r_{b'e} = h_{ie} - r_{bb'}$$

$$r_{b'c} = \frac{h_{ie} - r_{bb'}}{h_{re}}$$

$$g_m = \frac{h_{fe}}{h_{ie} - r_{bb'}}$$

$$\frac{1}{r_{ce}} = h_{oe} - \frac{(1 + h_{fe})h_{re}}{h_{ie} - r_{bb'}}$$

$$\alpha = \frac{g_m r_{b'e}}{1 + g_m r_{b'e}}$$

$$r_b = r_{bb'} + \frac{r_{b'e}}{1 + (r_{ce}/r_{b'c})(1 + g_m r_{b'e})}$$

$$\frac{1}{r_c} = \frac{1}{r_{b'c}} + \frac{1}{r_{ce}(1 + g_m r_{b'e})}$$

$$r_e = \frac{r_{b'e}}{(1 + g_m r_{b'e}) + r_{b'c}/r_{ce}}$$

A "Miller effect" is evident in the transistor because of the similarity between the "boxed" portion of Fig. 9–12 and the standard representation

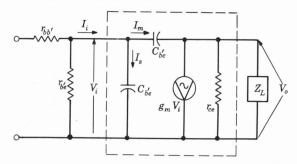

Fig. 9–12. Hybrid-π circuit analyzed for input capacitance. $r_{b'c}$ has been omitted from the diagram.

for a triode-tube equivalent circuit including interelemental capacities. The Miller effect is essentially a large input capacitance due to the mutual element, $C_{b'c}$ in this circuit. An investigation of I_i is enlightening:

$$I_i = I_m + I_s. \tag{9-28}$$

Now

$$I_s = j\omega C_{b'e} V_i, \tag{9-29}$$

and

$$I_m = -j\omega C_{b'c}(V_o - V_i). \tag{9-30}$$

Z_L is generally a small impedance compared with the other parallel paths. Consequently,

$$V_o = -g_m V_i Z_L. \tag{9-31}$$

A combination of the foregoing equations yields

$$\frac{I_i}{V_i} = Y_i = j\omega[C_{b'e} + C_{b'c}(1 + g_m Z_L)].$$ (9–32)

Notice that $C_{b'c}$ has effectively been multiplied by a term $(1 + g_m Z_L)$ considerably greater than unity. This, then, is the "Miller effect"; the total input capacitance is much greater than $C_{b'e}$. Typical parameter values will be given in an example to follow.

Should the load impedance, Z_L, be inductive it is easy to prove that Y_i will have a negative real part; a negative resistance physically means that power is being fed back from the output circuit through $C_{b'c}$, and under certain conditions oscillation may occur. Neutralization, discussed later, can be used to minimize this internal feedback.

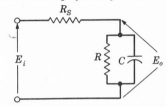

Use of the hybrid-π circuit to predict the frequency response of a transistor circuit is quick, convenient and fairly accurate. For a circuit

Fig. 9–13. R-C network simulates the input to a transistor stage.

of the form shown in Fig. 9–13, by voltage-division principles,

$$E_o = \frac{RE_i}{R + R_S + j\omega CRR_S}.$$ (9–33)

Now the voltage ratio will reduce to 0.707 of its reference value when the denominator is in the $K + jK$ form, or when

$$f_f = \frac{R + R_S}{2\pi CRR_S}.$$ (9–34)

We shall designate f_f as the upper-cutoff frequency, the frequency where the circuit-voltage gain is 3-db down from its reference value. Eq. (9–34) applies to the transistor, for the input circuit of the transistor may be approximated by the circuit of Fig. 9–13, with source resistance R_S (includes $r_{bb'}$), input resistance R of about $r_{b'e}$, and input capacitance C consisting of $C_{b'e}$ and Miller effect $C_{b'c}$ as given by Eq. (9–32).

A numerical example is in order. It is desired to find the upper-cutoff frequency for a stage coupling a 500-ohm source to a 1000-ohm load. Assume the transistor parameters to be:

$$f_{\alpha b} = 6 \text{ mc}, \qquad\qquad r_e' = 25 \text{ ohms},$$

$$\alpha_o = 0.98, \qquad\qquad r_b = 100 \text{ ohms},$$

$$C_c = 10 \ \mu\mu\text{f}, \qquad\qquad r_c = 2 \times 10^6 \text{ ohms}.$$

Calculation of hybrid-π parameters yields

$$g_m = \frac{\alpha_o}{r_e{}'} = 39 \text{ ma/volt,}$$

$$r_{b'e} = \frac{r_e{}'}{1 - \alpha_o} = 1250 \text{ ohms,}$$

$$C_{b'e} = \frac{1}{r_e'\omega_{\alpha b}} = 1060 \ \mu\mu\text{f,}$$

$$C_{in} = C_{b'e} + C_c(1 + g_m Z_L) = 1460 \ \mu\mu\text{f.}$$

The upper-cutoff frequency, as given by Eq. (9–34), is 300,000 cps. A lower load resistance will reduce C_{in} and raise the cutoff frequency. Also a smaller source resistance will allow operation to higher frequencies. Included with R_S is $r_{bb'}$, and therefore the limiting effect of that parameter is evident.

9–5. The Video Amplifier. A video-frequency or broadband amplifier is one capable of providing uniform amplification throughout a wide frequency range, often the required range is from 30 or 60 cps to about four megacycles. Sometimes the bandwidth requirement is different from the numbers cited, as they refer to applications in the television field, but in general a video amplifier must exhibit a flat response out to several megacycles.

To achieve a flat response, compensating networks are incorporated to couple stages and to provide a boost in amplification at the high-frequency end of the video spectrum where alpha deterioration and shunt capacitances have maximum effect. Transformer coupling is not used, because of its inherent narrow bandwidth; R-C coupling with associated peaking networks has become standard.

As discussed in the material of Chapter 5, a falloff in amplification is apparent at low frequencies in a transistor circuit because of the high reactances of coupling or blocking capacitors. At high frequencies, transistor capacitances, wiring capacitance, and reduction in alpha are to be contended with. The shunt capacitances will cause a minimum of difficulty if low input impedance connections (such as the common-base or common-emitter) are employed; however, the rapid reduction in α and β with frequency can cause a great deal of gain reduction.

For circuits employing the common-emitter connection, voltage amplification is satisfactory well beyond $f_{\alpha e}$; nevertheless, unless transistors with very high alpha cutoff frequencies can be afforded, it is necessary to provide some sort of compensation to extend the usable range.

Let us first discuss extension of flat response to low frequencies. Transistors themselves present no problems because parameters are real and constant. Direct-coupled video amplifier stages are possible, and will add no low-frequency operational restrictions, but the problem of drift with direct coupling has, in the past, caused most designers to choose capacitive coupling. The capacitor to be used must be of high value because impedance levels are low; since biasing potentials are also low (as compared with tube circuits) the physical size of large coupling capacitors is not objectional for most applications.

It is often desirable to employ a low-frequency compensating network for the purpose of extending flat response. Such a circuit appears in Fig. 9–14. At low frequencies current leaving the collector of the first transistor sees $R_1 - jX_{c2}$ in parallel with $R_i - jX_c$, and at higher frequencies the effective stage load is R_1 paralleled by R_i. It is desired that the current through R_i be independent of frequency at low frequencies, a condition that can be achieved if

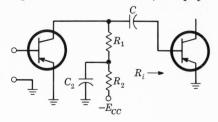

Fig. 9–14. Low-frequency compensating network coupling video amplifier stages.

$$\frac{R_1}{R_i} = \frac{C}{C_2}.$$
(9–35)

R_2 must be a great deal larger than X_{c2} for Eq. (9–35) to be valid. Proof of this criterion is left to the reader (Problem 9–9).

Should a practical size of R_2 cause unsatisfactory performance, improvement may be noted if a resistor in series with a very large capacitor is inserted to shunt C. This shunting resistor across C should match R_2 across C_2.

Turning our attention to high-frequency performance, it is usually desired to flatten the amplifier gain versus frequency curve to several megacycles. Here the problem is to compensate the transistor for its high-frequency limitations; this compensation is achieved in the interstage coupling network or in a transistor emitter leg where signal feedback is affected. The preceding chapter considered bandwidth versus feedback—bandwidth may be extended by using feedback, whether it be local or multistage.

For a common-emitter stage, current gain is given approximately by

$$A_i \cong \beta_o = \frac{\alpha_o}{1 - \alpha_o}.$$
(9–36)

The high-frequency current cutoff frequency is

$$f_h \cong f_{\alpha e} = (1 - \alpha_o)f_{\alpha b}.$$
(9–37)

It may be concluded that the potential gain-bandwidth product is

$$A_i f_h \cong \alpha_o f_{\alpha b}.$$
(9–38)

For a common-base stage, the same product is applicable. By addition of degenerative feedback, gain is reduced but bandwidth is increased, and, it is possible to trade gain for bandwidth when using the common-emitter connection.

One means of extending frequency response is to incorporate a frequency-sensitive collector-circuit network that steals a considerable current from the actual circuit load when low-frequency signals are present and transistor amplification is high, but drains little or no current away from the actual circuit load at high frequencies. Such a circuit is the R-L shunt of Fig. 9–15. The shunt inductance is a low reactance at low frequencies, and the transistor collector sees R_c paralleling Z_i. The high reactance of L_c at high frequencies results in an a-c circuit load which is essentially Z_i. Extension of response to higher frequencies may be achieved by adding a series "peaking" coil (in series with the coupling capacitor, C).

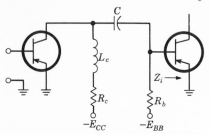

Fig. 9–15. Shunt peaking circuit for wide-band amplification.

Synthesis of video amplifiers generally proceeds experimentally because of the many complex quantities that are present, and some parameters change value with frequency. Shunt capacitances and reactive loads tend to make mathematical analysis difficult; such studies are undertaken in the more advanced texts.[15]

Video amplifiers often feed a high-impedance load, such as a cathode-ray tube, and consequently the final video stage is required to provide a large degree of voltage amplification. Capacitances represent a problem with high-impedance levels; another problem encountered is the required peak-to-peak voltage swing, and thus a high-frequency, high-voltage power transistor is required. A low-voltage CRT is available.

Some additional video amplifier considerations are evident in the circuit described in Appendix III. The reader is also referred to Sec. 11–2 of the text.

9–6. Tuned Circuit Theory. Before discussing the tuned amplifier a review of the applicable portion of circuit theory will be undertaken.

Impedance Transformations. First let us investigate the mathematical transformation of series and parallel impedances. Consider the series R-L and the parallel R-L circuits of Fig. 9–16. The impedance of the series circuit is

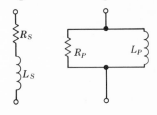

Fig. 9–16. Series and parallel R-L circuits.

$$Z_S = R_S + jX_{LS}, \tag{9-39}$$

and of the parallel circuit is

$$Z_P = \frac{jX_{LP}R_P}{R_P + jX_{LP}}. \tag{9-40}$$

The S and P subscripts pertain to series and parallel circuits respectively. If we wish to equate the two impedances, then

$$R_S + jX_{LS} = \frac{jX_{LP}R_P}{R_P + jX_{LP}}. \tag{9-41}$$

Multiplication of both numerator and denominator of the righthand side by the conjugate of the denominator, and separation of real and imaginary terms, gives

$$R_S + jX_{LS} = \frac{X_{LP}{}^2 R_P}{R_P{}^2 + X_{LP}{}^2} + \frac{jX_{LP}R_P{}^2}{R_P{}^2 + X_{LP}{}^2}. \tag{9-42}$$

To find the series resistance equivalent to the resistance of the parallel circuit, equate reals, thus

$$R_S = \frac{X_{LP}{}^2 R_P}{R_P{}^2 + X_{LP}{}^2}, \tag{9-43}$$

and the series inductive reactance that can take the place of the parallel circuit reactance is

$$X_{LS} = \frac{X_{LP}R_P{}^2}{R_P{}^2 + X_{LP}{}^2}. \tag{9-44}$$

If the admittances of each type of circuit are equated,

$$R_P = \frac{R_S{}^2 + X_{LS}{}^2}{R_S}, \tag{9-45}$$

and

$$X_{LP} = \frac{R_S{}^2 + X_{LS}{}^2}{X_{LS}}. \tag{9-46}$$

Eqs. (9–43), (9–44), (9–45), and (9–46) provide the tools for conversion from one circuit form to the other. These relationships can be employed when the circuits contain R and C rather than R and L. For this use it is only necessary to replace each X_L in Eqs. (9–43) through (9–46) by X_C.

Let us now define the Q or figure of merit of the series circuit previously considered as the ratio of inductive reactance to resistance

$$Q = \frac{X_{LS}}{R_S}, \tag{9-47}$$

at any designated frequency. The series definition of Q may be used for a parallel circuit by making use of the proved interrelations, Eqs. (9–43) and (9–44). The division indicated in Eq. (9–47) yields

$$Q = \frac{R_P}{X_{LP}}. \tag{9–48}$$

By equating admittances of the two circuits, the following relationships can be proved:

$$R_P = R_S(1 + Q^2) \tag{9–49}$$

and

$$X_{LP} = X_{LS}(1 + 1/Q^2). \tag{9–50}$$

A single inductance coil is, in reality, a series R-L circuit. Therefore such a coil is often described by its own Q, the ratio of its series reactance to resistance at a specific frequency. The discussion of the preceding paragraphs pertains to complete circuits or to single coils; in the material that follows, Q_C will be used to designate the quality factor of a single coil while the symbol Q will be reserved for use as a measure of overall circuit selectivity.

The circuit consisting of a parallel combination of capacitance and a practical inductance coil shown in Fig. 9–17a can now be replaced mathematically by the parallel R-L-C circuit of Fig. 9–17b; the value of R being given by Eq. (9–49). As an example consider a coil with a Q_C of 100 and R_S of 10 ohms. Equations (9–49) and (9–50) enable us to substitute parallel resistance of 10^5 ohms and inductive reactance of 1000 ohms (essentially the same as the series reactance because of the high quality of the coil).

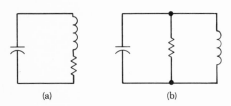

(a)   (b)

Fig. 9–17. Tuned circuit equivalence.

We have, therefore, an undamped or coil quality factor Q_C, and a circuit quality factor Q, the latter being defined by Eq. (9–48) as the ratio of parallel resistance to inductive reactance at the specified or resonant frequency. In the preceding numerical example Q and Q_C were identical, for no additional circuit resistance or inductance was present. Often, in practice, such tuned circuits will be "damped" by parallel resistance and a distinct difference will be observed between Q_C and Q.

Example. The coil with $Q_C = 100$ at 100 kc and $R_S = 10$ ohms is to be used in a tuned circuit to resonate at 100 kc, and the overall circuit shall exhibit a working Q of 20. Find the necessary parallel capacitance to resonate the entire circuit at the specified frequency, the circuit impedance at resonance, and the value of the additional parallel damping resistance necessary to provide the required Q.

At 100 kc, if $X_{CP} = X_{LP}$, the circuit will exhibit its maximum driving point impedance, total current and voltage will be in phase and resonance achieved. Therefore

$$\frac{1}{\omega C} = 1000.$$

The required value of shunt capacitance is

$$C = \frac{1}{2\pi(10^5)1000} = 0.0016 \ \mu f.$$

Q is the ratio of total parallel resistance to X_{LP}, and is given by

$$Q = 20 = \frac{R_a 10^5/(R_a + 10^5)}{1000},$$

so

$$R_a = 25,000 \text{ ohms.}$$

R_a must be inserted in parallel with the coil to achieve the proper degree of damping. The impedance of the composite circuit at the resonant frequency is

$$\frac{R_a 10^5}{R_a + 10^5} = 20,000 \text{ ohms.}$$

Insertion Loss. The analysis of the tuned circuit will now be extended to the more complete and practical configuration of circuit elements shown in Fig. 9–18. R_o is being used to represent the output resistance of a transistor stage, R_L is the terminating or load resistance, R_P is coil resistance, C is the total parallel capacitance and L_P the parallel inductance. The current generator I_o is feeding the circuit at the resonant frequency.

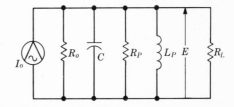

Fig. 9–18. General interstage circuit.

To find the insertion loss due to the finite Q_C of the coil in the circuit with an overall quality of Q we can compare the load power delivered under ideal and actual conditions.

Power to the load with an ideal coil $(R_P = \infty)$ is

$$P_L(\text{ideal}) = \frac{E^2}{R_L} = \frac{I_o{}^2 R^2}{R_L} \tag{9–51}$$

where R is the parallel combination of R_O and R_L and

$$\frac{1}{R} = G_O + G_L.$$

Power to the load with actual or practical coil having equivalent parallel resistance R_P is given by

$$P_L(\text{actual}) = \frac{E^2}{R_L} = \frac{I_o^2 R'^2}{R_L} \qquad (9\text{-}52)$$

with

$$\frac{1}{R'} = G_O + G_L + G_P.$$

The ratio of delivered powers is

$$\frac{P_L(\text{actual})}{P_L(\text{ideal})} = \frac{I_o^2 R'^2/R_L}{I_o^2 R^2/R_L} = \frac{R'^2}{R^2} = \left(\frac{G_O + G_L}{G_O + G_P + G_L}\right)^2. \qquad (9\text{-}53)$$

Circuit Q is

$$Q = \frac{R'}{X_P} = \frac{1}{(G_O + G_P + G_L)X_P}. \qquad (9\text{-}54)$$

After making the substitution that $X_P = R_P/Q_C$ we solve Eq. (9–54) for $G_O + G_L$

$$G_O + G_L = \frac{Q_C - Q}{QR_P}. \qquad (9\text{-}55)$$

Manipulation of Eqs. (9–54) and (9–55) yields

$$\left(\frac{G_O + G_L}{G_O + G_P + G_L}\right)^2 = \left(\frac{(Q_C - Q)/QR_P}{Q_C/QR_P}\right)^2. \qquad (9\text{-}56)$$

Therefore the required ratio is given by

$$\frac{P_L(\text{actual})}{P_L(\text{ideal})} = \left(\frac{Q_C - Q}{Q_C}\right)^2, \qquad (9\text{-}57\text{a})$$

and

$$\text{Insertion Loss (in db)} = 20 \log \frac{Q_C}{Q_C - Q}. \qquad (9\text{-}57\text{b})$$

Bandwidth. Bandwidth was defined in a preceding chapter as the frequency span between half-power points, and, of course, half-power points are the frequencies where power gain or power transmission has decreased to one half of its mid-frequency or reference value. The half-power points correspond to a reduction in voltage or current ratio to 0.707 or $1/\sqrt{2}$ of the reference value.

At this stage it is desired to find a relation between bandwidth, resonant frequency, and overall quality factor. The circuit of Fig. 9–19 uses single R, L and C elements to represent the composite of output, coupling, and load quantities. From a summation of currents,

$$I_o = \frac{E}{R} + Ej\omega C + \frac{E}{j\omega L},\qquad (9\text{--}58)$$

so

$$\frac{E}{I_o} = \frac{j\omega LR}{R(1 - \omega^2 LC) + j\omega L}.\qquad (9\text{--}59)$$

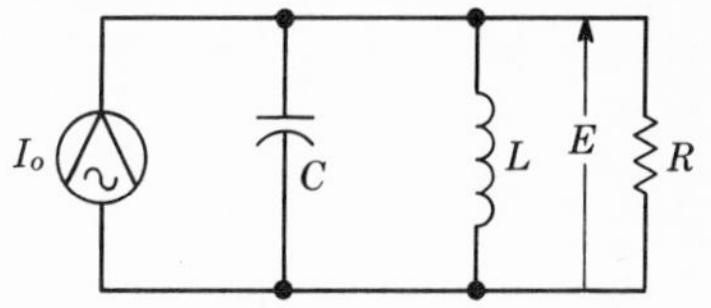

Fig. 9–19. Composite interstage circuit.

Load current is proportional to E, although the load resistance was not segregated in Fig. 9–19, and at resonance $E/I_o = R$. Therefore, to examine Eq. (9–59) at the half-power points where ω is designated as ω_3, we may write

$$\left|\frac{E}{I_o}\right| = \frac{R}{\sqrt{2}} = \frac{\omega_3 LR}{\sqrt{R^2(1 - \omega_3{}^2 LC)^2 + \omega_3{}^2 L^2}}.\qquad (9\text{--}60)$$

After making the substitutions that

$$Q = \frac{R}{\omega_r L_P} \quad \text{and} \quad \omega_r = \frac{1}{\sqrt{L_P C}}\qquad (9\text{--}61)$$

and rearrangement, Eq. (9–60) may be written as

$$\omega_3{}^4(Q^2/\omega_r{}^2) - \omega_3{}^2(1 + 2Q^2) + Q^2\omega_r{}^2 = 0.\qquad (9\text{--}62)$$

The solution for ω_3, if negative frequencies are omitted, is

$$\omega_3 = \sqrt{\frac{1 + 2Q^2 \pm \sqrt{1 + 4Q^2}}{2Q^2/\omega_r{}^2}}.\qquad (9\text{--}63)$$

Now bandwidth is defined by

$$(BW) = f_h - f_l = \frac{\omega_{3h} - \omega_{3l}}{2\pi}.\qquad (9\text{--}64)$$

Substitute Eq. (9–63) in Eq. (9–64) and square to eliminate the radicals. Finally take the square root of each side of the resulting equation to obtain

$$(BW) = \frac{f_r}{Q},\qquad (9\text{--}65)$$

the required relationship.

The relations involving (BW), Q, Q_C, R_o, R_L, R_P, R and ω_r can be juggled to arrive at a number of useful formulas; several such rearrangements will now be presented. From

$$(BW) = \frac{f_r}{Q}, \quad f_r = \frac{1}{2\pi\sqrt{L_P C}} \quad \text{and} \quad Q = \frac{R}{\omega_r L_P} \tag{9-66}$$

solution for C gives

$$C = \frac{1}{\omega_r^2 L_P}. \tag{9-67}$$

Eq. (9-67) can be written as

$$C = \frac{Q}{\omega_r R} \tag{9-68}$$

or as

$$C = \frac{1}{2\pi(BW)R}. \tag{9-69}$$

Recall that

$$Q_C = \frac{R_P}{\omega_r L_P} \quad \text{or} \quad R_P = \omega_r L_P Q_C \tag{9-70}$$

and that

$$Q = \frac{R}{\omega_r L_P}, \tag{9-71}$$

and furthermore that

$$\frac{1}{R} = \frac{1}{R_o} + \frac{1}{R_L} + \frac{1}{\omega_r L_P Q_C}, \tag{9-72}$$

to arrive at

$$Q = \frac{1}{\omega_r L_P \left(\dfrac{1}{R_o} + \dfrac{1}{R_L} + \dfrac{1}{\omega_r L_P Q_C} \right)}. \tag{9-73}$$

L_P may be obtained from Eq. (9-73). Thus

$$L_P = \frac{R_o R_L (Q_C - Q)}{\omega_r (R_L + R_o) Q Q_C}. \tag{9-74}$$

Under matched conditions, $R_o = R_L$ and Eq. (9-74) becomes

$$L_P = \frac{R_o (Q_C - Q)}{2\omega_r Q Q_C}. \tag{9-75}$$

9-7. Tuned Amplifiers. When an active circuit is required to amplify a specific band of frequencies and reject signals of higher or lower frequencies it is commonly referred to as a *tuned* or *narrow-band* amplifier. The word tuned, in this instance, refers to the circuit load that is normally a parallel L-C circuit designed to resonate at the carrier frequency (the middle frequency of the band to be passed). Although amplifiers of this type are referred to as narrow-band circuits, the bandwidth that is successfully passed may be many kilocycles or megacycles. Tuned circuits pass a band that is narrow when compared with the magnitude of the carrier frequency.

In communications receiver circuits, composite radio frequency signals are picked up by the antenna and fed to the *radio-frequency* (R.F.) amplifying stage; a circuit of this type is shown in Fig. 9–20. The antenna transformer is tuned to select the carrier frequency of the station to be received, and the load on the stage is also a tuned circuit. For the AM broadcast band, the R.F. stage is required to amplify signals from 550 to 1600 kc; a comparable

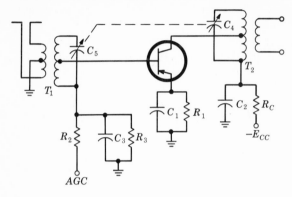

Fig. 9–20. Typical R.F. amplifying stage.

FM circuit covers 88 to 108 mc. For television reception, the R.F. amplifier must be capable of providing gain for signals of 54 to 88 mc, and 174 to 216 mc. The u.h.f. band is from 470 to 890 mc.

R.F. stages are not employed in all equipments, because of cost and design problems. When used their functions are:

1. To provide signal amplification where the signal is at its lowest level with the consequent advantage of increased receiver *sensitivity* (ability to receive weak signals).

2. To provide additional discrimination against signals in adjacent bands (*selectivity*) and improved image frequency rejection.

3. To reduce oscillator reradiation.

A lower gain is to be expected from an R.F. amplifier than can be obtained from other receiver stages because of the high frequencies it is called upon to handle. All present-day transistors provide greater gain at lower frequencies. Because of the low signal levels at this point in a receiver, noise is an important factor.

The *intermediate frequency* (I.F.) amplifier gets its name from the carrier frequency it must amplify, an intermediate value between the high or R.F.

and the low or audio spectrums. An I.F. stage always feeds a tuned load; high gain and the desired bandpass are thus obtained. In radio broadcast band receivers the generally accepted intermediate frequency is 455 kc, for TV, radar, FM and other bands a higher I.F. is necessary. The factors involved in selecting an I.F. are covered in books specifically devoted to communications.

As with R.F. stages, I.F. circuits are biased similarly to the audio amplifiers discussed in preceding chapters, and bypassed emitter resistance is often used for operating-point stability. With high-frequency stages, the coupling and bypass capacitors will be of much smaller value because capacitive reactance decreases with frequency.

Practical selective coupling networks will take on the forms of Fig. 9–21. In (a) and (b) of the figure a single-tuned two-winding transformer and a

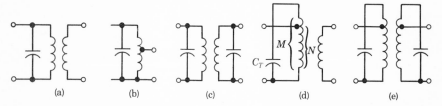

     (a)   (b)   (c)   (d)   (e)

Fig. 9–21. Practical selective coupling networks: (a) single-tuned, two winding transformer; (b) single-tuned, autotransformer; (c) double-tuned; (d) single-tuned, tapped primary, (e) double-tuned, tapped primary and secondary.

single-tuned autotransformer are shown. Since transistor output and input impedance levels are vastly different, the transformer serves to provide impedance matching as well as selectivity. Tuning of both primary and secondary inductances, as in the circuit of Fig. 9–21c, results in superior performance, a flatter frequency response and sharper cutoff at the edges of the passband. This network is called a *double-tuned coupling circuit*.

The single and double-tuned circuits of the diagram are modified in (d) and (e) of Fig. 9–21 to provide for a larger winding inductance and a smaller value of tuning capacitance for practical circuits. If N represents the number of turns as indicated on the diagram, M the total number of turns, and C is the required tuning capacitance for the portion of the winding designated by N, then a smaller capacitance, C_T, can be connected across M according to

$$C_T = \frac{N^2}{M^2} C. \qquad (9–76)$$

Typical of an I.F. stage is that shown in Fig. 9–22. This circuit bears a great deal of similarity to an audio-frequency transformer-coupled circuit; bypassed emitter resistance R_1 is used for operating-point stability, base bias is achieved by R_2 and R_3—the method called single-battery bias, and R_3 is bypassed to prevent signal loss in a resistance used for establishing the d-c operating point. As previously mentioned, 10 to 50 μf capacitors are not used for bypassing at these frequencies; for 455-kc stages capacitances of 0.05 to 0.1 μf adequately perform the necessary function of presenting low impedance to the a-c component of transistor currents. The tuning afforded by C is not exclusive with I.F. amplifiers; indeed, tuning is used in audio circuits to minimize the signal-shunting effects of transformer primary inductance at low frequencies. The need for C, in this circuit, is, of course, to resonate with

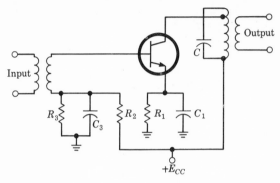

Fig. 9–22. Typical I.F. stage.

L at the carrier frequency, and the required bandpass characteristic is thereby obtained.

9–8. Instability of Tuned Amplifiers. The transistor is a non-unilateral device; its input circuit "senses" the applied load and output characteristics, and its output circuit "senses" the source termination and input circuit characteristics. At certain frequencies and under certain load conditions, as may be experienced with tuned loads, this sensing or internal feedback may result in the input impedance of a stage exhibiting a negative real part, a condition for self-oscillation. Calculations of conditions for oscillation are complicated by the fact that at high frequencies all parameters of the transistor are complex, the load is complex, and coupling circuits are complex functions of frequency.

If we consider the general h-parameter relationships for input and output impedance, namely

$$Z_i = h_i - \frac{h_r h_f}{h_o + Y_L}, \tag{9–77}$$

and

$$\frac{1}{Z_o} = h_o - \frac{h_r h_f}{h_i + Z_g}, \tag{9–78}$$

it is easy to prove that for certain source and load terminations the real portions of Z_i and Z_o may become negative. Internal feedback as represented by the right-hand members of the above equations may be minimized if $1/Z_L$ and Z_g are very large numbers so essentially

and

$$Z_i \cong h_i$$

$$Z_o \cong \frac{1}{h_o}.$$

Another method of minimizing the factors that contribute to instability is to make h_i and h_o more highly resistive. To accomplish this, a resistor may be placed in one of the input leads to the stage, and one may be placed in parallel with h_o across the transistor output terminal pair.

A third method of stabilizing high-frequency tuned amplifiers is by *neutralization*, the process of adding passive circuitry to provide external feedback tending to cancel the internal feedback that fosters instability. Neutralizing circuitry often practically consists of a single capacitor, or a resistance-capacitance parallel combination (or series combination) connected as in Fig. 9–23. The connection is often made from the base of a second transistor to the base of the preceding transistor with the coupling transformer supplying

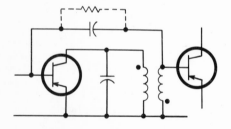

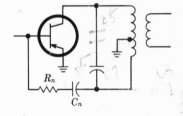

Fig. 9–23. Neutralized common-emitter tuned stage. No biasing is included in the figure.

Fig. 9–24. Another neutralizing scheme. Typical values: R_n—3000 to 8000 ohms; C_n—5 to 10 $\mu\mu$f. Numbers pertain to broadcast band. No biasing is shown in the figure.

180° of phase shift (for a typical 455-kc I.F. amplifier, the neutralizing capacitor will be of a value to 250 $\mu\mu$f, depending upon the transformer turns ratio, the transistor used, etc.). The neutralizing scheme of Fig. 9–24 is commonly employed in radio receiver I.F. strips.

Without neutralization, the non-unilateral aspects of the transistor make alignment of multistage-tuned amplifiers somewhat difficult, any change in the load of one stage affecting the operation of all other cascaded units.

Although one hears "neutralization" and "unilateralization" used interchangeably, actually unilateralization is a special case of neutralization in which the resistive as well as the reactive feedback parameters are balanced out, and therefore unilateralization changes a bilateral network into a unilateral network.

Shea [15] has concluded that potential instability occurs only up to a fraction of the alpha cutoff frequency (f_{ab}) in common-emitter circuits; at higher frequencies this configuration is unconditionally stable (the transistor cannot oscillate, no matter what passive terminations are used). For common-base and common-collector configurations, instability may occur throughout the entire range of frequencies.

9–9. Tuned-Amplifier Design. By making use of the principles discussed in the preceding sections of this chapter it is possible to design a tuned transistor amplifier; a sample design will be forthcoming. The hybrid-π equivalent of Fig. 9–11 will be used as the basis for design procedures even though this circuit is fairly complicated, and the addition of a tuned load and neutralizing elements result in even greater complexity. Some simplification of the overall equivalent circuit may be achieved by converting the hybrid-π to a normal-π of the type shown in the "boxed" portion of Fig. 9–25. (See Problem 9–16.)

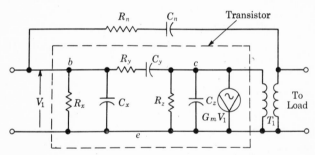

Fig. 9–25. Normal-π circuit with neutralizing components included.

After making this conversion the unilateralizing components R_n and C_n linking input and output and the transformer T_1 providing the phase reversal for this external feedback are added to the transistor equivalent in Fig. 9–25.

If the transformer turns ratio is 1:1, let us make $C_n = C_y$ and $R_n = R_y$. The current in the external feedback path will be opposite in phase to the current through R_y and C_y from base-to-collector, and it can be shown that net feedback from collector-to-base is cancelled. The resulting unilateralized stage is depicted in Fig. 9–26 and it is obvious that because of the isolation provided by the external elements, this circuit will be easy to work with.

Should the turns ratio of the coupling transformer be other than 1:1, let us say n:1, then, for isolation of input from load, and output from source, the

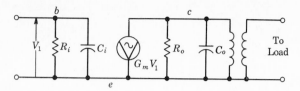

Fig. 9-26. Unilateralized common-emitter circuit with transformer coupling to load.

feedback elements must be

$$C_n = nC_y, \tag{9-79}$$

and

$$R_n = \frac{R_y}{n}. \tag{9-80}$$

The actual values of C_y and R_y in terms of the original hybrid-π parameters are

$$C_y = \frac{C_{b'c}}{1 + (r_{bb'}/r_{b'e}) - (r_{bb'}/r_{b'c})(C_{b'e}/C_{b'c})}, \tag{9-81}$$

and

$$R_y = r_{bb'}\left(1 + \frac{C_{b'e}}{C_{b'c}}\right) + \frac{1 + (r_{bb'}/r_{b'e})}{r_{b'c}\omega^2 C_{b'c}^2}. \tag{9-82}$$

Problem 9-17 may be used to derive these equations.

Solution for the other parameters of the circuit of Fig. 9-26 yields [22]

$$R_i = r_{bb'} + r_{b'e}\left[\frac{r_{b'e} + r_{bb'}}{r_{b'e} + r_{bb'} + \omega^2(C_{b'e} + C_{b'c})^2 r_{b'e}^2 r_{bb'}}\right] \tag{9-83}$$

$$C_i = \frac{C_{b'e} + C_{b'c}}{[1 + (r_{bb'}/r_{b'e})]^2 + \omega^2(C_{b'e} + C_{b'c})^2 r_{bb'}^2} \tag{9-84}$$

$$\frac{1}{R_o} = g_{ce} + g_{b'c} + g_m\left[\frac{g_{b'c}(g_{bb'} + g_{b'e}) + \omega^2 C_{b'e}C_{b'c}}{(g_{bb'} + g_{b'e})^2 + \omega^2 C_{b'e}^2}\right] \tag{9-85}$$

$$C_o = C_{b'c}\left[1 + \frac{g_m(g_{bb'} + g_{b'e})}{(g_{bb'} + g_{b'e})^2 + \omega^2 C_{b'e}^2}\right] \tag{9-86}$$

$$G_m = \frac{g_m}{\sqrt{[1 + (r_{bb'}/r_{b'e})]^2 + [r_{bb'}\omega(C_{b'e} + C_{b'c})]^2}}. \tag{9-87}$$

Conductances have been used in Eqs. (9-85) and (9-86) to somewhat simplify those formulas. Eqs. (9-83) through (9-86) pertain to the unilateralized transistor exclusively; to determine input and output resistances and capacitances for the entire stage, R_n and C_n should be considered as paralleling those terminal pairs. (See Problems 9-19 and 9-20.)

The load to be fed is often the input impedance of the following stage and it is desired, for maximum power transfer, to reflect the resistive component of this load to the first transistor collector at a level equal to R_o. The interstage transformer performs this function. Input capacitance of the following (load) stage parallels the tuned circuit, and if of significant value must be considered a portion of the overall tuning capacitance. This composite tuning capacitance (C_T) required to resonate with transformer inductance at the carrier frequency is made up of the parallel elements C_o, reflected load C_i, stray capacitance, and purposely added capacitance.

I.F. Amplifier Stage Design Example

Object. To design a single I.F. amplifying stage according to the following specifications:

1. Carrier frequency: 455 kc
2. Bandwidth: 10 kc
3. Load: Z_i of identical unilateralized transistor
4. Power supply available: -9 volts

Solution. A suitable transistor for this service is the RCA 2N139, a germanium p-n-p alloy-junction type. Small-signal hybrid-π parameters are here given for an operating point of $V_{CE} = -9$ volts and $I_C = 1$ ma

$$r_{bb'} = 75 \text{ ohms} \qquad C_{b'e} = 1560 \text{ } \mu\mu f$$

$$g_{b'e} = 800 \text{ } \mu mhos \qquad C_{b'c} = 9.5 \text{ } \mu\mu f$$

$$g_{ce} = 8.6 \text{ } \mu mhos \qquad g_m = 38,600 \text{ } \mu mhos$$

$$g_{b'c} = 0.25 \text{ } \mu mho$$

Preliminary calculations:

$$r_{b'e} = \frac{1}{g_{b'e}} = 1250 \text{ ohms} \qquad g_{bb'} = 1.33 \times 10^{-2} \text{ mho}$$

$$r_{ce} = \frac{1}{g_{ce}} = 0.116 \times 10^6 \text{ ohms} \qquad \omega_r = 2\pi f_r = 2.86 \times 10^6 \text{ rad/sec}$$

$$r_{b'c} = \frac{1}{g_{b'c}} = 4 \times 10^6 \text{ ohms} \qquad \omega_r{}^2 = 8.18 \times 10^{12} \text{ rad}^2/\text{sec}^2$$

It is necessary to determine the values of the elements of the circuit of Fig. 9–27. The biasing resistances R_2 and R_3 are chosen so that $I_C = 1$ ma, and the reactance of C_3 at 455 kc made much smaller than the resistance of R_3 (if $R_3 = 5\ K$, C_3 can be chosen to be 0.05 to 0.1 μf). For bias stability, R_1 will be included, 1000 ohms is typical, bypassed by C_1 of 0.1 μf. The decoupling circuit shall be composed of $R_C = 500$ ohms and $C_C = 0.05$ μf.

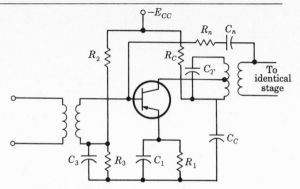

Fig. 9–27.   Circuit for I.F. amplifier design example.

Because of the d-c potential drops across R_C, R_1 and the winding resistance of the transformer, V_{CE} will not be 9 volts, but will have some lesser value. In the absence of parameter correction information for this transistor and because the deviation from 9 volts is not too great, the 9-volt parameters will be used.

We may calculate feedback elements C_y and R_y by using Eqs. (9–81) and (9–82). From Eq. (9–81)

$$C_y = \frac{9.5 \times 10^{-12}}{1 + (75/1250) - (75/4 \times 10^6)(1560/9.5)}$$

$$= 9.0 \ \mu\mu f.$$

From Eq. (9–82)

$$R_y = 75\left(1 + \frac{1560}{9.5}\right) + \frac{1 + (75/1250)}{(8.18 \times 10^{12})(4 \times 10^6)(9.5 \times 10^{-12})^2}$$

$$= 12{,}760 \text{ ohms.}$$

Insertion of appropriate external feedback elements will cancel the effects of C_y and R_y and result in a unilateralized stage of the form of Fig. 9–28.

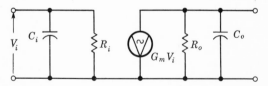

Fig. 9–28.   Unilateralized equivalent circuit.

The five parameters of the circuit of Fig. 9–28 can be calculated.   From Eq. (9–83)

$$R_i = 75 + \frac{1250(1250 + 75)}{1250 + 75 + (8.18 \times 10^{12})(1569.5 \times 10^{-12})^2(1250)^2(75)}$$

$$= 528 \text{ ohms.}$$

From Eq. (9–84)

$$C_i = \frac{1569.5 \times 10^{-12}}{[1 + (75/1250)]^2 + (8.18 \times 10^{12})(1569.5 \times 10^{-12})^2(75)^2}$$

$$= 1270 \ \mu\mu f.$$

From Eq. (9–85)

$$\frac{1}{R_o} = 30.8 \times 10^{-6}$$

Therefore

$$R_o = 32,400 \text{ ohms.}$$

From Eq. (9–86)

$$C_o = 33.1 \ \mu\mu f$$

From Eq. (9–87)

$$G_m = 34.8 \text{ ma/volt.}$$

Now to specify the transformer to be used, match R_o to the load resistance, which is R_i of an identical stage.

$$\text{Impedance ratio} = 32,400:530.$$

Therefore the turns ratio is

$$n = \sqrt{\frac{32,400}{530}} = 7.8:1.$$

The feedback elements were given by $R_n = R_y/n$ and $C_n = nC_y$.

$$R_n = \frac{12,760}{7.8} = 1640 \text{ ohms}$$

and

$$C_n = (7.8)(9.0) = 70 \ \mu\mu f.$$

The paralleling effects of these elements upon terminal properties will not be considered here. Problem 9–24 may be used to determine these effects.

A few other calculations are needed to satisfactorily specify circuit operation and circuit elements. The expected power gain must be predicted, so, from Fig. 9–29,

$$P_i = \frac{V_i^2}{R_i}.$$

$R_L = n^2 R_i = R_o$, and, if load current is symbolized by I_o, then load power is

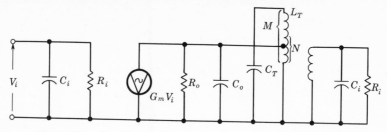

Fig. 9–29.   Coupling and load added to the circuit of Fig. 9–28.

given by

$$P_o = I_o{}^2 R_L = I_o{}^2 R_o$$

$$= \left(\frac{G_m V_i}{2}\right)^2 R_o.$$

Then

$$G = \frac{P_o}{P_i} = \frac{G_m{}^2 R_o R_i}{4},$$

$$= \frac{(34.8 \times 10^{-3})^2 (32{,}400)(528)}{4},$$

$$= 5{,}200, \text{ or } 37.2 \text{ db.}$$

This figure assumes a perfect coil. Because an actual coil has losses, less gain will be available. To find the overall Q required, use Eq. (9–65).

$$Q = \frac{f_r}{(BW)} = \frac{455{,}000}{10{,}000},$$

$$= 45.5.$$

If a coil with $Q_C = 100$ is available, then, from Eq. (9–57b),

$$\text{Insertion loss} = 20 \log \frac{Q_C}{Q_C - Q} = 20 \log \frac{100}{100 - 45.5}$$

$$= 5.3 \text{ db.}$$

The overall power gain to be expected is, therefore, $37.2 - 5.3$, or 31.9 db. From Eq. (9–75), a calculation of the coil inductance can be made.

$$L = \frac{R_o(Q_C - Q)}{2\omega_r Q Q_C} = \frac{32{,}400(100 - 45.5)}{2(2.86 \times 10^6)(45.5)(100)}$$

$$= 68 \ \mu h.$$

Using the standard equation for parallel resonance permits the determination of parallel capacitance.

$$C = \frac{1}{\omega_r^2 L} = \frac{1}{(8.18 \times 10^{12})(68 \times 10^{-6})}$$

$$= 1800 \ \mu\mu f.$$

Of this total required capacitance, C_o makes up 33 $\mu\mu f$ and reflected C_i of stage two accounts for $1270/(7.8)^2$ or 21 $\mu\mu f$. The contribution of a separate tuning capacitor must be 1746 $\mu\mu f$.

If a tapped coil is to be used, and if 200 $\mu\mu f$ of additional tuning capacitance (C_T) is decided upon, then from Fig. 9–29

$$\frac{M}{N} = \sqrt{\frac{1746}{200}} = 2.96.$$

The C_o and reflected C_i capacitances amount to 54 $\mu\mu f$ and are across N turns of the transformer primary. Their contribution to total tuning capacitance is $54/(2.96)^2 = 6.2 \ \mu\mu f$. The total primary inductance now is given by

$$L_T = \frac{1}{\omega_r^2 C} = \frac{1}{(8.18 \times 10^{12})(206 \times 10^{-12})}$$

$$= 592 \ \mu h.$$

Summary. To meet the listed specifications:

Coil requirements:

$$Q_C = 100$$

$$L = 592 \ \mu h$$

$$M/N = 2.96$$

$$32,400:530 \text{ ohms}$$

Circuit elements: (Refer to Fig. 9–27)

$C_T = 200 \ \mu\mu f$	$R_2 = $ Approx. 25,000 ohms	$R_1 = 1000$ ohms
$R_n = 1640$ ohms	$R_3 = 5,000$ ohms	$C_1 = 0.1 \ \mu f$
$C_n = 70 \ \mu\mu f$	$C_3 = 0.05 \ \mu f$	$R_C = 500$ ohms
		$C_C = 0.05 \ \mu f$

Performance:

$$\text{Power gain} = 1550, \text{ or } 31.9 \text{ db.}$$

PROBLEMS

9-1. Calculate the thermal noise voltage generated by a 500,000-ohm resistor at 100° C. The useable bandwidth is 2 megacycles.

9-2. For the volume control arrangement of Fig. 9-3c, calculate the voltage gain of the interstage network for various control settings and sketch gain vs. K.

9-3. A particular transistor has the following low-frequency parameters: $h_{ie} = 2500$ ohms, $h_{re} = 2 \times 10^{-3}$, $h_{fe} = 50$, $h_{oe} = 5 \times 10^{-5}$ mho, $r_{bb'} = 60$ ohms.

(a) Draw a hybrid-π network and calculate the values of the parameters.

(b) Draw a current-generator equivalent tee and calculate the values of the parameters.

9-4. Consider a transistor with the parameters given in Problem 9-3, and, in addition, $C_c = 10$ $\mu\mu$f, $f_{ab} = 10$ mc, $R_L = 2000$ ohms and $R_g = 100$ ohms.

(a) Calculate the input capacitance including the Miller effect.

(b) At what frequency will E_o/E_g be $1/\sqrt{2}$ of its mid-frequency value.

9-5. Measurements of the input impedance of a particular common-emitter stage indicate that the 1000-cycle value is 800 ohms and at 90,000 cycles the magnitude had diminished to 566 ohms. From this data determine the effective input resistance and input capacitance.

9-6. If it is known that the transistor of Problem 9-5 is feeding a 1000-ohm load from a 1000-ohm source, and that $C_{b'c} = 20$ $\mu\mu$f and $g_m = 30$ ma/volt, calculate:

(a) The emitter diffusion capacitance.

(b) The alpha cutoff frequency.

(c) The upper voltage gain cutoff frequency.

9-7. Derive expressions for the common-emitter h-parameters in terms of low-frequency hybrid-π parameters.

9-8. Derive expressions for the T-parameters in terms of low-frequency hybrid-π parameters. Use the relationships of Tables 4-5 and 4-7.

9-9. Confirm Eq. (9-35).

9-10. At 800 kc a 200-μh inductor exhibits an equivalent-series R.F. resistance of 8 ohms. Determine:

(a) The series Q_C.

(b) The equivalent shunt inductance at that frequency.

(c) The equivalent shunt resistance at that frequency.

(d) The parallel Q_C.

9-11. Find the insertion loss when using a coil with $Q_C = 52$ in a circuit with half-power points at 600 kc and 612 kc and with the resonant frequency at the center of the band.

9–12. The resonant frequency of the circuit of the figure is 3.1 mc. Calculate the following:

(a) The overall circuit Q.

(b) The bandwidth.

(c) The coil (transformer) insertion loss.

(d) The load seen by I at the resonant frequency.

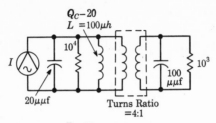

Problem 9–12.

9–13. Derive an expression for the resonant frequency of a circuit with C paralleling a series R-L branch.

9–14. Devise tests to determine the characteristics of an I.F. transformer, i.e., Q_C, ω_r, L, C, and turns ratio, if the assembly is that of Fig. 9–21a. C may be considered removable if necessary.

9–15. To achieve a wide band "stagger" tuning is useful. Each I.F. stage is tuned to a different center frequency, and the overall response of the cascade amplifier is much flatter than the response of a like number of stages single tuned to the center of the passband. If each stage of a two-stage amplifier has a Q of 10, and the center of the band is at 24 mc, graphically determine the bandwidth of the overall I.F. strip. Stage no. 1 is tuned to 23 mc and no. 2 is tuned to 25 mc.

9–16. To convert from the hybrid-π circuit to the normal-π circuit a simple method involves equating the network y-parameters (see Chapter 4) obtained

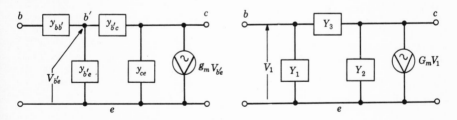

Problem 9–16.

from each of the circuits. Derive expressions for the normal-π parameters in terms of the hybrid-π parameters.

9–17. Y_3 in the circuit of Problem 9–16 may be expressed in terms of hybrid-π admittance parameters thus:

$$Y_3 = \frac{y_{b'c}y_{bb'}}{y_{b'e} + y_{bb'} + y_{b'c}}.$$

Show that separation of the real and imaginary parts of the impedance represented by this expression provides confirmation of Eqs. (9–81) and (9–82). Make the assumptions that $r_{b'c}$ is very large and $C_{b'e} \gg C_{b'c}$.

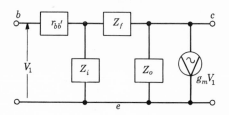

Problem 9–18.

9–18. Confirm the following formulas which have been derived for the hybrid-π circuit of the above figure.

$$A_i = \frac{Z_i Z_o[1 - g_m Z_f]}{Z_o[Z_i + Z_f] + Z_L[Z_i + Z_f + Z_o + g_m Z_i Z_o]}$$

$$A_v = \frac{Z_i Z_o Z_L r_{bb'}[1 - g_m Z_f]}{[Z_o + Z_L][r_{bb'}(Z_i + Z_f) + Z_i Z_f + Z_o Z_L(r_{bb'} + Z_i + g_m r_{bb'} Z_i)]}$$

$$R_i = \frac{Z_o[r_{bb'}(Z_i + Z_f) + Z_i Z_f] + Z_L[r_{bb'}(Z_i + Z_f + Z_o + g_m Z_o Z_i) + Z_i(Z_f + Z_o)]}{Z_o(Z_i + Z_f) + Z_L(Z_i + Z_f + Z_o + g_m Z_o Z_i)}$$

$$R_o = \frac{Z_o[(Z_i + Z_f)(Z_g + r_{bb'}) + Z_i Z_f]}{[Z_g + r_{bb'}][Z_i + Z_f + Z_o + g_m Z_i Z_o] + Z_i[Z_f + Z_o]}.$$

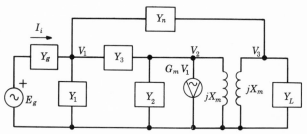

Problem 9–19.

9–19. Consider the normal-π circuit of the preceding figure. The transformer has unity turns ratio but provides phase reversal so $V_3 = -V_2$.

(a) Write the nodal equation at V_1 and show that input impedance $\left[Z_i = \dfrac{V_1}{I_i} \right]$ is independent of the load termination provided that $Y_3 = Y_n$.

(b) Write the nodal equations at V_3 and V_1 and show that output impedance is independent of source impedance.

9–20. It has been established in Problem 9–16 that, for the normal-π circuit,

$$Y_1 = \frac{y_{b'e} y_{bb'}}{y_{bb'} + y_{b'e} + y_{b'c}}.$$

Problem 9–17 gives Y_3 and the solution to Problem 9–19 provides an expression for Z_i. Using this information confirm Eq. (9–83). Note the statement in the text explaining that Eq. (9–83) does not include the paralleling effects of R_n and C_n. Consider the conductance of the $b'c$ branch to be very small compared to $b'e$ and bb'.

9–21. A unilateralized transistor stage at the carrier frequency of 600 kc exhibits the following terminal properties: $Z_i = 900 - j550$; $Z_o = 20,000 - j14,000$. If the transistor is feeding a load that is an identical stage, a coil $Q_C = 60$ may be assumed, and the required bandwidth is 20 kc, answer the following:

(a) What is the required coil inductance?

(b) With a transformer of the Fig. 9–21a type, what impedance ratio should be used?

(c) What is the total required shunt capacitance and how much must be made up by additional capacitance?

(d) What is the gain of the stage including coil losses? Assume that $G_m = 25$ ma/volt.

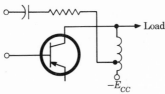

Problem 9–22.

9–22. Design an I.F. stage to meet the following requirements:

1. Carrier frequency: 455 kc
2. Bandwidth: 20 kc
3. Load: 10,000 ohms paralleled by 35 $\mu\mu$f
4. Transistor type: 2N139
5. Operating point: 1 ma and −9 volts

6. Coupling: inductors available with $Q_C = 70$. Transformers not to be used.

7. Unilateralization provided by feedback from inductor tap as shown in diagram.

The problem essentially requires determination of coil inductance, additional tuning capacity, and expected gain.

9–23. Discuss the factors involved in choosing an intermediate frequency for a communications receiver. *Theory and Design of Television Receivers*, by S. Deutsch, McGraw-Hill, 1951, will be of assistance.

9–24. Alter the text design example by including the paralleling effects of R_n and C_n upon Z_i and Z_o (see Problem 9–20). It is suggested that R_n and C_n first be transformed to equivalent parallel elements to simplify the combination. Compare values obtained with the listed coil requirements, circuit element values, and performance.

REFERENCES

1. Bevitt, W. D., *Transistors Handbook*, Prentice-Hall, Inc., Englewood Cliffs, New Jersey, 1956.
2. DeWitt, D., and Rossoff, A. L., *Transistor Electronics*, McGraw-Hill Book Company, New York, 1957.
3. Garner, L. E., Jr., "Transistors in the TV Set," *Radio Electronics*, vol. 59 (May and June, 1958).
4. Giacolletto, L. J., "Study of P-N-P Alloy Junction Transistors from D.C. through Medium Frequencies," *RCA Review*, vol. 15 (Dec., 1954).
5. Gibson, J. E., and Tuteur, F. E., *Control System Components*, McGraw-Hill Book Company, New York, 1958.
6. Hunter, L. P., *Handbook of Semiconductor Electronics*, McGraw-Hill Book Company, New York, 1956.
7. Hurley, R. B., *Junction Transistor Electronics*, John Wiley & Sons, Inc., New York, 1958.
8. Kiver, M. S., *Transistors in Radio and Television*, McGraw-Hill Book Company, Inc., New York, 1956.
9. Lo, et al., *Transistor Electronics*, Prentice-Hall, Inc., Englewood Cliffs, New Jersey, 1955.
10. Middlebrook, R. D., *An Introduction to Junction Transistor Theory*, John Wiley & Sons, Inc., New York, 1957.
11. Pritchard, R. L., "Electric-Network Representation of Transistors—A Survey," *IRE Trans.*, CT-3, No. 1 (Mar., 1956).
12. Pritchard, R. L., "High-Frequency Power Gain of Junction Transistors," *Proc. IRE*, vol. 43 (Sept., 1955).
13. Riddle, R. L., and Ristenbatt, M. P., *Transistor Physics and Circuits*, Prentice-Hall, Inc., Englewood Cliffs, New Jersey, 1958.
14. Shea, R. F., *Principles of Transistor Circuits*, John Wiley & Sons, Inc., New York, 1953.
15. Shea, R. F., *Transistor Circuit Engineering*, John Wiley & Sons, Inc., New York, 1957.

16. Shockley, W., *Electrons and Holes in Semiconductors*, D. Van Nostrand Co., Inc., New York, 1950.
17. Terman, E. F., and Pettit, J. M., *Electronic Measurements*, McGraw-Hill Book Company, New York, 1952.
18. van der Ziel, A., *Noise*, Prentice-Hall, Inc., Englewood Cliffs, New Jersey, 1954.
19. van der Ziel, A., "Noise in Junction Transistors," *Proc.* IRE, vol. 46 (June, 1958).
20. van der Ziel, A., *Solid State Physical Electronics*, Prentice-Hall, Inc., Englewood Cliffs, New Jersey, 1957.
21. Volkers, W. K., and Pedersen, N. E., "The Hushed Transistor Amplifier," *Proc. Natl. Electronics Cont.*, vol. 11 (1955).
22. Wolfendale, E., *The Junction Transistor and Its Applications*, The Macmillan Company, New York, 1958.

Chapter 10

COMMUNICATIONS CIRCUITS AND SYSTEMS

The discussion up to this point has been centered about signal amplification —the raising of a signal level—with the transistor as the active circuit element. The transistor, however, may be used for purposes other than amplification, and in this chapter, and in the subsequent chapter, such applications will be examined. Because many of the principles thus far considered with reference to amplification apply equally well to the processes of oscillation, modulation, and detection, analysis and synthesis of these new circuits will not appear completely foreign to the transistor-amplifier designer.

10–1. Oscillation. Oscillators are of extreme importance in the communications field for they are the source of the high-frequency voltages that are generated both in the transmitter and in the receiver portions of a complete system. Actually an oscillator is a power converter in the sense that its only input is the direct-supply potential (and hence supply power) and its output is a time-varying waveform that is usually, but not necessarily, of a frequency well above that which can be generated with rotating equipment. It is therefore customary that no signal input terminal is apparent in the circuit diagram for an oscillator; the output is usually, but not always, taken between transistor collector and ground.

If the generated waveform is basically sinusoidal and the active circuit element is continuously supplying power to the passive circuit elements, the composite is termed a *harmonic oscillator.* Included in this category are *negative-resistance* and *feedback oscillators.* Another broad category among generators includes the *relaxation* types, characterized by nonsinusoidal waveforms (sawtooth, square, etc.) and the switched interchange of energy between active and passive circuit elements. Concern in this section is directed toward the harmonic oscillators, with limited discussion of relaxation oscillators reserved for Chapter 11.

An oscillator may, in some instances, be required to furnish very little power, or, by itself, cannot furnish the power required by the circuit load. However, once the desired time-varying signal is obtained, no matter how weakly, it is then possible to build it up with separate amplifying stages. Because a non-sinusoidal wave or a distorted sinusoidal wave is available from certain oscillator circuits, filtering circuitry can be useful in extracting the fundamental and can help in the attainment of a pure sinusoid if one is required.

A generally quoted "rule of thumb" describes the limiting frequency of oscillation for any transistor as its alpha-cutoff frequency. The treatment here will be concerned with oscillation at frequencies considerably below that limit and will be centered about operation in the audio-frequency band, but the discussion will be useful in analyzing any oscillator when transistor terminal reactances do not play an important part in circuit operation.

From the discussion of feedback in amplifiers presented in Chapter 8 it will be recalled that a unique condition existed when the denominator of the overall amplification formula equaled zero. Repeated here,

$$A_f = \frac{A}{1 - BA} = \frac{V_o}{V_i}. \tag{10-1}$$

Thus when $BA \rightarrow +1$, $A_f \rightarrow \infty$. This represents oscillation, the situation existing when an input signal is unnecessary for the maintenance of an output signal. It is now desired that this generated signal be sinusoidal, and of constant amplitude, and furthermore that its frequency be predictable, and in some cases adjustable.

The loop gain (BA) must actually be greater than unity in all practical feedback oscillators, for if it were precisely unity then aging of circuit components would in all likelihood eventually result in discontinuance of the desired waveform generation, because of gain reduction. When BA is made slightly greater than unity, more signal is being fed back than originally was present, and a buildup in signal level results; this buildup will always be limited by nonlinearities within the transistor (the collector-supply voltage also presents a limit). Such nonlinearities always result in distortion of the output waveform, but in good oscillator designs this distortion may be very slight.

Because transistor gain and input and output impedances are so sensitive to ambient temperature it is mandatory for stable oscillation that the frequency be solely dependent upon high quality, stable, external tuning elements and not upon the transistor reactances. Elements that determine the frequency of oscillation include R-C networks for phase shifting, resonant L-C pairs, and piezoelectric crystals. In addition, stable biasing is used to keep circuit operation predictable.

A frequency-determining device or circuit is required in all oscillator circuits; inductance-capacitance circuitry can perform this function. It can be recalled from the transient analysis portion of electrical network theory that oscillations are developed in the response of even a simple R-L-C circuit when subjected to a step or suddenly applied d-c shock. See Fig. 10–1. The d-c transient, however, always decays because of the inescapable damping effect

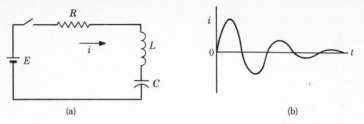

(a)   (b)

Fig. 10–1. Transient in a simple d-c circuit, and the frequency-determining properties of an L-C circuit.

of ever-present resistance.

The current in the simple R-L-C circuit shown can be expressed by

$$i = \frac{E}{L} \frac{\epsilon^{-t/T}}{\omega} \sin \omega t \qquad (10\text{–}2)$$

for the case when $(\sqrt{L/C}) > R/2$. The exponential term causing the decay is dictated by $T = 2L/R$. Angular frequency of the sine term is given by

$$\omega = \sqrt{\frac{1}{LC} - \left(\frac{R}{2L}\right)^2}.$$

It is clear that R causes the reduction in amplitude and slightly determines the frequency of oscillation. In the absence of R, never-ending oscillation would exist, because of the interchange of stored energy between inductance and capacitance.

The active element in an oscillator circuit, a transistor in this instance, may be thought of as supplying, to the circuit of Fig. 10–1, or to its parallel counterpart, a negative resistance of sufficient value to overcome the positive resistance R in the figure, and consequently the complete oscillator, including both resonant circuit and negative resistance, when shocked, will oscillate continuously. Oftentimes the only shock needed is the application of power to the circuit.

Oscillators are studied from a negative-resistance standpoint and from a feedback point-of-view, but mathematically there is no rigid division between the two and any particular oscillator may be considered from either approach. In the so-called negative-resistance type of waveform generator, internal positive feedback is present and serves to provide a negative resistance to an external resonant circuit. The so-called feedback-oscillator type employs positive external feedback in order to overcome natural damping.

Two-Terminal Negative-Resistance Oscillators. One cannot purchase a negative resistance from a components supplier, nor will one see such a device listed in any catalog, so a negative resistance characteristic must be obtained from a common active device when operated in a specific manner, or when used in conjunction with other common circuit elements.

Some transistor types, the point-contact and *p-n-p-n* hook varieties, for example, possess alphas greater than unity, and it is rather easy to show that negative terminal resistance properties may be forthcoming with these devices. Consider the approximate equation listed in Table 4–1 for the input resistance of a transistor connected common-emitter. Repeated here,

$$R_i \cong r_b + \frac{r_e}{1 - \alpha}. \tag{10-3}$$

For a device exhibiting $\alpha > 1$, input resistance will be negative when

$$\frac{r_e}{\alpha - 1} > r_b,$$

a condition that suggests that in some cases additional series emitter resistance may be required to attain negative input resistance. See Fig. 10–2 and note the change in polarity of the collector branch current generator when alpha exceeds unity.

The foregoing oscillator discussion, for devices with alpha greater than unity that exhibit negative input terminal resistance, can be alternately thought of as a positive feedback phenomenon, for output circuit current in r_e and R_e of the emitter branch decidedly affects the input circuit.

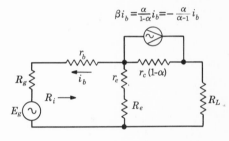

Fig. 10–2. Simple common-emitter *T*-equivalent with series emitter resistance added.

The approximate expression for output resistance, from Table 4–1, is

$$R_o \cong \frac{R_g r_c (1 - \alpha) + r_e r_c}{r_e + r_b + R_g}. \tag{10-4}$$

Although a negative sign is already in the equation, it is easy to show that R_o cannot be negative, for positive parameters and $\alpha < 1$. If, however, α is greater than unity then output terminal resistance becomes negative when

$$R_g(\alpha - 1) > r_e.$$

This relation suggests that source resistance is important in this consideration.

A typical point-contact transistor oscillator circuit is shown in Fig. 10–3. R_1, R_2, R_3, and R_L are used for the maintenance of a satisfactory operating

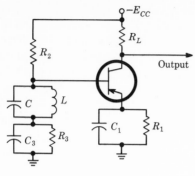

point, and C_1 and C_3 serve as bypass or a-c grounding capacitors. C and L are the prime tuning elements.

Feedback Oscillators. There is a multiplicity of possible circuit arrangements useful as feedback oscillators. If one starts with a transistor in the common-emitter orientation, 180° of phase shift is inherent between input and output quantities. To feed some of the output signal back to the input in order to provide positive feedback, an additional shift of 180° is required. A transformer can, of course, be used to sup-

Fig. 10–3. Negative-resistance oscillator circuit.

ply this necessary phase reversal and in the circuit of Fig. 10–4 one is shown doing just that. The transformer secondary winding is connected into the transistor base circuit, and the capacitor C is being used to complete the frequency-determining circuit in conjunction with the transformer winding inductance. The element R_e is offering some control over gain and can be used to keep the waveshape fairly clear of distortion. The circuit shown

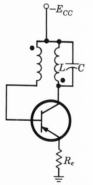

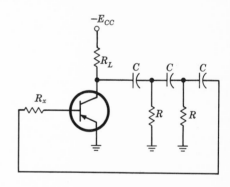

Fig. 10–4. Common-emitter oriented feedback oscillator with transformer providing phase reversal.

Fig. 10–5. Phase-shift oscillator. Base biasing not shown.

contains all the elements necessary for oscillation. Frequency is controlled by C and to a minor extent by R_e.

An *R-C* network can be designed to provide the additional phase shift needed for regeneration. In the circuit of Fig. 10–5, the transistor collector and base are connected through a three-stage phase shift network; each R-C pair is therefore required to supply about $60°$ of phase shift.

Now let us consider an approach to the mathematical analysis of oscillator circuits. Nonlinearities of characteristics impose limits upon waveform magnitude and shape, and because circuit analysis involving nonlinear elements is often to be avoided, on account of the relative complexity, our approach will be to treat the circuit as comprised of linear elements and to predict the frequency of oscillation and the circuit conditions necessary to support oscillation.

Consider an oscillator circuit, with, of course, no driving potential, because no input is specified. If it is assumed that the circuit is oscillating, and further assumed that those oscillations can be represented by sinusoidal circuit quantities, then a normal set of loop (mesh) or nodal equations may be written for steady-state analysis. Such equations were written for the derivation of gain and impedance formulas in Chapter 4, and when solved for circuit currents gave rise to expressions of the form

$$I = \frac{f(E_i)}{D}. \tag{10-5}$$

E_i represents the driving potential, and D the circuit determinant. Because $E_i = 0$ in oscillator circuits, Eq. (10–5) may be written as

$$I = \frac{0}{D}.$$

But I does exist and is not zero as this expression seems to indicate; therefore, the denominator must also be zero. Then

$$I = \frac{0}{0}$$

and is indeterminate. It is therefore necessary for the circuit determinant D to equal zero for oscillations to exist. It will be recalled that D, when using the loop method of analysis, is composed of functions of both the transistor parameters and the impedances of external elements. This determinant will have a real and an imaginary part, and to equal zero, each part must equal zero. The real part equated to zero yields, upon solution, the necessary conditions for oscillation: a relation between the current-gain parameter h_f and circuit inductances and capacitances. Upon equating the imaginary portion of the determinant to zero, one can solve for the frequency of oscillation, always a function of the circuit parameters, and dependent upon the transistor but essentially determined by the external tuned circuit. In fact, a good approximation to the circuit oscillation frequency is the resonant condition for the L-C combination,

$$f = \frac{1}{2\pi\sqrt{LC}},$$ (10–6)

which applies to either series resonant or parallel resonant (antiresonant) loss-less circuits.

Now returning in our oscillator discussion to the phase-shift type of Fig. 10–5, let us apply the foregoing treatment to this circuit. A complete a-c equivalent using h-parameters is shown in Fig. 10–6a with R_x being used to

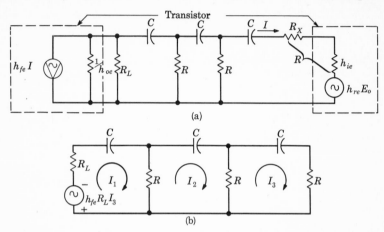

(a)

(b)

Fig. 10–6. A-c equivalent of the circuit of Fig. 10–5; (a) current-generator form; (b) simplified voltage-generator form.

bring the total resistance of the input branch up to R in value ($R_x + h_{ie} = R$). Loop equations will be written after some simplifications are made. If we consider $h_{re}E_o$ as small and $1/h_{oe}$ as very large, those two parameters may be omitted. A source transformation allows us to redraw Fig. 10–6a in the form of Fig. 10–6b. The equations are

$$0 = I_1(R_L + R - jX_C) - I_2R + I_3h_{fe}R_L,$$
$$0 = -I_1R + I_2(2R - jX_C) - I_3R,$$
$$0 = 0 - I_2R + I_3(2R - jX_C).$$
(10–7)

The numerator of every current expression is zero, and all denominators are equal and will be set to zero. The imaginary part of the determinant provides

$$\omega^2 = \frac{1}{C^2(4RR_L + 6R^2)}.$$ (10–8)

Using this value for ω^2 in the real part of the denominator yields

$$h_{fe} = 23 + \frac{29R}{R_L} + \frac{4R_L}{R}. \qquad (10\text{–}9)$$

Eq. (10–8) gives us the frequency of oscillation and Eq. (10–9) provides the necessary condition for sustained oscillations. Should $C = 0.1$ μf, $R_L = 10\ K$ and $R = 2\ K$, then the equations predict oscillations at about 160 cps and require h_{fe} to be 49 or larger.

If a common-base amplifying stage (see Fig. 10–7a) is supplying a load that

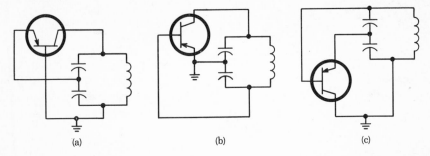

(a)   (b)   (c)

Fig. 10–7.   Colpitts-type oscillator: (a) common-base; (b) common-emitter; (c) common-collector.

is a tuned circuit and a feedback connection is made from the junction of the split load capacitors to the transistor input (emitter) terminal, and if sufficient positive feedback is available, the circuit is a *Colpitts* type oscillator. The a-c portion of this classical circuit is shown in Fig. 10–7 in the several possible ways in which it can be arranged, for the circuit may be drawn in such a way as to look like a common-base stage, or it can be common-emitter or common-collector oriented.

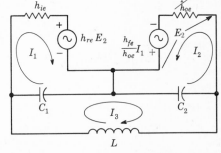

Fig. 10–8.   Circuit for analysis of the Colpitts-type oscillator.

To perform a linear analysis of the Colpitts oscillator the a-c equivalent circuit of Fig. 10–8 has been drawn, with common-emitter h-parameters used. For the lower audio frequencies they are real and will be so considered here. Note that

$$E_2 = \frac{I_2}{h_{oe}} - I_1 \frac{h_{fe}}{h_{oe}}.$$

The three loop equations are

$$0 = I_1\left(h_{ie} - \frac{h_{re}h_{fe}}{h_{oe}} - jX_{C1}\right) + I_2\left(\frac{h_{re}}{h_{oe}}\right) - I_3(-jX_{C1}),$$

$$0 = -I_1\left(\frac{h_{fe}}{h_{oe}}\right) + I_2\left(\frac{1}{h_{oe}} - jX_{C2}\right) + I_3(-jX_{C2}),$$

$$0 = -I_1(-jX_{C1}) + I_2(-jX_{C2}) + I_3(jX_L - jX_{C1} - jX_{C2}).$$

$$(10\text{--}10)$$

Equating the imaginary portion of the circuit determinant to zero allows calculation of the frequency of oscillation. The complete expression is

$$\omega^2 = \frac{h_{oe}}{C_1 C_2 h_{ie}} + \frac{1}{LC_1} + \frac{1}{LC_2}. \qquad (10\text{--}11a)$$

For practical values of the parameters, oscillator angular frequency is

$$\omega^2 = \frac{C_1 + C_2}{LC_1 C_2}. \qquad (10\text{--}11b)$$

This expression represents the resonant frequency of a tank circuit with L paralleling a series branch of C_1 and C_2.

Under the assumptions that $\omega^2 = (C_1 + C_2)/LC_1C_2$ and $h_{re} \ll 1$, the real portion of the determinant, equated to zero, yields

$$\frac{h_{fe}}{\Delta^{h_e}} = \frac{C_1}{C_2}, \qquad (10\text{--}12)$$

with

$$\Delta^{h_e} = h_{ie}h_{oe} - h_{re}h_{fe}.$$

Because h_{fe} may have a value of perhaps 50 and Δ^{h_e} of perhaps 0.5, it follows that in workable Colpitts type oscillators a big difference will be observed between the values of C_1 and C_2.

The a-c portion of the classical Hartley oscillator, when transistorized, would appear as in Fig. 10–9. The Hartley and Colpitts oscillators are very similar circuits, with just inductance and capacitance interchanged. Therefore the circuit determinant for the Hartley is identical to the determinant previously described, Eq. (10–10), except that for the Hartley circuit jX_{L1} and jX_{L2} must replace $-jX_{C1}$ and $-jX_{C2}$, and $-jX_C$ must replace jX_L. An analysis similar to that made for the Colpitts circuit results in, for the oscillating frequency of the

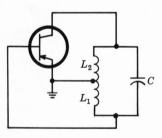

Fig. 10–9. A-c portion of the Hartley-type oscillator, common-emitter oriented.

Hartley,

$$\omega^2 = \frac{1}{C(L_1 + L_2) - L_1 L_2 h_{oe}/h_{ie}}. \tag{10–13}$$

The condition for oscillation is

$$h_{fe} = \frac{L_1}{L_2} + \Delta^{h_e} \frac{L_2}{L_1}. \tag{10–14}$$

If the L_2/L_1 term is considered as a variable z, then $h_{fe} = 1/z + \Delta^{h_e}z$, and solution for z yields, with $h_{fe}^2 \gg 4\Delta^{h_e}$,

$$\frac{h_{fe}}{\Delta^{h_e}} \cong \frac{L_2}{L_1} \tag{10–15}$$

as the desired relationship.

Mutual inductance may be present between the two inductive elements, resulting in expressions for ω and h_{fe} that also include M (see Problem 10–7). Some have found that the drawing of a more-or-less universal equivalent circuit similar to the figure of Problem 10–8 but using generalized Z elements and including mutual impedance (between Z_1 and Z_2 in that figure) can provide a basis for the derivation of formulas for the Colpitts, Hartley, and Clapp circuits, and for any variations of the basic circuit.

Stability Considerations. Drifting of the frequency of oscillation is an important engineering problem, for certain types of oscillator applications require a very great degree of frequency stability. It has already been noted that in good design the oscillation frequency should be solely dependent upon high-quality external tuning elements and not upon the transistor reactances, for the latter are subject to aging and climatic conditions as well as power-supply variations. The R, L, and C external parameters also will show a tendency to vary with temperature excursions and on occasion, if compensatory circuits and highest quality components do not suffice, the elements of importance may be located in a constant temperature bath.

Clapp's modification of the Colpitts oscillator type can result in greater frequency stability, and is accomplished by insertion of an additional capacitor in series with the tuning inductance of the Colpitts circuit.[1] The Wien bridge oscillator enjoys excellent frequency stability; further discussion is reserved for the literature.[6]

A piezoelectric crystal can be used as the prime tuning element and will provide exceptionally stable oscillation. A vibrating electromechanical system is formed within such a crystal (quartz, for instance) when a potential is applied to its opposite faces and the device is properly excited. The frequency of the resulting oscillations depends upon crystal dimensions, mounting and cut, and units are available that resonate at from several kilocycles to frequencies in the lower megacycle range.

A circuit diagram symbol and the electrical equivalent circuit for a crystal are shown in Fig. 10–10. R, L, and C are electrical equivalents of the mechanical parameters, while C_h represents electrical capacitance of the crystal between electrodes. The crystal represents a very high Q circuit, with values of Q in the thousands; if we therefore omit R from the determination of resonant frequency, no significant error is introduced. Also because C_h may be 100 or more times larger than C, it can be shown that the resonant frequency of the crystal may be approximated by

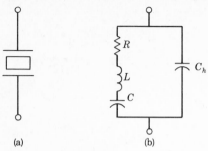

(a)   (b)

Fig. 10–10. Piezoelectric crystal: (a) circuit diagram symbol; (b) equivalent electrical circuit.

$$f = \frac{1}{2\pi\sqrt{LC}}.$$

A crystal may be substituted for an L-C resonant circuit in order to improve the stability of oscillation frequency.

Bias Considerations. Oscillators as discussed in this section may be biased Class-A by the methods previously considered for amplifiers. For higher efficiency Class-B or Class-C operation may be chosen. Starting generally requires that the circuit be initially self-biased somewhere in the active region unless some auxiliary starting means is included.

Bypassed emitter resistance permits Class-C transistor operation in a manner somewhat similar to the grid leak method used with vacuum-tube oscillators. An average voltage builds up across the emitter R-C combination that provides reverse bias for the emitter diode (see Fig. 3–12). With an initial operating point near cutoff, rising oscillations will first result in clipping at the low-current end of the load line, and eventually the buildup will be limited by nonlinearities at the high-current end. The operating point will eventually lie in the cutoff region.

Radio-Frequency Oscillators. Because of the requirement for multichannel reception, adjustable frequency waveform generation at frequencies well above the audio is necessary in the superheterodyne type of communications receiver. Transistor reactances, temperature excursions, and power-supply variations must be contended with, but the basic principles of oscillation previously discussed naturally pertain. Of course, as in any design, economic considerations are also of great importance.

A practical local oscillator for broadcast-band radio receiver circuits is shown in Fig. 10–11. The circuit employs L-C resonance, and might be called a phase-shift type of harmonic oscillator, for the transformer provides the required shift and C_a and C_f resonate with transformer inductance. Capacitor C_1 is a-c grounding the emitter terminal of the transistor, and emitter bias is being used. Quiescent base current is returned to ground through part

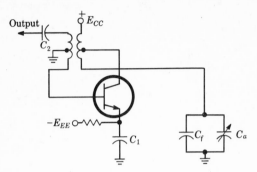

Fig. 10–11.   Transistor local oscillator.

of the transformer's base circuit winding. Typical values for the blocking capacitors C_1 and C_2 are 0.01 to 0.05 μf.

10–2. Modulation. If the output of an oscillator is connected to an antenna, some of the output is radiated into space and a fraction of the radiated signal may be intercepted by a receiving antenna. This, then, is a communications system, but to convey intelligence some characteristic of the radiated signal must be varied with time. If the phase or frequency of carrier oscillation changes as a result of coded intelligence, the method is called frequency modulation (FM). Changing carrier amplitude in accordance with intelligence yields amplitude modulation (AM), and pulse modulation (PM) results from on-off control of the carrier.

Modulation, therefore, is the process of producing a composite waveform some characteristic of which varies in accordance with the instantaneous value of another wave, called the modulating wave (the signal).

Amplitude Modulation. The process of amplitude modulation may be illustrated by first considering the mathematical relations. The carrier wave may be described by the standard sinusoidal waveform equation

$$e_c = E_{cm} \cos \omega_c t, \tag{10–16}$$

and will generally be of high frequency. The modulating signal, if a simple sinusoidal function of time, may be described by

$$e_m = E_{mm} \cos \omega_m t \tag{10–17}$$

a low-frequency signal.

If the magnitude of the carrier is changed in proportion (K_a) to e_m so that

$$e = (E_{cm} + K_a E_{mm} \cos \omega_m t) \cos \omega_c t \tag{10–18a}$$

then this equation describes amplitude modulation. In a slightly different form, Eq. (10–18a) becomes

$$e = E_{cm}\left(1 + \frac{K_a E_{mm}}{E_{cm}}\cos \omega_m t\right)\cos \omega_c t \qquad (10\text{--}18b)$$

or

$$e = E_{cm}(1 + m_a \cos \omega_m t)\cos \omega_c t. \qquad (10\text{--}18c)$$

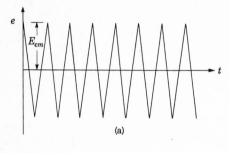

(a)

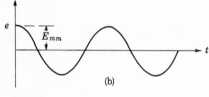

(b)

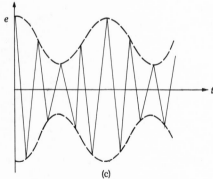

(c)

Fig. 10–12. Amplitude modulation: (a) unmodulated carrier (sinusoidal shape not used, in order to simplify the diagram); (b) modulation signal; (c) modulated wave, $m_a = 0.5$.

m_a is proportional to the ratio of maximum amplitudes of the component waves and is called the *modulation factor* or *modulation index*. Fig. 10–12 illustrates the waveforms of interest. Should m_a exceed unity, distortion is introduced.

All of the intelligence given by Eq. (10–17) is contained in the envelope of the composite waveform, for the envelope (the dashed curve joining peaks in Fig. 10–12c) can be described by

$$E_{cm}(1 + m_a \cos \omega_m t).$$

Its time-varying component is

$$E_{mm} \cos \omega_m t,$$

which is Eq. (10–17).

Should the composite waveform relationship given by Eq. (10–18c) be expanded trigonometrically, we obtain

$$e = E_{cm} \cos \omega_c t$$
$$+ \tfrac{1}{2}m_a E_{cm} \cos (\omega_c + \omega_m)t$$
$$+ \tfrac{1}{2}m_a E_{cm} \cos (\omega_c - \omega_m)t. \qquad (10\text{--}19)$$

Eq. (10–19) represents the sum of three waveforms, one of the carrier frequency, one higher and another lower than the carrier frequency. The higher frequency is part of the *upper sideband*, while the lower frequency portion lies in the *lower sideband*. Should the modulating signal contain waves of many frequencies, as one would find in broadcasting, the sidebands too would be made up of many different frequencies.

The amplitude modulation process can occasionally be useful for frequency shifting. Should ω_m and ω_c be supplied to a modulator, the frequencies ω_c, $\omega_c - \omega_m$ and $\omega_c + \omega_m$ are available from a perfect process. Not only is the low- or audio-frequency signal shifted to a higher level in the spectrum as evidenced by the second and third terms of Eq. (10–19), but the carrier frequency is also shifted higher and lower according to those same terms.

The AM Amplifier. A method for amplitude-modulating a carrier is to feed the carrier through an amplifying stage whose gain varies in accordance with the frequency of the modulating signal. We have already seen that the gain of transistor stage is highly dependent upon quiescent emitter current. Suppose that total emitter current is caused to follow the instantaneous modulating wave as in

$$i_E = I_E + K'E_{mm} \cos \omega_m t. \tag{10–20}$$

Amplitude modulation will result provided that the maximum signal amplitude E_{mm} is smaller than the direct emitter current I_E. If gain is a function of total emitter current, and, more specifically if

$$A_v = K''i_E,$$

then voltage amplification is

$$A_v = K''(I_E + K'E_{mm} \cos \omega_m t). \tag{10–21}$$

Output voltage may be given by

$$v_o = A_v e_c. \tag{10–22}$$

Substitution of Eqs. (10–16) and (10–21) into Eq. (10–22) yields

$$v_o = K''(I_E + K'E_{mm} \cos \omega_m t)(E_{cm} \cos \omega_c t). \tag{10–23a}$$

This may be written as

$$v_o = K''I_E E_{cm} \cos \omega_c t$$

$$+ \frac{K'K''E_{mm}E_{cm}}{2} [\cos (\omega_c + \omega_m)t + \cos (\omega_c - \omega_m)t]. \tag{10–23b}$$

Thus

$$v_o = K \left\{ E_{cm} \cos \omega_c t + \frac{m_a E_{cm}}{2} [\cos (\omega_c + \omega_m)t + \cos (\omega_c - \omega_m)t] \right\}. \tag{10–23c}$$

This represents an amplitude-modulated wave as required by Eq. (10–19). The modulation factor m_a in the above equation equals $K'E_{mm}/I_E$.

Because a perfectly proportional relationship between gain and bias was previously assumed, the expression for v_o contained no harmonics or signals of unwanted frequencies. Undesirable signals always result from practical modulation techniques, and a tuned circuit is used in the collector of the modulator stage to provide the necessary frequency selectivity. Naturally the bandpass characteristic of such a circuit must include the carrier and both sidebands.

The modulating signal may be injected into a carrier-amplifying stage as base signal, emitter signal, or collector signal. Because the frequency of the carrier is always much higher than the modulating frequency, capacitors and transformers may be used to maintain separation of signals. Thus the capacitor across the modulation input in each circuit, C_e, C_b and C_c in a, b and c of Fig. 10–13 respectively, is chosen as a short-circuit for the carrier only; one

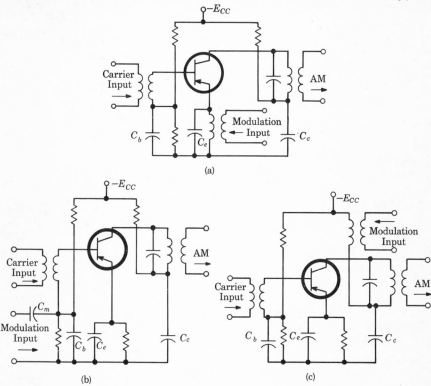

Fig. 10–13. Modulator circuits: (a) emitter modulation; (b) base modulation; (c) collector modulation.

would naturally not want to ground the modulation at its input. C_m in Fig. 10–13b blocks d-c; the remaining capacitors in each circuit are useful in bypassing all a-c from the parallel d-c path.

Base and emitter modulation are very similar, both methods represent a sort of "low-level modulation," because operation is limited to the most linear portion of the gain vs. i_E curve. Shea [10] has shown almost perfect linearity using emitter injection up to 92% modulation, with base injection resulting in more distortion.

Collector modulation causes collector-to-emitter voltage to vary with the modulation voltage. The most linear region of the gain vs. v_{CE} curve is at low levels of potential, therefore collector injection will also be limited to low signal levels.

Frequency Modulation. A frequency modulated wave results when the instantaneous deviation in frequency from the carrier is proportional to the instantaneous value of the modulating signal. Thus the angular frequency of the FM wave is described by

$$\omega = \omega_c + K_f E_{mm} \cos \omega_m t. \qquad (10\text{--}24)$$

Total phase angle $\phi = \omega t$, so that, if ω is variable,

$$\phi = \int_o^t \omega dt = \int_o^t (\omega_c + K_f E_{mm} \cos \omega_m t) dt.$$

Therefore

$$\phi = \omega_c t + \frac{K_f E_{mm}}{\omega_m} \sin \omega_m t, \qquad (10\text{--}25a)$$

or

$$\phi = \omega_c t + m_f \sin \omega_m t. \qquad (10\text{--}25b)$$

The *modulation index* is m_f. Substitution of Eq. (10–25b) into the carrier equation, $e = E_{cm} \cos \phi$, yields

$$e = E_{cm} \cos (\omega_c t + m_f \sin \omega_m t). \qquad (10\text{--}26)$$

This is the general equation for a frequency-modulated wave. Phase modulation results in a similar voltage equation.

The methods for attaining an FM waveform will not be discussed here. Our interest in FM in this chapter will center about the reception of a frequency-modulated wave and not in its generation.

10–3. Detection. It is, of course, necessary to separate the amplitude-modulated wave into its components, carrier and signal, in order to retrieve the intelligence in a communications system. The process of separation of information from the carrier and sidebands is called *detection* or *demodulation*. The carrier can be looked at as a tool for the successful transmission of electromagnetic radiations; it is discarded at the receiver after its purpose has been served.

Diode Detection. Two-electrode devices, the semiconductor diode in particular, are very popular elements for detection. The volt-ampere characteristic of the diode, even when idealized as in Fig. 10–14, is nonlinear in the sense that it will pass only signals of a particular polarity, and it can be shown that a nonlinear characteristic is essential for both the modulation and the demodulation processes.

The ideal diode characteristic is given mathematically by

$$i_b = \frac{e_b}{r_p} \quad \text{for } e_b > 0$$

and

$$i_b = 0 \quad \text{for } e_b < 0$$

i_b and e_b are the instantaneous plate current and plate-to-cathode voltage respectively, and r_p the dynamic plate resistance (forward diode resistance).

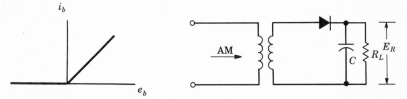

Fig. 10–14. Idealized diode characteristic.   Fig. 10–15. Simple diode detector circuit with filter and load.

All diodes, as stated in Chapter 1, whether they be of the semiconductor or the vacuum types, are discussed in terms of vacuum-tube quantities (i_b, e_b, r_p, etc.).

For an analysis of diode detection, we shall consider only the popular circuit of Fig. 10–15, operating so as to perform what is commonly referred to as *envelope detection* or *linear detection*. In appearance this is merely a rectifier type of circuit with capacitor input filter, so rectification studies will prove helpful in analyzing such an envelope detector.

The waveform available to the circuit is that of an amplitude-modulated wave, with a high-frequency carrier and a low-frequency envelope usually varying according to audio-frequency modulation. In other words, the diode slices off negative-going portions of the composite waveform. The capacitor may be thought of as shorting all of the carrier to ground, or, alternatively, providing a low impedance to the carrier so that most of the carrier voltage will drop across r_p. The capacitor charges up to the peak of the composite wave through the fairly low r_p, and then, on negative half cycles of the carrier, tries to discharge through the relatively high-resistance load R_L. Because the capacitor is chosen so that this discharge is very slight in the time available between carrier half cycles, the voltage available at R_L is simply the audio-frequency modulation superimposed upon a constant level, that level resulting from the rectification process.

An average or direct voltage exists across the load during all periods when the circuit is in operation, and that potential will alter the preceding idealized discussion, for the diode operating point, in the presence of signal, will be at $-E_R$ volts along the e_b axis instead of 0. Although, in reality, E_R is not a constant-valued quantity, it will herein be assumed constant in order to simplify the analysis. The instantaneous potential applied to the diode can now be written as

$$e_b = E_{cm}(1 + m_a \cos \omega_m t) \cos \omega_c t - E_R. \qquad (10\text{--}27a)$$

In a further quest for simplicity, this equation will be written as

$$e_b = E' \cos \theta - E_R, \qquad (10\text{--}27b)$$

with $E' = E_{cm}(1 + m_a \cos \omega_m t)$. E' will be treated as a constant when only a few cycles of the carrier are being investigated. Over a single cycle of the carrier the average of the load current is given by an integration of the current waveform. Thus

$$I_R = \frac{1}{2\pi} \int_{-\pi}^{\pi} \frac{e_b}{r_p} d\theta. \qquad (10\text{--}28)$$

Because there is conduction between $-\theta_s$ and $+\theta_s$, as shown in Fig. 10–16,

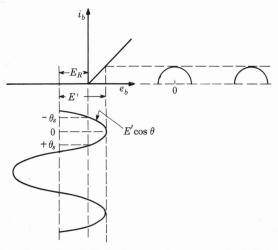

Fig. 10–16.   Operation of diode detector during a cycle of the carrier.

the integration limits in Eq. (10–28) may be changed. Substitution of Eq. (10–27b) into the integral and evaluation yields

$$I_R = \frac{1}{\pi r_p} (E' \sin \theta_s - E_R \theta_s). \qquad (10\text{--}29)$$

Recall that $E_R = I_R R_L$ if $R_L \gg 1/\omega_c C$. Observation of Fig. 10–16 shows

$\cos \theta_s = E_R/E'$, and therefore

$$E_R = \frac{E'R_L}{\pi r_p} (\sin \theta_s - \theta_s \cos \theta_s). \tag{10-30}$$

Removal of E' gives

$$E_R = \frac{E_{cm}R_L}{\pi r_p} (\sin \theta_s - \theta_s \cos \theta_s) + \frac{E_{mm}R_L}{\pi r_p} (\sin \theta_s - \theta_s \cos \theta_s) \cos \omega_m t. \tag{10-31}$$

Eq. (10-31) indicates that a substantial direct voltage is present across the load, and that it is highly dependent upon carrier magnitude. The second term shows that the modulating frequency has been recovered without distortion.

Practically, distortion is evident in most demodulators because of curvature in the diode characteristic, and because for some modulation frequencies the capacitor cannot discharge at the same rate as the modulation envelope decreases. An empirically derived relation [9] for designers indicates that distortion is not excessive if

$$\frac{1}{R_L C} \geq m_a \omega_m. \tag{10-32}$$

Transistor Detectors. The transistor is used occasionally as a detector. It is capable of detection because of the diode-like characteristic of its emitter-base input circuit. When operated at a very low quiescent emitter current (less than 50 μa), the detection performance of a transistor is good; it provides signal gain and therefore may be used to play the dual roles of detector and first audio amplifier. Where AGC is used, more control power is available with a transistor detector.

As we have seen in Chapter 5, low emitter current results in low gain, and therefore the gain provided by a transistor detector will not be as great as that of a regular audio amplifier. A simple transistor detector stage is illustrated in Fig. 10-17. A small base-bias is provided by R_2 and R_3; the d-c

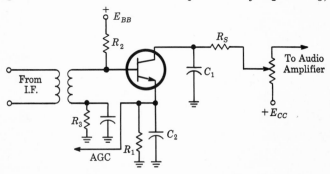

Fig. 10-17.   Transistor detector.

level at the emitter, after detection, is fed back for AGC purposes. Capacitors C_1 and C_2 are of 0.01 µf, a size consistent with the requirement for low I.F. impedance in broadcast receiver operation, but they do not effectively short the audio modulation. R_s helps to maintain a direct collector potential that is fairly constant, and therefore not too seriously affected by volume control setting.

FM Demodulation. An FM detector must be capable of changing variations in frequency into variations in amplitude. Because it is desired that amplitude variations caused by noise and unwanted signals not be reproduced in the loudspeaker, the FM receiver sometimes includes an amplitude-limiting circuit. This *limiter* precedes the detector and provides the detector with a substantially constant amplitude signal above a certain low level. Limiting action is possible through use of the saturation and cutoff regions of transistor characteristics. When a *ratio detector* is being used, the translation from FM to AM can be accomplished without external limiting, for the ratio detector circuit is insensitive to amplitude variations. Because ratio detectors are primarily diode circuits, and because analysis is fairly involved, no description of such circuits will be attempted. The reader is referred to the excellent treatment available in other texts.[8, 9]

10–4. Conversion and Mixing. In the superheterodyne receiver, the incoming modulated carrier (R.F.) is combined with a locally generated waveform to produce a new frequency, the I.F., which is also modulated and is at

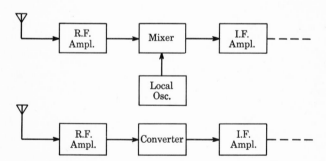

Fig. 10–18. Block diagrams of receiver front end—local oscillator and converter systems for obtaining the I.F.

lower frequency than the original carrier. This combining of waveforms may be accomplished in a *mixer* stage, or the local oscillator and mixing functions may be combined in a single stage. When this latter procedure is used the process is described as *frequency conversion* and the stage is said to be a frequency converter. The two possible methods for producing the amplitude-modulated I.F. are shown in Fig. 10–18 in block form.

Some choose to view frequency conversion as a modulation process because the amplitude of one signal is made to follow the variations of another signal. The local oscillator output corresponds to the waveform to be modulated and the R.F. wave is the modulating signal. Others feel that frequency conversion is detection, and the converter is frequently called the "first detector" because a frequency shifting from the R.F. level to I.F. level is accomplished.

The mixing of two waveforms in a linear device does not result in the generation of waveforms of new frequencies. Therefore, again, a nonlinear characteristic will be necessary. A square-law characteristic such as

$$i_c = K e_b{}^2 \tag{10-33}$$

satisfies the requirements. Consider the amplitude-modulated waveform mathematically described by

$$e_1 = E_{cm} \cos \omega_c t + \frac{m_a E_{cm}}{2} \cos (\omega_c - \omega_m)t + \frac{m_a E_{cm}}{2} \cos (\omega_c + \omega_m)t. \tag{10-34}$$

The local oscillator voltage is given by

$$e_2 = E_{xm} \cos \omega_x t. \tag{10-35}$$

Addition of these two voltages to give e_b and squaring their sum as indicated by Eq. (10-33) results in a host of terms; those involving ω_c, ω_x, $\omega_c + \omega_x$ and $\omega_c + \omega_x \pm \omega_m$ and their harmonics will be discarded because it is desired that ω_i, the intermediate frequency, be lower than the carrier, ω_c, and that tuned coupling to the following stage will pass only those frequencies in the neighborhood of the I.F. Thus, the angular I.F. will be

$$\omega_i = \omega_c - \omega_x. \tag{10-36}$$

The terms of interest are

$$i_c = K E_{xm} E_{cm} \left[\cos (\omega_c - \omega_x)t + \frac{m_a}{2} \cos (\omega_c - \omega_x + \omega_m)t \right.$$

$$\left. + \frac{m_a}{2} \cos (\omega_c - \omega_x - \omega_m)t \right]. \tag{10-37}$$

This equation may be written in terms of the I.F.

$$i_c = K E_{xm} E_{cm} \left[\cos \omega_i t + \frac{m_a}{2} \cos (\omega_i + \omega_m)t + \frac{m_a}{2} \cos (\omega_i - \omega_m)t \right]. \tag{10-38}$$

A comparison of Eq. (10-38) with Eq. (10-34) clearly shows the frequency translation that has taken place.

A typical converter stage is shown in Fig. 10-19. Emitter injection of the oscillator coil (T_1) signal is used to minimize interaction between the oscillator and R.F. sections. Resistors R_1, R_2 and R_3 provide and maintain the

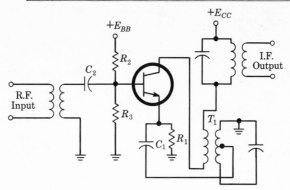

Fig. 10–19. Transistor converter stage.

operating point, with C_1 bypassing R_1 and C_2 blocking d-c from the input transformer secondary.

10–5. The AM Receiver. The preceding material will now be integrated in order to briefly study the complete superheterodyne AM receiver. A general block diagram of this type of receiver is shown in Fig. 10–20. In operation only the R.F. stage and the local oscillator are tuned to receive a specific station. All other portions of the set are pretuned at the factory or in service alignment. The I.F. stages must handle only the intermediate frequency (455 kc or 262 kc for example) and sidebands; the audio stages just amplify the modulation frequencies. Thus each incoming signal is converted

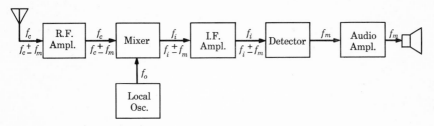

Fig. 10–20. Block diagram for complete AM receiver.

to the same I.F. and amplified by high-gain, fixed-tuned stages designed for the required selectivity.

The frequencies at various points within the receiver are shown in the diagram with the following abbreviations:

$$f_c = \text{carrier frequency}$$
$$f_m = \text{modulation frequency (audio)}$$
$$f_o = \text{local oscillator frequency}$$
$$f_i = \text{intermediate frequency}$$

Deviations from the general block diagram are common. The R.F. stage may be omitted in certain receiver designs, because of economic considerations; the functions of separate local oscillator and mixer circuits may be performed by a single converter stage; and AGC may be shown on the diagram connecting the appropriate blocks. The number of transistors used in the I.F. portion may differ among designs owing to costs or owing to the theory that greater receiver gain is achievable from additional audio stages because transistors provide more gain at low frequencies.

Naturally the receiver takes on the form dictated by design specifications regarding sensitivity, output power, frequency response, distortion, costs, etc.

In our brief study of the AM receiver, attention will be focused upon the complete radio schematic shown in Fig. 10–21. Because this circuit offers a number of interesting features, it was selected to be included here. A discussion of these features follows.

Upon first examination, notice that both p-n-p and n-p-n types are used with a single 9-volt supply, negative grounded. The common-emitter orientation is used throughout. The n-p-n transistors use $+9$ volts as their collector supply; p-n-p units have their collectors at d-c ground with the $+9$ volts supplied to their emitters. Notice that base-bias resistors are more or less opposites when using different transistor conductivity types; this is apparent when the converter stage is compared with the second I.F. stage.

The AGC line is from the plate of the detector diode to the base of the first I.F. stage. Base bias for that stage is obtained from the AGC line, and in the absence of signal there is a quiescent base current because of the connection through R_{10} to the supply. The output pair is conventional Class-B push-pull with some base bias for the elimination of crossover distortion. Bypassed emitter resistance is used in all Class-A stages and what we have called single-battery bias is used throughout except where AGC feedback is introduced.

The a-c path commences with signal pickup in the antenna coil L_1. For the frequency that C_1 is adjusted for, series resonance results in the greater portion of the signal being available at the base of the converter. Unwanted signals (off resonance) find C_1 part of a high reactance and drop across the untuned L-C series combination, leaving little signal at the relatively low-impedance converter input.

Collector-to-emitter coupling through the oscillator coil L_2 provides the adjustable locally generated frequency. The I.F., formed from signal mixing in the converter, is transformer coupled to the first I.F. stage. The I.F. stages are unneutralized. Detection is accomplished with a point-contact diode in the conventional manner; the driver and output pair are also conventional.

10–6. The FM Receiver. FM receivers use the superheterodyne principle, and in Fig. 10–22 a block diagram of such a system is shown. The frequencies

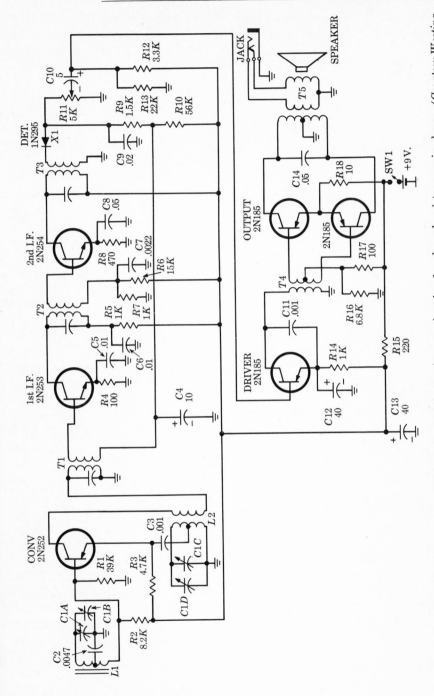

Fig. 10-21. Typical battery-powered AM receiver. All capacitors are in microfarads and resistors are in ohms. (*Courtesy Westing-house Electric Corporation.*)

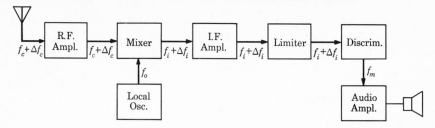

Fig. 10–22. Block diagram for complete FM receiver.

at various points within the receiver are shown and the following abbreviations are used:

$$f_c = \text{carrier frequency}$$
$$\Delta f_c = \text{carrier variation due to modulation}$$
$$f_o = \text{local oscillator frequency}$$
$$f_i = \text{intermediate frequency}$$
$$\Delta f_i = \text{I.F. variation due to modulation}$$
$$f_m = \text{modulation frequency (audio)}$$

Because high-frequency audio signals are accentuated by a *preemphasis* network in the FM transmitter in order to improve the signal strength relative to noise, the FM receiver must include a response-shaping network (*deemphasis*) to reduce the highs.

The application of transistors to FM circuits has proceeded rather slowly because of the poor transistor performance of early production types at FM frequencies (88 to 108 mc). The advent of modern high-frequency types such as the drift transistor with its small effective base width and low feedback capacitance has resulted in satisfactory FM reception.

J. W. Englund and H. Thanos at the Radio Corporation of America have described a complete all-transistor battery-operated FM receiver.[3] The schematic diagram of this receiver is shown in Fig. 10–23. Nine transistors, three semiconductor diodes and a thermistor are used in the circuit in addition to the normal complement of usual passive circuit elements. This circuit will be discussed because it makes use of many of the aforementioned electronic principles. In the paragraphs to follow some of the many engineering considerations associated with the design of a circuit of this type will be mentioned.

Starting with the front end, it is immediately obvious that the R.F., mixer and oscillator stages are common-base oriented. This configuration provides a higher usable gain than does the common-emitter connection and simplifies the design of the output coil by providing a higher output resistance which results in a more favorable operating circuit Q. Because the drift transistor used is inherently stable over the FM bandwidth when used in the common-base configuration, maximum available gain can be realized consistent with economical transformer construction. Some ten to fifteen db of power gain can be attained from the R.F. amplifier.

The input and output coils of the R.F. amplifier stage (L_1 and L_3) are designed to provide a match at 108 mc to give the highest circuit gain at the frequency at which the transistor has inherently less gain, and also to provide a good signal-to-noise ratio by minimizing input-circuit loss. An emitter current of 1.5 ma was chosen as the operating bias of the R.F. stage because this value provides the best balance between maximum available gain, good signal-to-noise ratios and AGC performance.

Coupling between the R.F. coil L_3 and the mixer is achieved through capacitor C_{12}, which results in a match between the input resistance of mixer, the parallel combination of the R.F. transistor output resistance, and the R.F. coil parallel-tuned resistance. The mixer transistor is operated at an emitter current of 0.6 milliampere and a collector-to-base voltage of 11.1 volts, with 125 millivolts rms of oscillator injection voltage. This operating point and value of injection voltage result in minimum noise contribution of the mixer and maximum gain, while avoiding any tendency of the base-to-emitter junction to become reverse-biased because of excessive oscillator swing. The first I.F. coil in the collector circuit of the mixer is designed to provide an approximate match to the output resistance of the mixer for increased front-end gain.

The oscillator circuit operates as a grounded-base circuit and needs no phase shift in the feedback network to sustain oscillation. Careful circuit design must be utilized, however, to compensate for the transconductance phase shift at the highest frequency of oscillation (118.7 mc). Feedback from collector to emitter is obtained through a 4-$\mu\mu$f capacitor, C_8. Inductor L_2 is placed in the emitter-base circuit to correct for the transconductance phase shift. Because the oscillator transistor phase shift is controlled, a fixed value of inductance may be used. The design of the oscillator d-c bias circuit is such that the emitter current and collector-to-base voltage vary in a prescribed manner to provide oscillator-frequency compensation with a change in supply voltage. Frequency compensation with temperature, although not included in this design, can be added by the use of a temperature-sensitive capacitor. The over-all circuit gain of the front end of the receiver at 88 and 108 mc is 26.5 and 22.5 db, respectively, with a noise factor of 6 db.

In the design of the I.F. amplifier transformers, it is necessary to know the power gain at the intermediate frequency (10.7 mc). Based on amplifier stability considerations, a usable gain of 23 db per stage may be obtained. This usable gain figure is obtained by reference to the input and output resistance of the device. R_{in} is 325 ohms and R_{out} is 24,000 ohms at 10.7 mc for the transistor type selected.

The I.F. amplifier portion of the receiver shown in Fig. 10–23 has two transistors operating in the neutralized common-emitter configuration and one transistor in the unneutralized common-emitter configuration. Three double tuned transformers T_1, T_2 and T_3 are used for coupling. The design of the primary impedance of the ratio-detector transformer, which is dictated by the large-signal capabilities of the driver transistor, does not require neutralization because sufficient mismatch is provided for stability.

Although AGC voltage is available at the output of the ratio detector, it is advisable to obtain AGC from the driver transformer through a 1N295 diode to prevent undue loading at the output of the ratio detector. AGC is applied to the I.F. stage first, and then amplified. AGC derived from the emitter of the first I.F. stage is applied to the base of the R.F. amplifier stage. The large-signal capabilities are further improved by the incorporation of a limiter resistor R_{27} in the output of the second I.F. amplifier.

The ratio-detector circuit is of conventional design and incorporates balancing resistors to provide good AM rejection. Also in conjunction with these balancing resistors, resistor R_{28} is placed in series with the tertiary winding to provide further AM rejection. The audio signal is derived from this point and fed through a volume control to the base of the audio-driver stage. The standard deemphasis curve is obtained through the use of a 0.001 microfarad capacitor, C_{45}, across the driver transformer and a 0.02-microfarad capacitor, C_{49}, across the output transformer. The output stage is operated Class-B and is capable of delivering one watt of audio-output power at 10 per cent distortion. The over-all audio gain is approximately 70 db.

Parts List for FM Receiver

C_1 C_{23} C_{30} C_{36} = 5 $\mu\mu$f
C_2 C_7 C_9 C_{10} C_{17} C_{18} C_{21} C_{24} C_{25} C_{27} C_{28} C_{31} C_{33} C_{34} C_{35} = 0.005 μf
C_3 C_5 C_{14} = 1–10 $\mu\mu$f
C_4 C_6 C_{15} = 3–15 $\mu\mu$f
C_8 = 4 $\mu\mu$f
C_{11} C_{16} = 470 $\mu\mu$f
C_{12} = 8.2 $\mu\mu$f
C_{13} = 3 $\mu\mu$f
C_{19} C_{22} C_{29} = 31 $\mu\mu$f
C_{20} C_{26} C_{32} = 33 $\mu\mu$f
C_{37} C_{44} = 5 μf, electrolytic, 6 v
C_{38} = 47 $\mu\mu$f
C_{39} = 120 $\mu\mu$f
C_{40} C_{41} = 330 $\mu\mu$f
C_{43} = 2 μf, electrolytic, 6 v.
C_{45} = 0.001 μf
C_{46} C_{47} C_{48} = 100 μf, electrolytic, 12 v
C_{49} = 0.02 μf
L_1 = 4 turns No. 18 Heavy Formvar, $\frac{3}{8}$″ diameter, spaced, $\frac{3}{4}$″ long, tapped at 1$\frac{1}{2}$ turns from bottom
L_2 L_5 = 6.2 μh
L_3 = 4 turns No. 18 Heavy Formvar, $\frac{3}{8}$″ diameter, spaced, $\frac{3}{4}$″ long
L_4 = 3 turns No. 18 Heavy Formvar, $\frac{3}{8}$″ diameter, spaced, $\frac{3}{4}$″ long
R_1 R_2 R_{14} = 820 ohms
R_3 R_6 = 39,000 ohms
R_4 R_7 R_{11} R_{12} R_{15} R_{23} = 680 ohms
R_5 R_9 R_{29} R_{30} = 4700 ohms
R_8 R_{18} R_{22} R_{27} = 1000 ohms
R_{10} = 68,000 ohms
R_{13} = 43,000 ohms
R_{16} R_{20} R_{32} = 33,000 ohms
R_{17} R_{21} R_{24} = 5600 ohms
R_{19} = 220 ohms
R_{25} = 470 ohms
R_{26} = 1000 ohms
R_{36} = 3300 ohms
R_{28} = 100 ohms

R_{31} = potentiometer, 25,000 ohms
R_{33} R_{35} = 6800 ohms
R_{34} = 1500 ohms
R_{36} = 3300 ohms
R_{37} = 68 ohms
R_{38} R_{39} = 3.9 ohms
R_T = 100 ohms at 25° C
T_1: Q_{OU} (unloaded, uncoupled) of primary is 90 and of secondary is 66; Q_{LU} (loaded, uncoupled) is 53.
T_2, T_3: Q_{OU} of primary and secondary is 67; Q_{LU} is 53.
T_4: Q_{OU} of primary is 41 and secondary is 90; Q_{LU} is 20 and 9.
T_5: impedance ratio (primary to secondary) is 10,000 ohms to 1000 ohms.
T_6: primary impedance 250 ohms collector-to-collector, center-tapped; secondary 3.2 ohms.

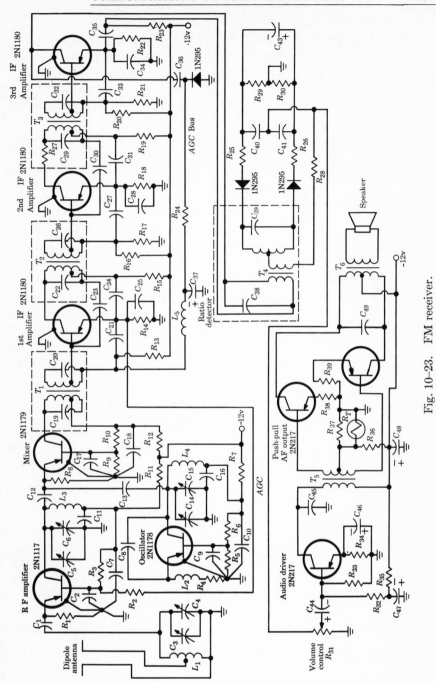

Fig. 10-23. FM receiver.

Fig. 10-24 shows the tuning characteristic of this FM receiver for input signals of 11, 110, 1,100, and 11,000 microvolts. The peak-to-peak separation varies from about 160 kilocycles at 11 microvolts to 330 kilocycles at 110,000 microvolts. The AM rejection ratio of the receiver varies from -20 db at sensitivity level of 2.5 microvolts to a maximum of -36 db at 12 microvolts and stabilizes at -35 db up to 100,000 microvolts. (For a definition of unfamiliar terms, see, for example, Reference 11.)

Fig. 10-25 contains curves for sensitivity, image rejection, and I.F. rejection from 88 to 108 megacycles. Sensitivity varies from 4 to 5 microvolts, image rejection from 40 to 25 db, and I.F. rejection from 72 to 74 db. Frequency response for this receiver is down 3 db at 230 cps and 12,000 cps. Additional performance information concerning the circuit is available.

Certain additional considerations are appropriate. Stabilization of oscillator frequency with variations in temperature and supply voltage, reduction in noise, incorporation of automatic frequency control and cost reduction through use of fewer transistors are some of the many areas that warrant further study by the designers.[3]

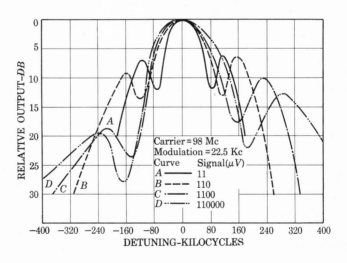

Fig. 10-24. Tuning characteristics of transistor FM receiver.[3]

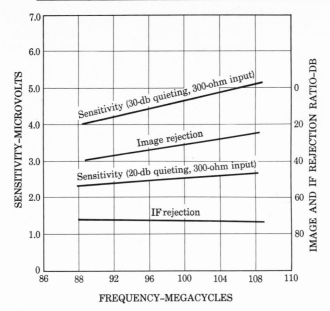

Fig. 10–25. Sensitivity, image rejection and I.F. rejection of receiver over the FM band.

PROBLEMS

10–1. Solve for the expression for the instantaneous current in the series R-L-C circuit of Fig. 10–1 suddenly supplied with a direct voltage of E volts. The circuit has been at rest for some time prior to switching. Make necessary assumptions so that the current wave will be comprised of a damped oscillation. Express the frequency of this oscillation in terms of the circuit parameters.

10–2. Analyze the common-base oriented transistor with $\alpha > 1$ for the required conditions for a negative input resistance.

10–3. A common-base connected transistor is to be used as an oscillator with a transformer coupling its input and output circuits. Draw the complete circuit and describe all differences between your circuit and that shown in Fig. 10–4.

10–4. Confirm Eqs. (10–8) and (10–9) for the phase-shift oscillator.

10–5. Confirm Eqs. (10–11) and (10–12) for the Colpitts-type oscillator.

10–6. Confirm Eqs. (10–13) and (10–14) for the Hartley-type oscillator.

10–7. Include mutual inductance in the derivations for starting conditions and frequency of oscillation for a Hartley-type oscillator.

10–8. Write the circuit determinant for the generalized oscillator shown in the accompanying diagram.

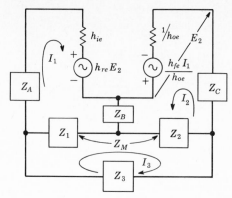

Problem 10–8.

10–9. Can you find a relationship among external elements, from the solution to Problem 10–8, that will result in the frequency of oscillation being completely independent of the transistor parameters?

10–10. A quartz crystal has the following equivalent parameters: $L = 10$ h., $C = 0.04$ $\mu\mu f$, $R = 5,000$ ohms, $C_h = 3$ $\mu\mu f$.

(a) Determine the resonant frequency of the series portion of the circuit.

(b) Determine the Q of the series branch.

(c) Determine the resonant frequency of the entire parallel circuit (neglect R but include C_h).

(d) By what per cent does the parallel resonant frequency differ from the series resonant frequency?

10–11. In the tuned-emitter, tuned-base oscillator of the accompanying

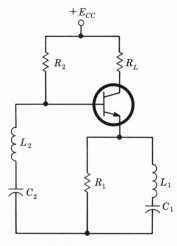

Problem 10–11.

diagram R_1 and R_2 are large-valued resistances useful for biasing. Prove that the frequency of oscillation for this circuit is given by

$$\omega^2 \cong \frac{C_1 + C_2}{(L_1 + L_2)C_1C_2}.$$

10–12. So-called *square-law* or *small-signal* modulation is produced when a device with a nonlinear transfer characteristic, for example one of the form

$$i_c = K_1e_b + K_2e_b{}^2,$$

is excited with a base voltage that is the sum of modulation and carrier frequency terms as

$$e_b = E_{mm} \cos \omega_m t + E_{cm} \cos \omega_c t.$$

(a) Show that the resulting expression for collector current contains terms involving ω_c, ω_m, $(\omega_c + \omega_m)$, $(\omega_c - \omega_m)$, and harmonics of the two input frequencies.

(b) Derive the expression for i_c that contains only terms in ω_c, $(\omega_c + \omega_m)$ and $(\omega_c - \omega_m)$ by assuming that a frequency selective network eliminates all terms not in the vicinity of ω_c.

(c) Prove that the modulation index may be given by $m_a = 2K_2E_{mm}/K_1$.

10–13. For a modulated wave given by

$$e = 100(1 + 0.4 \cos 2000t) \sin 10^6t$$

find the three frequencies contained in the wave and the peak amplitude of each.

10–14. Derive an expression for the sideband power as a percentage of carrier power in terms of the modulation factor m_a. 5000 watts of 30% amplitude-modulated R.F. power contains how much sideband power?

10–15. Square-law detection depends upon a voltage-current characteristic of the form

$$i_b = Ke_b{}^2.$$

If an amplitude-modulated wave

$$e_b = E_{cm}(1 + m_a \cos \omega_m t) \cos \omega_c t$$

is impressed upon a device with a characteristic as given above, show that i_b will contain terms in ω_m, $2\omega_m$, $2\omega_c$ and in the sum and difference of harmonics of the carrier and modulating frequency. Find the coefficients for each term of the expansion.

10–16. For the square-law detector of Problem 10–15, determine the highest allowable modulation index in order for second harmonic distortion to be limited to 10% of the fundamental (ω_m).

10–17. Show that a circuit element with a square-law characteristic (see

Problem 10–15) can be used as a frequency multiplier when $e = E_{\max} \sin \omega t$ is applied.

10–18. A superheterodyne AM receiver contains an R.F. amplifier, separate oscillator, three I.F. amplifiers, and a Class-B audio-amplifier pair. The I.F. is 455 kc, and the receiver is tuned to a station at 1050 kc, modulated at 1000 cps.

(a) Draw a block diagram clearly showing all necessary functions.

(b) On the diagram indicate the frequencies present in each stage.

10–19. Draw a block diagram for the AM receiver of Fig. 10–21.

10–20. Describe the function of each resistor in the circuit of Fig. 10–21.

10–21. Describe the function of each capacitor in the circuit of Fig. 10–21.

10–22. Describe the function of each inductor and transformer in the circuit of Fig. 10–21.

10–23. For the circuit of Fig. 10–21, compare the reactance of emitter bypass capacitors with the resistance they bypass for the audio and I.F. stages. The I.F. is 455 kc.

10–24. In the circuit of Fig. 10–21, what approximate direct voltages would be measured from base-to-ground and collector-to-ground for the I.F. and audio stages? Consider that the I.F. stages each operate at 1 ma, the driver at 2 ma, and the output pair at 0 ma.

10–25. Redraw the circuit of Fig. 10–21 showing only those components that make up the d-c portions of the circuit, in other words the components affecting the operating points.

10–26. Redraw the circuit of Fig. 10–21 showing only those components that make up the a-c portions of the circuit, in other words the components affecting the signal.

10–27. Repeat Problem 10–25 for the circuit of Fig. 10–23.

10–28. Repeat Problem 10–26 for the circuit of Fig. 10–23.

10–29. For the circuit of Fig. 10–23, draw a complete block diagram. Include the AGC path.

10–30. Discuss the operation of a ratio detector such as that used in the circuit of Fig. 10–23.

10–31. Discuss the crystal oscillator of the accompanying figure.

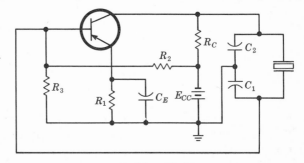

Problem 10–31.

REFERENCES

1. Clapp, J. K., "An Inductance-Capacitance Oscillator of Unusual Frequency Stability," *Proc.* IRE, vol. 36 (Mar., 1948).
2. DeWitt, D., and Rossoff, A. L., *Transistor Electronics*, McGraw-Hill Book Co., Inc., New York, 1957.
3. Englund, J. W., and Thanos, H., "Application of RCA Drift Transistors to FM Receivers," *IRE Trans.*, vol. BTR-5, no. 1 (Jan., 1959).
4. Happel, G. E., and Hesselberth, W. M., *Engineering Electronics*, McGraw-Hill Book Co., Inc., New York, 1953.
5. Hurley, R. F., *Junction Transistor Electronics*, John Wiley & Sons, Inc., New York, 1958.
6. Millman, J., *Vacuum-Tube and Semiconductor Electronics*, McGraw-Hill Book Co., Inc., New York, 1958.
7. Riddle, R. L., and Ristenbatt, M. P., *Transistor Physics and Circuits*, Prentice-Hall, Inc., Englewood Cliffs, New Jersey, 1958.
8. Ryder, J. D., *Electronic Fundamentals and Applications*, 2nd Ed., Prentice-Hall, Inc., Englewood Cliffs, New Jersey, 1959.
9. Seely, S., *Radio Electronics*, McGraw-Hill Book Co., Inc., New York, 1956.
10. Shea, R. F., *Transistor Circuit Engineering*, John Wiley & Sons, Inc., New York, 1957.
11. Terman, F. E., and Pettit, J. M., *Electronic Measurements*, McGraw-Hill Book Co., Inc., New York, 1952.
12. Wolfendale, E., *The Junction Transistor and Its Applications*, The Macmillan Co., New York, 1958.

Chapter 11

PULSE CIRCUITS

Continuous and generally sinusoidal currents and voltages were considered in the foregoing chapters. There are a great many applications where discontinuous and nonsinusoidal waveforms play an important role, and consequently this chapter will be devoted to *pulse* and *switching circuits*, those circuits wherein abrupt and often large changes in the important quantities occur. Changes of this sort often result from the presence or absence of an input drive, and faithful reproduction of the input waveform is sometimes not a requirement. Switching circuits are not conveniently analyzed by steady-state methods because operation involves the saturation and cutoff regions as well as the active region of the transistor characteristics.

Pulse circuits are required to perform certain functions; these functions may be summarized as follows:

1. Generation of pulse waveforms
2. Amplification of pulse waveforms
3. Shaping of pulse waveforms
4. Storage of digital information
5. Switching and gating

Generation and storage will be described in the section of this chapter devoted to multivibrators; item 2, the amplification of nonsinusoidal waveshapes, will be given some further attention and may also be classified under the video amplifier heading of Chapter 9. Item 3 will not be discussed here as it is primarily a passive-device function, but general switching theory, item 5, does warrant some attention here, and our discussion will proceed with the considerations involved.

11-1. Switching. The resistive load R_L shown in Fig. 11-1a is connected in a series circuit with a switch and a d-c supply. The resistor is to be supplied with current, and hence power, from the supply when the switch is closed. The generalized switch of the figure may take on one of many forms. For instance, it may be an electromechanical, a purely mechanical or a purely

304

electrical device. Often the power available to control the switch (to change its state from ON to OFF or vice versa) is small, and therefore the switch may also be required to provide amplification, for then, from a small-signal

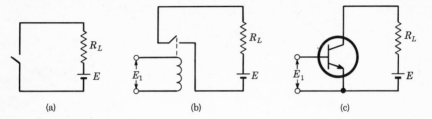

Fig. 11–1. Switching: (a) general circuit; (b) the relay as a switch; (c) the transistor as a switch.

command, it can control a great deal of load power by completing the R_L-E circuit.

An electromechanical switch, the relay for example, combines amplification with control. A small signal of either polarity (or even a-c) supplied to the relay coil will close the switch and complete the R_L-E circuit as shown in Fig. 11–1b. The signal applied must be more than a specified minimum in order for the relay to actuate and close the contacts; the relay will "drop out" and the contacts will open when the voltage E_1 decreases below a specified level.

The transistor may be used as a switch. In the circuit of Fig. 11–1c a transistor takes the place of the relay of the preceding figure. The low-power n-p-n transistor depicted requires, for the full ON condition, a potential E_1 of several hundred millivolts, or, alternately, a base current of several hundred microamperes of the correct polarity. The full ON condition exists when the transistor is in saturation, and consequently the resistance of the collector-to-emitter branch is very low. Various ON conditions are possible and correspond to operation within the active region of the collector characteristics, but for the time being let us concern ourselves with full ON. To turn the transistor OFF, opening of the base lead may not suffice, for I_{CEO} is the resulting collector-to-emitter current. The full OFF condition is attained when a small negative potential is applied to the input terminal pair to reverse-bias the emitter junction. The resulting load current is I_{CO} and may be just a few microamperes.

Let us now examine the advantages and disadvantages of the transistor in relation to the relay as a switching device. One measure of comparison is the ratio of open- to closed-circuit resistance introduced into the load circuit by the switching device. An ideal switch has infinite resistance when open, zero resistance when closed, and therefore an infinite resistance ratio. The relay approaches this ratio. However, the transistor when full ON or saturated does have a finite collector-emitter resistance, and when full OFF does pass some leakage current, so a finite resistance ratio is apparent. For a typical low-power germanium transistor, the saturation resistance may be of the order of 4 ohms and I_{CO} may be 5 μa at $V_{CE} = 10$ volts. These figures indicate an OFF-to-ON resistance ratio of 0.5×10^6. A silicon transistor for the same job may have a saturation resistance of 200 ohms, and I_{CO} may be 0.1 μa at $V_{CE} = 10$ volts. These numbers also yield a ratio of 0.5×10^6. Higher power transistors have lower saturation resistance but more leakage current.

The transistor is, as we have seen, inferior to an electromechanical switch in the aspect discussed above, but the devices may be compared on other counts. Because the transistor has no moving parts and therefore lacks mechanical contacts that are subject to wear, the semiconductor device is far more reliable. The transistor as a switch is smaller, quieter, more efficient electrically and costs less than a relay. A great advantage in electronic switching is the speed of that operation. Operating time is reduced by a factor of more than 1000 when the transistor is compared with a mechanical device. Where applicable, then, it may be concluded that electronic switching provides many advantages.

A brief discussion regarding transistor orientation is always appropriate when new uses for the device are considered. If switching were to be accomplished with a common-base oriented transistor, about as much input current (i_e) would be required as load current (i_c) to be controlled. With the common-emitter configuration a small base current can control a much larger collector current, and because of this internal amplification this configuration is the most widely used in switching circuits.

Limits. The common-emitter collector characteristics for a low-power transistor are illustrated in Fig. 11–2. A 2500-ohm load line has been drawn linking $E_{CC} = 15$ volts with $E_{CC}/R_L = 6$ ma. Point A represents the upper limit of the OFF region and point B represents saturation or full ON. Switching as previously discussed could occur between these extremes and should base current assume values of 125 μa or greater to drive collector current to point B, the transistor would be called a *saturating switch*. A *nonsaturating switch* is one in which base current variations cause operation between the region of point A and a point such as C. C represents the ON condition, and is located somewhere in the active region of the characteristics.

A saturating switch requires more base current "drive" and longer switching time, but results in a much lower ON resistance than does the nonsaturating type. With respect to collector dissipation the saturating type of switch has advantages. Both types exhibit low dissipation in the standby or OFF condition, but when ON the saturating switch has a much lower V_{CE}-I_C product. Should the load line as shown in Fig. 11–2 cut across the maximum-dissipation contour it is possible that the maximum allowable junction temperature of the transistor will not be exceeded, provided that the switching time is fast. Therefore, because their average dissipation is low, switching

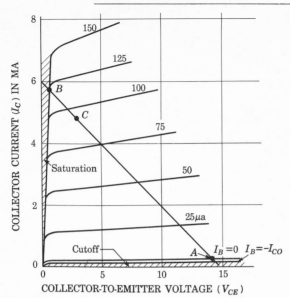

Fig. 11–2. Load line on collector characteristics with points of interest noted.

transistors can handle much larger voltages and currents without exceeding the rated maximum dissipation. A nonsaturating switch with a load line intersecting the maximum-dissipation contour must be carefully designed in order not to exceed the junction temperature limit; the duty cycle and tolerances must be accurately known.

In order to investigate more clearly the transistor operated in a switching mode, the common-emitter input characteristics for a typical low-power unit are illustrated in Fig. 11–3.

There are several possible OFF conditions for the common-emitter connected transistor, three of which are shown in Fig. 11–4. In (a) of the figure,

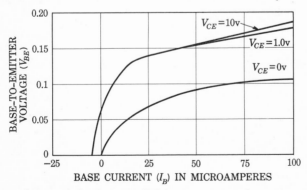

Fig. 11–3. Input characteristics for a typical low-power transistor, common-emitter connected.

zero base-to-emitter voltage is available because of the obvious short circuit across the input terminal pair; the resulting collector current is often given the symbol I_{CBS}. When the base terminal is open, as in Fig. 11–4b, no base

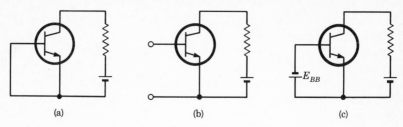

(a)   (b)   (c)

Fig. 11–4. OFF conditions for common-emitter connected transistor: (a) zero input voltage; (b) zero input current; (c) restraining input voltage.

current can exist, and collector current is symbolized by the familiar I_{CEO}. Collector current I_{CEO} is two or more times greater than I_{CBS}. A third method of turning OFF the transistor is by applying a restraining input voltage to reverse-bias the base-emitter diode. By choosing a suitable reverse bias the collector current can be most efficiently turned OFF; I_{CO}, the inevitable leakage, is then the remaining collector current.

To summarize switching states, it may be concluded that in the OFF condition transistor input and output resistances are high, small leakage currents are apparent, and collector voltage approaches the supply voltage E_{CC}. The saturated ON condition results in $I_C \cong E_{CC}/R_L$, $V_{CE} = I_C R_{CS} < 1$ volt, and a fairly low input resistance, with several hundred millivolts needed to supply the input terminal pair with the several hundred microamperes of base current necessary for the saturation of low-power transistor.

Drive. A universal test for transistors used as switches is their response to a *step* input function. A step function $Au(t)$ is a voltage or current that at $t = 0$ rises immediately and instantaneously from a value of zero to a value A and remains at that level afterwards. (A unit step function has a plateau value, A, of unity.) A plot of $Au(t)$ is shown in Fig. 11–5a. Mathematically, if the step function does not start at $t = 0$ but rather at some other time t_1,

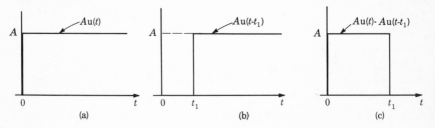

(a)   (b)   (c)

Fig. 11–5. Step functions.

the function can be described by $Au(t - t_1)$. Should a rectangular pulse be considered that rises at $t = 0$, and falls at $t = t_1$, then an addition of the two functions $u(t)$ and $-u(t - t_1)$ can describe the pulse. Thus, for Fig. 11–5c, $A[u(t) - u(t - t_1)]$ describes the resultant function.

Naturally, the ideal step function can only be approached in practice, for the ideal pulse, if described by a Fourier series, contains terms of frequencies to infinity. A device that would pass an ideal pulse must have an infinite frequency response. The transistor does not follow an ideal rectangular pulse, because of transit time and minority-carrier storage in its base.

The base current produced by a given base-to-emitter voltage will vary because of production tolerances and consequently a constant current source is generally used to provide a controlled value of I_B in saturating switching circuits.

Turn-on and Turn-off. Consider an ideal step function of voltage shown in Fig. 11–6a applied between base and emitter of an *n-p-n* transistor. The tran-

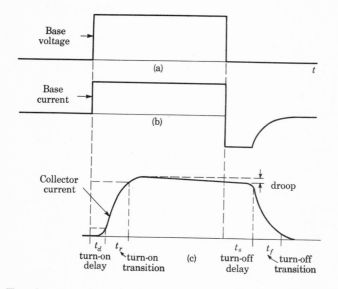

Fig. 11–6. Transistor step function response: (a) step of base voltage; (b) resulting base current; (c) resulting collector current.

sistor was in the OFF condition and the pulse is turning it ON. Base current is immediately evident, as in (b) of the figure, but collector current does not instantaneously respond. Electrons from the emitter must travel across the *p*-type base, and a finite time is required for their travel. This time is shown in (c) of the diagram as "turn-on delay." Electrons arriving at the collector travel by various paths; some paths are longer than others and consequently a finite time is again required before normal operation is achieved. This effect, wherein faster electrons traveling shorter paths arrive at their destination ahead of the less energetic and dispersed carriers, is referred to in the diagram as "turn-on transition." Delay time is generally measured from the beginning of the input pulse to the 10% point on the output waveform. Transition or rise time has, for its limits, the 10% and 90% marks.

When the transistor is driven into saturation, the collector junction is forward-biased, and the collector then emits electrons into the base (for *n-p-n*). This causes an excess of minority carriers in the base region. A saturated transistor cannot be effectively turned OFF until this "stored base charge" is reduced. Therefore the high current level in the collector is supported by this charge during the time interval immediately after the OFF command is given to the input terminals. *Minority-carrier storage effect* is the name given to the "turn-off delay" encountered. The "turn-off transition" results from different velocities and path lengths that affect the arrival time of the last electrons to reach the collector. Note that the base current suffers a reversal in direction when the base-driving voltage is removed; stored charge accounts for this base current.

To measure stored base charge a voltage pulse is applied to a circuit such as Fig. 11-7. If the pulse saturates the transistor, and the output (v_{ce}) wave-

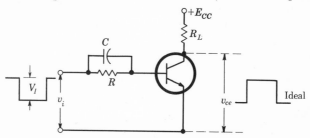

Fig. 11-7. Turn-off of a transistor with a voltage pulse. A speed-up capacitor is included, and ideal v_{ce} is shown.

form is observed for various test values of C, a "clean" or best turn-off will be observed with a particular value of C. In this instance clean means that v_{ce} will be straight-sided. The amount of stored base charge is then given by

$$Q_s = CV_I.$$

The capacitor, C, is often referred to as a "speed-up" capacitor. In circuit design, knowledge of Q_s from given data or from a test such as just described can be combined with information concerning the voltage amplitude of the pulse and base current required for saturation (I_B''). Then R can be determined from

$$R = \frac{V_I}{I_B''}.$$

It is of course desirable to minimize the total time required for a switching operation to be performed. Turn-on delay may be reduced by driving the base with a high current, for this provides a greater number of available carriers in that region. The rise time, t_r, is dependent in part upon the frequency response characteristics of the device, but can be reduced by application of transient circuit theory.

A speed-up in the switching time required to turn a transistor ON (t_r) can be accomplished by overdriving, supplying the base with a current pulse of sufficient amplitude to drive the transistor deep into saturation, rather than just to E_{CC}/R_L. Transistor performance can be approximated by the differential equations given in Problem 11–5 and derived in Problem 11–6, namely

$$\frac{di_c}{dt} + \omega_{\alpha e} i_c = \beta_o \omega_{\alpha e} i_b. \qquad (11\text{–}1)$$

The solution of Eq. (11–1), for a step function base current of Δ_B, is

$$i_c = \beta_o \Delta_B (1 - \epsilon^{-t/T}) \qquad (11\text{–}2)$$

with the time constant T equal to $1/\omega_{\alpha e}$. This expression predicts an exponential rise in collector current with time, as would be found in the current response of a series R-L circuit to a suddenly applied direct potential.

The time constant is the value of t that causes the exponential term to assume the form ϵ^{-1}, and represents the time required for 63.2% of the total transient change to occur. It would appear that a speed-up in i_c could be accomplished only by a reduction in T; however, it is to be remembered that we are dealing with a quantity, i_c, that will enter the saturation region of the collector characteristics, and saturation will end the transient, for collector current can be no larger than its saturated value. Consequently, to speed-up switching times we wish to get to saturation as rapidly as possible.

Fig. 11–8 shows the collector-current response to three input pulses. The A curve rises to a value of E_{CC}/R_L, or just to saturation. Curves B and C would rise (dotted lines) to twice and thrice the saturation collector current respectively were it not for saturation which prevents their complete rise. It is obvious from examination of the figure that curve C has the shortest transient time (t_3), and curve A has the longest (t_1).

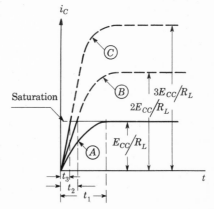

Fig. 11–8.   Collector-current response to input pulses.

Although the transition times are measured from 10% of the final value of the changing quantity to 90% of the final value; the regular network theory rules also apply here—95% of the total change occurs in time equal to three time constants and the transient is over in four time constants, for 98% of the total change has then occurred.

When turning OFF a transistor that has been in the ON state, the base region must be swept clean of minority carriers before collector current can cease. The turn-off period (t_f) is characterized by the same parameters as dictated turn-on, except that an initial collector current is apparent, which shall be designated as I_C'. If we consider that i_c will fall to zero, then

$$i_c = I_C'(\epsilon^{-t/T}). \tag{11-3}$$

But if a base-current drive is to be used to reduce the time required to reach cutoff,

$$i_c = I_C'\epsilon^{-t/T} - \beta_o\Delta_B(1 - \epsilon^{-t/T}) \tag{11-4}$$

more clearly describes the process. Just as overdriving can speed up the turn-on operation, so it can also be used, in the opposite sense, to turn off a transistor quickly.

Overdriving, when used to saturate or cut off a transistor, may tend to cause a higher input-junction dissipation than is apparent for normal operation, and consideration must often be given to this additional power conversion. An ideal base-current waveform for fast turn-on and turn-off is shown in Fig. 11–9. This waveform results in a speed-up of the drive into saturation, levels off at a value just necessary for saturation so that storage effects will be minimized, and overdrives into the cutoff region when shutoff is required.

A waveform approaching this ideal can be achieved when the speed-up capacitor previously discussed is incorporated into the input circuit of a switching transistor. If, again as in Fig. 11–9, the saturated base-current level is designated as I_B'' and the entire pulse height as I_B', then it is desired that the overdrive, represented by $I_B' - I_B''$, be supplied by the capacitive branch during the transient. The duration of time, designated as t_o, during which an overdrive is required need only be as long as is necessary for the collector current to reach saturation.

Consider the circuit of Fig. 11–10. What appears to be base bias, namely the $E_{BB} - R_2$ branch, also seems at first glance to be backwards, for E_{BB} is a negative potential and the circuit uses an n-p-n transistor. The function of E_{BB} and R_2 is to provide a base bias at cutoff; that is, to reverse-bias the input junction. This reverse bias on the emitter-base diode will allow only I_{CO} as the collector current.

Now, turning our attention to the C-R branch, we recall that the instantaneous current through a capacitor is given by

$$i = C\frac{dv}{dt}.$$

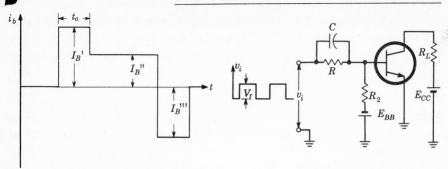

Fig. 11-9. Ideal base-current drive for a saturating switch.

Fig. 11-10. Switching circuit.

For the present problem the increment of voltage is V_I; the signal is going to change from 0 to $+V_I$ volts. The desired capacitive current, as previously stated, amounts to $I_B' - I_B''$, and if the switching time increment necessary and desired is designated as t_o, then the capacitance may be determined from

$$C = \frac{(I_B' - I_B'')t_o}{V_I}. \qquad (11\text{-}5)$$

A numerical example may be of assistance. Suppose that V_I is to step between 0 and $+10$ volts and a one microsecond rise and fall time is allowed for v_{ce}. The transistor used has a 2500-ohm load, $E_{CC} = 15$ volts and therefore the saturation collector current is 6 ma. The worst leakage current (I_{CO}) to be expected is 40 μa. Available $E_{BB} = 5$ volts, and consider that Figs. 11-2 and 11-3 apply.

For the same circuit, namely that of Fig. 11-10, R_2 may be calculated from $E_{BB}/I_{CO} = 5/40 \times 10^{-6} = 125{,}000$ ohms. To drive the transistor represented by the average curve (Fig. 11-2) just into saturation requires 125 μa of base current, so $I_B'' = 125$ μa. From Fig. 11-3, the V_{BE} drop, is found to be, for $V_{CE} = 0$, about 0.1 volt. Therefore, to determine R

$$R = \frac{V_I - 0.1}{I_B'' + I_{CO}} = \frac{9.9}{165 \times 10^{-6}} = 60{,}000 \text{ ohms.}$$

The reason that the denominator of the above fraction takes on the form shown is clear when one realizes that base current, for the turn-on operation, starts at $-I_{CO}$ and must rise to $+I_B''$, therefore its total excursion is $I_B'' + I_{CO}$.

Because the capacitor should handle a current pulse considerably greater than the saturation requirement, and because one microsecond has been allotted as the rise time for this example, a transient study can be made to determine the base-current overdrive needed to reach collector-current saturation in one microsecond. For a transistor with $f_{ab} = 5$ mc, from Eq. (11-2),

$$6 \times 10^{-3} = 50\Delta_B \left[1 - \epsilon^{-\left(\frac{10^{-6}}{1/[1-50/51][5 \times 10^{+6}][2\pi]} \right)} \right],$$

so

$$\Delta_B = 257 \ \mu\text{a}.$$

Because the resistive branch will supply the base with the plateau value of 125 μa, the remaining 132 μa must come thru C:

$$132 \times 10^{-6} = C \frac{10}{10^{-6}}.$$

So $C = 13.2 \ \mu\mu\text{f}$ is the required value for the speed-up capacitor.

A nonsaturated switch with its ON levels in the active region of the collector characteristics can provide faster operation because storage time, t_s, will be extremely short. Many circuits have been proposed to "clamp" collector voltage at an unsaturated value. The reader is referred to the literature.

11-2. Pulse Amplifiers. It is naturally necessary that amplifying devices for pulse waveforms be available. Such amplifiers must have a very wide bandwidth if the pulse is to be passed without the introduction of a great deal of distortion. Video amplifiers briefly discussed in Chapter 9 have similar specifications.

As an example of a successful pulse amplifier, "NBS Preferred Circuit No. 201" has been chosen. This circuit, one of the first "preferred" transistor circuits, is part of the nationwide program inaugurated by the U. S. Navy Bureau of Aeronautics in conjunction with the National Bureau of Standards to list proved electronics circuits for the help of circuit designers, equipment manufacturers, and the military services. The objectives of the preferred circuits program are to conserve engineering manpower, simplify maintenance, provide greater operational reliability, lower inventories and original equipment prices, and to provide for faster production of complex electronic equipment.

NBS Preferred Circuit No. 201, Silicon Transistor Video Amplifier, is a two-stage circuit employing feedback from the collector of stage two to the emitter of stage one. Appendix III contains a complete description of the circuit, its specifications, and operational characteristics. Typical performance is discussed for several values of the feedback resistor located in the emitter leg of the first transistor. It is obvious from the information given that more feedback results in lowered gain, higher input resistance, lower output resistance, greater input-signal amplitude handling capacity, faster rise time and less droop (greater bandwidth), and increased insensitivity to temperature, transistor parameter variations, etc.

Frequency response information for the pulse amplifier is not offered in the description given, but transient response is available. A rule for converting step-function response to frequency response has been given [9] and pertains to low-pass amplifiers (as opposed to band-pass amplifiers) without excessive overshoot. Denoting T as the 10% to 90% rise time of the step function response, and (BW) as the 3-db bandwidth, then

$$T(BW) = 0.35 \text{ to } 0.45. \tag{11-6}$$

The 0.35 value is used for overshoots of less than 5%.

Problem 11-15 contains additional information regarding this circuit. Another type of pulse amplifier will be considered under the *monostable multivibrator* heading, which follows.

11-3. Multivibrators. The multivibrator circuit is important from both a classical and a practical point of view. Three classes of multivibrators are common: The *astable* or free-running circuit is a square-wave oscillator; the *monostable* or one-shot circuit is useful as a regenerative pulse amplifier, and the *bistable* or flip-flop can store information. The term "multivibrator" suggests the abundance of harmonics present in the associated nonsinusoidal waveshapes.

Astable. The astable circuit is an oscillator in the sense that it exhibits characteristics similar to oscillators as set forth in the earlier discussion of Chapter 10, namely that a time-varying waveform is generated although no input other than the d-c supply is necessary, and that feedback is evident. In one aspect it differs from a true oscillator. The circuit possesses two conditions of stable equilibrium, and generally the active element switches from its conducting to its non-conducting state and vice versa because of a timing transient determined by external circuit elements. Thus a particular transistor in an astable multivibrator is OFF part of the time and ON during the remainder of its period. Although its ON period may be a saturated or unsaturated condition, it will be assumed in the discussion of this chapter that a saturating switch will always be considered because saturation provides certain advantages.

A typical astable multivibrator circuit is shown in Fig. 11-11. E_{CC} is available to the transistor collectors through R_{c1} and R_{c2}, and E_{BB} supplies the bases through R_{21} and R_{22}, although the bases could utilize the collector supply if conditions so warrant. Capacitor C_1 joins the collector of $TR1$ with the base of $TR2$, so it is through this element that the signal will come to change the state of $TR2$. The circuit is symmetrical with C_2 joining the $TR2$ collector to the $TR1$ base.

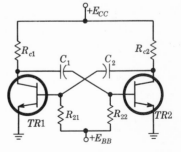

Fig. 11-11. Sample astable multivibrator.

If the transistors are to be operated between saturation and cutoff, then the aforementioned simplified conditions prevail. Repeated here, for a saturated n-p-n transistor,

$$v_c \cong 0$$

$$v_b = +$$

$$i_c \cong E_{CC}/R_c$$

and for a cutoff unit

$$v_c \cong E_{CC}$$

$$v_b = -$$

$$i_c \cong 0$$

Operation is dictated by the fact that the charge on a capacitor and hence the voltage across its plates cannot change instantaneously. Each capacitor in the figure is tied to points in the circuit where the potential will vary between wide limits when switching states change. Although only positive direct voltages are supplied to this circuit, the switching action will actually result in voltages that are negative with respect to ground.

When supply voltage is initially applied, currents flow in the various circuit branches and the capacitors build up charge. Because the two halves of the circuit are similar, currents will be alike at first, but even the slightest unbalance will result in a cumulative difference in the two collector currents. This unbalance, no matter how slight, will result in the saturation of one transistor and cutoff of the other. The starting requirements are, therefore, that a dissymmetry exist—this is unescapable—and that the other conditions to be presently introduced be satisfied.

To analyze the operation of switching circuits such as the astable multivibrator, simplified circuit diagrams of the Fig. 11–12 type give an indication of the ultimate capacitor potentials if the circuit would allow complete buildup to take place. From (a) and (c) of the figure it can be noted that C_1 would tend to go through an excursion of $E_{CC} + E_{BB}$ for with $TR1$ ON it will try to charge to E_{BB} volts, positive on the right, and with $TR1$ OFF it will try to charge to the E_{CC} potential magnitude, positive on the left. Actually, from (a) of the figure, C_1 will not charge up to E_{BB}, for when the voltage on b_2 gets slightly positive, switching occurs.

If the time constants $R_{c1}C_1$ and $R_{c2}C_2$ are made short (compared with the firing time constants $R_{22}C_1$ and $R_{21}C_2$), collector potentials v_{c1} and v_{c2} will reach their ultimate or steady-state values rapidly, and therefore collector potentials during the OFF periods can be described by a simple exponential expression obtained from Fig. 11–12 (a) and (c). For example

$$v_{c1} = E_{CC}(1 - \epsilon^{-t/T_1}) \tag{11-7}$$

with

$$T_1 = R_{c1}C_1.$$

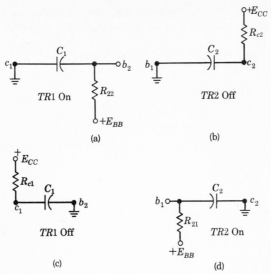

Fig. 11–12. Portions of Figure 11–11 used for analysis.

This expression assumes that collector voltage is zero during the ON or saturated condition.

At the instant that $TR1$ is turned ON by the voltage on its base terminal, the capacitor C_1 holds accumulated charge which is positive on its left hand or c_1 terminal because of its previous history; but that terminal is switched to approximately ground potential when $TR1$ is turned ON, and b_2, which is directly attached to the other terminal of the capacitor, must become $-E_{CC}$ volts with respect to ground potential because of the switching just described. For an expression for the voltage on b_2, with this initial condition included, we have

$$v_{b2} = (E_{BB} + E_{CC})(1 - \epsilon^{-t/T_2}) - E_{CC}, \qquad (11–8)$$

where

$$T_2 = R_{22}C_1.$$

This transient never reaches the ultimate value mathematically predicted because when v_{b2} becomes but slightly positive the transistor saturates.

If we set Eq. (11–8) for v_{b2} equal to zero and solve for the time period (T_a) necessary for that voltage to build up to zero and hence turn ON transistor No. 2, we find

$$0 = (E_{BB} + E_{CC})(1 - \epsilon^{-T_a/T_2}) - E_{CC},$$

so

$$T_a = -T_2 \ln \left(\frac{E_{BB}}{E_{BB} + E_{CC}} \right). \qquad (11–9)$$

This, then, is the OFF period for $TR1$. Expressions for the other transistor

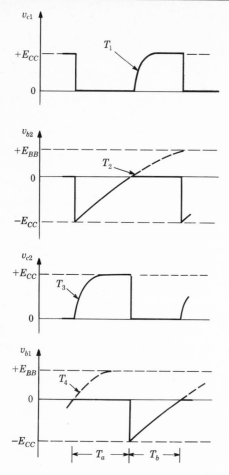

Fig. 11–13. Waveforms for the astable multivibrator.

are similar, with $T_3 = R_{c2}C_2$ and $T_4 = R_{21}C_2$

$$v_{c2} = E_{CC}(1 - \epsilon^{-t/T_3})$$

$$v_{b1} = (E_{BB} + E_{CC})(1 - \epsilon^{-t/T_4}) - E_{CC}$$

$$T_b = -T_4 \ln\left[\frac{E_{BB}}{E_{BB} + E_{CC}}\right]. \quad (11\text{–}10)$$

The frequency of oscillation is given by

$$f = \frac{1}{T_a + T_b}.$$

It is obvious from this discussion that the designer is free to control the duration of each half cycle, and has good control over the frequency of oscillation. He must also select component sizes to assure transistor saturation and to control performance by external elements rather than transistor reactances.

Monostable. The monostable multivibrator circuit, when triggered by a small pulse, generates a larger pulse, the width of which is under the control of the circuit designer.

In the monostable circuit of Fig. 11–14 transistor $TR1$ is biased so that its collector current is in saturation, and $TR2$ is biased normally at cutoff. A negative-going pulse on the base of $TR1$ will turn OFF that transistor, and an interesting sequence of circuit activity follows.

Because the capacitor C determines the timing of the operation it will be studied in detail with the aid of Fig. 11–15. In part (a) of that figure, the simplified circuit is shown with $TR2$ OFF and $TR1$ ON. It can be seen that C will charge through R_{c2} to E_{CC}, positive on the right. When $TR1$ is turned OFF by the incoming pulse, $TR2$ turns ON because of the change in $TR1$ collector voltage, and the circuit with C in it switches to the form of Fig. 11–15b. Consequently, $TR1$ will remain OFF until the capacitor loses its charge and b_1 goes slightly positive. An equation describing the performance of this portion of the monostable multivibrator can be written from observa-

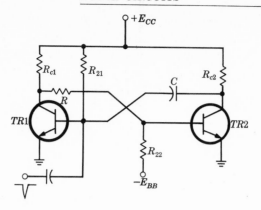

Fig. 11–14. Sample monostable multivibrator.

tion by noting that the capacitor potential starts at E_{CC} and would eventually charge to E_{CC} of the opposite polarity if it were not for switching occurring when v_b goes positive. Therefore

$$v_{b1} = 2E_{CC}(1 - \epsilon^{-t/T_1}) - E_{CC}, \tag{11–11}$$

with

$$T_1 = R_{21}C.$$

This transient never reaches its ultimate predicted by Eq. (11–11) because $TR1$ saturates when v_{b1} reaches a slightly positive value.

The sequence of operation will now be summarized. An externally generated pulse, applied to the base of the ON transistor turns $TR1$ OFF and $TR2$ ON. $TR2$ remains ON during the time interval determined by the discharge of capacitor C. $TR1$ is then switched ON and $TR2$ returns to the OFF state (Problem 11–21).

Bistable. The basic multivibrator circuit of the preceding discussion can be altered to provide us with a circuit with two stable states, capable of remaining in either state indefinitely until triggered by an external signal. The circuit that exhibits this type of operation has been given the name of *bistable multivibrator* but is more commonly known as a *flip-flop.* This sort of opera-

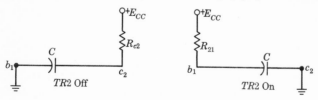

Fig. 11–15. Simplified version of Fig. 11–14 showing timing circuitry.

tion indicates that the flip-flop has a memory—it will remember the last signal received until another signal is forthcoming.

One form of the bistable multivibrator is the emitter-coupled circuit of Fig. 11–16. Capacitors are for speed-up and not for timing. Input signals are fed to the transistor bases in this diagram and outputs are taken at the collectors.

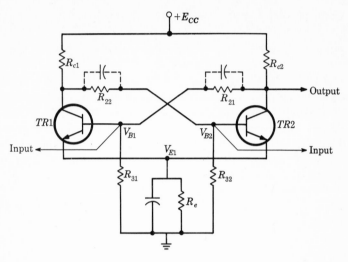

Fig. 11–16.   Typical bistable multivibrator.

If it is assumed that $TR1$ is conducting and $TR2$ cutoff, then the base bias for the conducting transistor is provided by the divider action of resistors R_{c2}, R_{21}, and R_{31} on E_{CC}. $TR1$ may or may not be saturated by this bias circuit, which effectively provides a base-to-emitter potential of $V_{B1} - V_{E1}$; the latter voltage, V_{E1}, is equal to $I_{E1}R_e$.

The OFF transistor stays in that state because its base-to-emitter potential is essentially

$$(V_{CE1} + V_{E1})\frac{R_{32}}{R_{22} + R_{32}} - V_{E1}.$$

This results, for practical component values, in the input junction being reverse-biased.

Assume that a signal pulse of positive polarity and of sufficient amplitude and width is supplied to the base of the OFF transistor. It immediately turns ON, lowering its collector voltage because of the $I_{C2}R_{C2}$ drop. When v_{c2} does decrease, the biasing that originally dictated that $TR1$ be ON is now nonexistent, and $TR1$ must switch to an OFF condition, to be held OFF by $I_{E2}R_e$.

The output waveshape obtained from either collector will be a constant potential with a magnitude of nearly E_{CC} at certain times, and of approximately $I_E R_e$ at other times, depending upon the history of supplied pulses.

PROBLEMS

11-1. Compare the junction transistor with the triode vacuum tube as a simple switch.

11-2. A power transistor with a spread in H_{FE} of 30 to 100 is to be used as a saturating switch. R_{CS} has a spread of 0.1 to 0.3 ohm. If the load resistance is 5 ohms, E_{CC} is 10 volts, and the switching circuit is designed for a constant base current drive, calculate the minimum base current necessary to cause saturation.

11-3. A saturating transistor switch has a cutoff at $V_{CE} = 20$ volts and $I_{CO} = 10$ μa and saturation at $V_{CE} = 1$ volt and $I_C = 20$ ma. Allow 10% for losses in the base circuit.

(a) Compute the OFF dissipation.

(b) Compute the ON dissipation.

(c) If the duty cycle is 0.5 millisecond ON and 1.0 OFF, and the switching time is 10 microseconds, compute the average rate of dissipation.

11-4. For the transistor whose collector characteristics are depicted in Fig. 11-2, with the load line as drawn, it is required that a switching circuit be designed to handle an ideal input voltage pulse of 5 volts. The circuit of Fig. 11-7 will be used.

(a) Determine R for a saturation base current of 400 μa. Use Fig. 11-3 to estimate the transistor input resistance.

(b) The stored base charge is known to be 750 $\mu\mu$-coulombs. Find C.

11-5. The differential equation for common-base operation is given as

$$\frac{di_c}{dt} + \omega_{\alpha b} i_c = \omega_{\alpha b} \alpha_o i_e,$$

and for common-emitter operation as

$$\frac{di_c}{dt} + \omega_{\alpha e} i_c = \omega_{\alpha e} \beta_o i_b.$$

(a) Derive the equation for i_c of a common-base connected transistor subjected to a step-input disturbance ($i_e = \Delta_1$).

(b) Derive the equation for i_c of common-emitter connected transistor subjected to a step-input disturbance ($i_b = \Delta_2$).

(c) Should $\Delta_1 = \Delta_2$, show that the initial rate of rise of i_c (di_c/dt at $t = 0$) for each of the above connections may be expressed by the same relationship.

11–6. The differential equations of the preceding problem may be derived from the knowledge that

$$\alpha = \frac{\alpha_o}{1 + j\omega/\omega_{\alpha b}},$$

and

$$\alpha = \frac{i_c}{i_e}.$$

Make use of the Laplace transform, recalling that $s = j\omega = d/dt$, to derive the two equations referred to.

11–7. For typical transient of the form

$$i = K(1 - \epsilon^{-t/T})$$

with T the time constant, and K the steady-state value of the quantity i, make a listing of the percentage of total change occurring in times of $T/2$, T, $2T$, $3T$, $4T$, and $5T$.

11–8. From your solution to problem 11–5, and considering a common-emitter connected transistor with $f_{\alpha b} = 5$ mc, and $\beta_o = 50$, make a plot of i_c vs. t for values of t from 0 to $5T$. Consider Δ_B equal to one milliampere.

11–9. Compare the time required for an exponential transient to build up from 10% of its final value to 90% of that value with the time required for 0 to 90% and 0 to 95%. Express your results in terms of the circuit time constant T.

11–10. Derive a mathematical expression for a current transient that rises from zero to a value of I_s, a value somewhat lower than its steady-state value, I_{ss}, and then remains at I_s for all values of time after t_s. The expression will explain the saturating curves of Fig. 11–8.

11–11. Fig. 11–2 and 11–3 apply to a transistor to be used in the circuit of Fig. 11–10. A voltage pulse of 5 volts will trigger the circuit, which has $R_L = 2000$ ohms, $E_{CC} = 10$ volts, and $E_{BB} = 10$ volts. It is possible that with temperature variations I_{CO} will reach 50 μa. Determine R, R_2, and C for a turn-on time of 0.5 μsec. Consider $f_{\alpha b}$ to equal 4 mc.

11–12. If the turn-on time specification listed in problem 11–11 was tightened to become 0.4 μsec, which circuit elements need be changed, and what new values must they take on?

11–13. Consider that the resistors and capacitors used in the circuit of problem 11–11 have a tolerance of $\pm 10\%$, of their nominal value, and H_{FE} can vary $\pm 20\%$ from unit-to-unit. Discuss the operation of this circuit by considering the poorest operation that may be encountered.

11–14. Using 0.35 in Eq. (11–6), calculate the approximate bandwidth for the "NBS Preferred Circuit No. 201" for various values of $R5$ at 25° C and 150° C. Consider the rise times listed as 10% to 90% values.

11-15. The stabilization ratio referred to in Appendix III is defined as

$$1 - \frac{\partial I_C/\partial I_{CO} \text{ (for the stabilized circuit)}}{\partial I_C/\partial I_{CO} \text{ (for the unstabilized transistor)}}.$$

The numerator of the fraction may be represented by S, as in Chapter 3, and the denominator by $\beta + 1$. Stabilization ratio as defined here approaches unity for a highly stable circuit and approaches zero for an unstabilized circuit. Show that when Eq. (3–17a) is used in the above expression, the stabilization ratio quoted in Appendix III results.

11-16. Redraw the astable multivibrator circuit of Fig. 11–11 as a two-stage feedback amplifier.

11-17. An astable multivibrator of the form of Fig. 11–11 is to be designed to generate a 400 cps waveform with symmetrical half periods. $E_{CC} = E_{BB} = 10$ volts. Determine the values of all circuit elements in your design.

11-18. What effect would a $\pm 20\%$ tolerance on the nominal values of all passive circuit elements have upon the frequency of oscillation of the circuit designed in Problem 11–17?

11-19. What effect would a $\pm 10\%$ variation in E_{CC} and E_{BB} have upon the frequency of oscillation of the circuit designed in Problem 11–17?

11-20. Instead of considering that collector current in the OFF state is zero, consider it to be I_{CO}, and consider base voltage and collector voltage for saturated ON periods to be V_{BE}' and V_{CE}' rather than zero. Derive equations that include I_{CO}, V_{CE}', and V_{BE}' to predict the effect of these quantities upon the frequency of oscillation of the circuit of Problem 11–17. If these quantities have values of 10 μa, 0.2 volt, and 0.2 volt respectively, predict the frequency of oscillation.

11-21. For a monostable multivibrator of the Fig. 11–14 form, draw the portion of the circuit that affects the turn-on and turn-off of $TR2$ and describe the cause of this switching.

REFERENCES

1. Bright, R. L., "Junction Transistors Used as Switches," *Trans. AIEE, Communications and Electronics*, vol. 74 (Mar., 1955).
2. Ebers, J. J., and Moll, J. L., "Large-Signal Behavior of Junction Transistors," *Proc.* I.R.E., vol. 42 (Dec., 1954).
3. "Handbook PREFERRED CIRCUITS Navy Aeronautical Electronic Equipment," NAVAER 16-1-519 Supplement no. 1 (1958).
4. Hurley, R. B., *Junction Transistor Electronics*, John Wiley & Sons, Inc., New York, 1958.
5. Ivy, W., "Some Comments on Frequency and Transient Response," *Device-Circuit Notes* No. A-58-9, Texas Instruments, Inc.
6. Lo, A. W., *et al.*, *Transistor Electronics*, Prentice-Hall, Inc., Englewood Cliffs, New Jersey, 1955.

7. Pressman, A. I., *Design of Transistorized Circuits for Digital Computers*, John F. Rider Publisher, Inc., New York, 1959.
8. Shea, R. F., *Transistor Circuit Engineering*, John Wiley & Sons, Inc., New York, 1957.
9. Valley, G. E., Jr., and Wallman, H., *Vacuum-Tube Amplifiers*, McGraw-Hill, Inc., New York, 1948.
10. Von Tersch, L. W., and Swago, A. W., *Recurrent Electrical Transients*, Prentice-Hall, Inc., Englewood Cliffs, New Jersey, 1953.

Appendix I

SELECTED TRANSISTOR DATA

The following pages contain data as supplied by the various manufacturers on five commercial transistor types. This information is useful in solving the end-of-chapter problems. It can be noted that some of the symbols and conventions used here differ among manufacturers and differ from those of the text.

The types selected are:

2N43 Germanium general purpose, p-n-p, junction
2N344 Germanium, high frequency, p-n-p, surface barrier
2N414 Germanium, high frequency, p-n-p, junction
2N475 Silicon, general purpose, n-p-n, junction
2N539 Germanium, power, p-n-p, junction

325

GENERAL ELECTRIC TYPE 2N43 *P-N-P* GERMANIUM JUNCTION TRANSISTOR

The General Electric Type 2N43 alloy junction triode transistor is a *p-n-p* unit particularly recommended for low- to medium-power applications. A hermetic enclosure is provided by the use of glass-to-metal seals and welded seams.

ABSOLUTE MAXIMUM RATINGS (25° C)

Voltages
Collector to Base	V_{CB}	-45 volts
Collector to Emitter	V_{CE}	-30 volts
Emitter to Base	V_{EB}	-5 volts
Collector Current	I_C	-300 ma
Temperatures		
Storage	T_{STG}	Max. $+100°$ C Min. $-65°$ C
Operating Junction	T_J	Max. $+85°$ C
Total Transistor Dissipation	P_{AV}	(See note 1)

ELECTRICAL CHARACTERISTICS (25° C)

Small Signal Characteristics

(Unless otherwise specified;
$V_C = -5$ v common base;
$I_E = 1$ ma; f = 270 cps.)

		Min.	Design Center	Max.	
Output Admittance (Input A-C open circuited)	h_{ob}	0.1	0.8	1.5	μmhos
Forward Current Transfer Ratio (Common Emitter; Output A-C short circuited)	h_{fe}	30	42	66	
Input Impedance (Output A-C short circuited)	h_{ib}	25	29	35	ohms
Reverse Voltage Transfer Ratio (Input A-C open circuited)	h_{rb}	1	5	15	$\times 10^{-4}$
Output Capacity (f = 1 mc; input A-C open circuited)	C_{ob}	20	40	60	$\mu\mu$f
Noise Figure (f = 1 kc; BW = 1 cycle)	NF		6	20	db
Frequency Cut-off	$f_{\alpha b}$	0.5	1.3	3.5	mc

		Min.	Design Center	Max.	

D-c Characteristics

Forward Current Gain, Common
Emitter I_C/I_B

		Min.	*Design Center*	*Max.*	
($V_{CE} = -1$ v; $I_C = -20$ ma)	h_{FE}	34	53	65	
($V_{CE} = -1$ v; $I_C = -100$ ma)	h_{FE}	30	48		
Collector Saturation Voltage	$\{V_{CE\ (SAT)}$	65	90	130	mv
($I_C = -20$ ma; I_B as indicated)	$\{@I_B =$	2	2	2	ma
Base Input Voltage, Common Emitter					
($V_{CE} = -1$ v; $I_C = -20$ ma)	V_{BE}	-180	-230	-280	mv
Collector Cutoff Current					
($V_{CBO} = -45$ v)	I_{CO}		-8	-16	μamps
Emitter Cutoff Current					
($V_{EBO} = -5$ v)	I_{EO}		-4	-10	μamps
Collector to Emitter Voltage ($R_{BE} = 10$ K ohms; $I_C = -0.6$ ma)	V_{CER}	-30			volts
Punch-through Voltage	V_{PT}	-30			volts

Thermal Resistance (k)

Junction Temperature Rise/Total Transistor Dissipation;

Free Air (Note 2)	0.25 °C/mw
Infinite Heat Sink	0.11 °C/mw
Clip-on Heat Sink in Free Air (Note 2) (0.95 sq. in. radiating surface)	0.20 °C/mw

Note #1. The transistor power dissipation is limited by the operating junction temperature. In a properly stabilized circuit, the permissible maximum operating junction temperature is 85° C. The method for computing the operating junction temperature is:

$$T_J = T_A + kP_{AV}$$

The method for computing the maximum allowable transistor power dissipation is:

$$P_{AV} = \frac{85° \text{ C} - T_A}{k}$$

where T_J = Operating Junction Temperature in °C
T_A = Operating Ambient Temperature in °C
P_{AV} = Transistor Power Dissipation in mw
k = Thermal Resistance in °C/mw

Note #2. Free air means unrestricted air flow around the transistor.

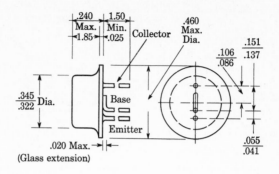

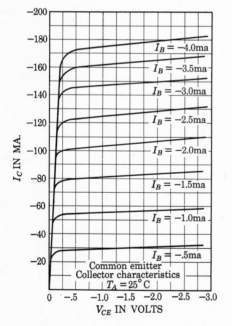

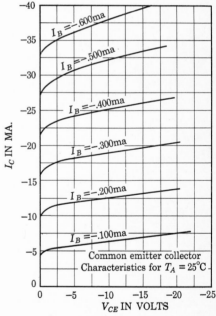

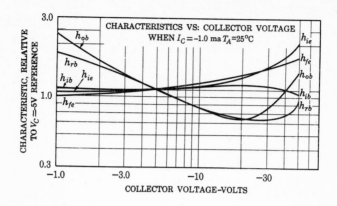

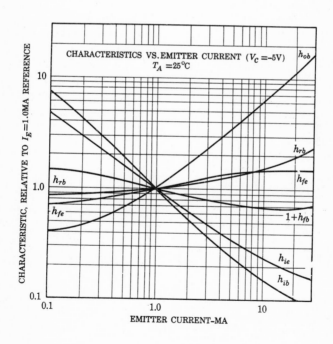

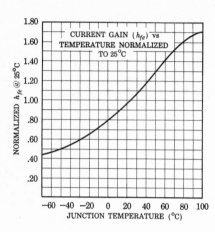

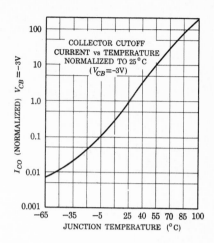

PHILCO TYPE 2N344 GERMANIUM SURFACE BARRIER TRANSISTOR

The 2N344 is a germanium surface barrier transistor intended for general purpose high-frequency applications. This transistor type can be used as RF, IF, and video amplifiers, converters, oscillators and in switching circuits. For general high-frequency use the 2N344 provides a transistor for any purpose requiring a narrow beta range. Other features are long flexible leads for easy insertion into the circuit and a true hermetic seal. The polarities of the emitter and collector voltages are similar to those of p-n-p junction transistors.

ABSOLUTE MAXIMUM RATINGS (NOTE #1)

Storage Temperature (Note #2)...........................85° C
Junction Temperature....................................55° C
Junction Temperature Rise (free air)...............0.75° C/mw
Collector Voltage, V_{CB} or V_{CE} (Note #3)................−5 volts
Collector Current, I_C................................−5 ma
Collector Dissipation at 40° C..........................20 mw
Lead Temperature, at $\frac{1}{16}'' \pm \frac{1}{32}''$ from case.....230° ± 5° for 10 sec

ELECTRICAL CHARACTERISTICS

Static Characteristics

(T = 25° C)

$Max.$

Collector Cutoff Current, I_{CBO} ($V_{CB} = -5$ v)...............3 μa
Emitter Cutoff Current, I_{EBO} ($V_{EB} = -5$ v)................3 μa

Small Signal Parameters

($V_C = -3.0$ V, $I_C = -0.5$ ma, T = 25° C)

		Max.
Input Resistance, h_{ib}	....	100 ohms
Output Conductance, h_{ob}	....	5 μmhos
Extrinsic Base Resistance Collector Capacitance		
Product, $r_b'C_c$	....	1200 $\mu\mu$sec
Output Capacitance, C_{ob}	....	6 $\mu\mu$f

	Min.	*Typ.*	*Max.*	
Current Amplification Factor, h_{fe}	11		33	
Maximum Frequency of Oscillation, f_{os} max	30	50		mc

NOTES

1. The maximum ratings are limiting absolute values above which the serviceability may be impaired from the viewpoint of life or satisfactory performance.
2. For maximum reliability storage at temperatures above 55° C is not recommended for extended periods of time.
3. In surface barrier transistors the maximum collector voltage is limited by the punch through phenomenon.

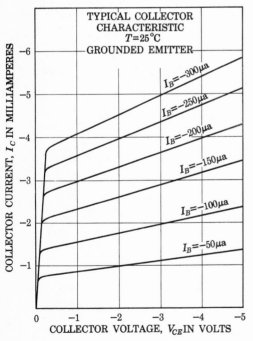

TYPICAL COLLECTOR
CHARACTERISTIC
$T = 25\,°C$
GROUNDED EMITTER

$I_B = -300\mu a$
$I_B = -250\mu a$
$I_B = -200\mu a$
$I_B = -150\mu a$
$I_B = -100\mu a$
$I_B = -50\mu a$

COLLECTOR CURRENT, I_C IN MILLIAMPERES

COLLECTOR VOLTAGE, V_{CE} IN VOLTS

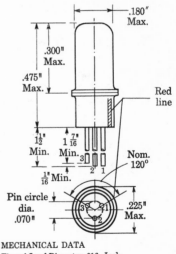

DIMENSIONAL OUTLINE AND
MECHANICAL SPECIFICATIONS

.180″ Max.
.300″ Max.
.475″ Max.
Red line
$1\frac{1}{2}$″ Min.
$1\frac{7}{16}$″ Min.
$\frac{1}{16}$″ Min.
Nom. 120°
Pin circle dia. .070″
.225″ Max.

MECHANICAL DATA

Tinned Lead Diameter .016 Inch
Base   E3-34
Lead Orientation-Red Line adjacent to lead #1
Basing
  Lead #1   Collector
  Lead #2   Base
  Lead #3   Emitter

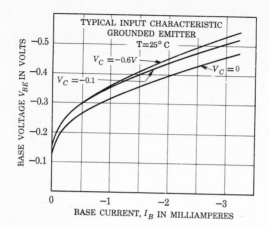

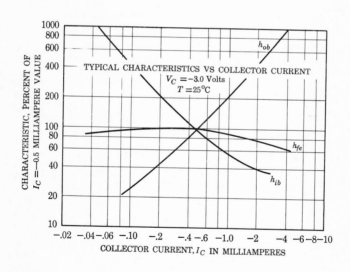

RAYTHEON TYPE 2N414 *P-N-P* GERMANIUM JUNCTION TRANSISTOR

The 2N414 is a medium gain PNP fusion alloy junction transistor especially intended for high frequency amplifier applications up to 8 megacycles. This transistor features rigid processing control to insure reliability and stability of electrical characteristics. Reliable hermetic sealing is assured by use of a welded package.

MECHANICAL DATA

Case: Metal
Base: Metal with glass eyelets. 0.017″ silver plated flexible leads.
Length: 1.5″ min. Spacing: 90° on 0.200″ circle diameter.
Terminal Connections:
Lead 1 Emitter
Lead 2 Base
Lead 3 Collector
Mounting Position: Any

ELECTRICAL DATA

Absolute Maximum Ratings:

Collector to Base Voltage (Emitter Open)	-30 volts
Emitter to Base Voltage (Collector Open)	-20 volts
Collector to Emitter Voltage (Base Open)	-15 volts
Collector to Emitter Voltage ($V_{BE} = +0.1$ volt)	-20 volts
DC Collector Current	-200 ma
Peak Collector Current	-400 ma
Dissipation Coefficient (in air) Ka*	0.4 °C/mw
Dissipation Coefficient (in sink) Ks*	0.18 °C/mw
Junction Temperature (Operating or Storage)	-65 to $+85$ °C
Lead Temperature (at $\frac{1}{16}″ \pm \frac{1}{32}″$ from case)	240 °C for 10 seconds

Characteristics: @25° C ($V_{CB} = -6$ V, $I_E = 1$ ma, f = 1 Kc, except as noted)

Parameter	Sym.	Conditions	Min.	Design Values Avg.	Max.	Units
Collector Cutoff Current	I_{CO}	$V_{CB} = -12$ V	....	-2.0	-5.0	μa
Emitter Cutoff Current	I_{EO}	$V_{EB} = -12$ V	....	-2.0	-5.0	μa
Input Impedance	hib		....	25	....	ohms
Base Current Gain	hfe	$V_{CE} = -6$ V	....	60	....	....
Voltage Feedback Ratio	hrb		....	0.5	....	$\times 10^{-3}$
Output Admittance	hob		....	0.62	....	μmhos
Alpha Cutoff Frequency	fαb		....	7	....	Mc
Collector Capacitance	Cob	f = 2 Mc	....	12	....	$\mu\mu$f
Extrinsic Base Resistance	rb″	f = 2 Mc	....	55	....	ohms
Noise Figure	N.F.	$V_{CE} = -6$ V f = 1.5 Mc	....	6	....	DB
Power Gain	Gp	$V_{CE} = -6$ V f = 1.5 Mc	....	16	....	DB

* Maximum allowable total transistor power dissipation at any ambient temperature is given by the relation: $P = (\text{Max. } Tj - Ta)/K$ where Tj is junction temperature, Ta is ambient temperature and K is the dissipation coefficient.

COLLECTOR CHARACTERISTICS
(Grounded Emitter)

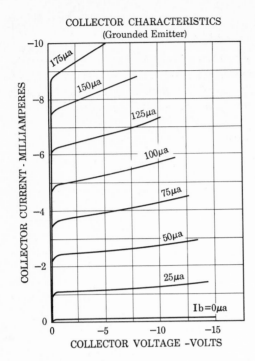

COLLECTOR CURRENT - MILLIAMPERES

175μa
150μa
125μa
100μa
75μa
50μa
25μa
Ib=0μa

COLLECTOR VOLTAGE –VOLTS

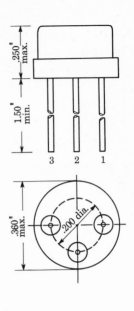

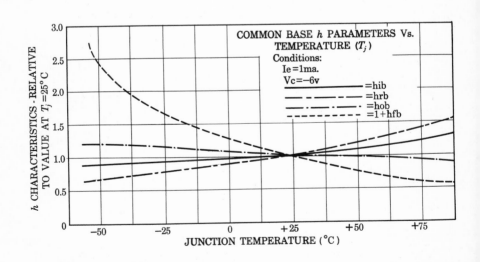

COMMON BASE *h* PARAMETERS Vs. TEMPERATURE (T_j)

Conditions:
Ie =1ma.
Vc=−6v

——————— =hib
— — — — — =hrb
—·—·—·— =hob
— — — — — =1+hfb

h CHARACTERISTICS - RELATIVE TO VALUE AT T_j=25°C

JUNCTION TEMPERATURE (°C)

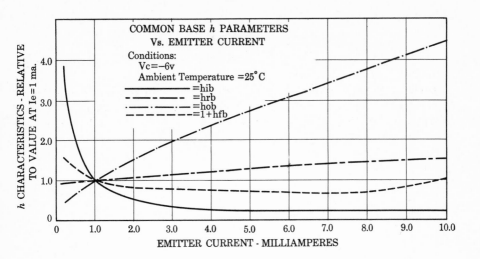

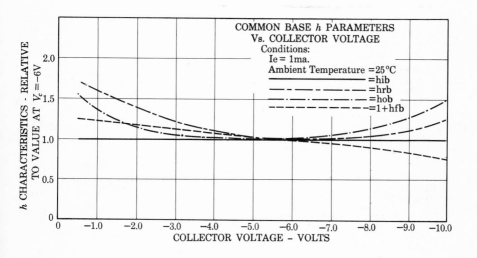

TRANSITRON TYPE 2N475 N-P-N SILICON JUNCTION TRANSISTOR

Transitron's medium gain NPN silicon transistors are designed for low level signal applications up to 200° C.

High temperature reliability is insured through close process control which results in a stable and low I_{CO} up to the maximum voltage rating. Extensive temperature cycling and storage, as well as mechanical and hermetic seal tests, are included as a regular part of the manufacturing process.

ABSÓLUTE MAXIMUM RATINGS

Collector to Emitter Voltage		V_{CE}	45 Volts
Collector to Base Voltage		V_{CB}	45 Volts
Emitter to Base Voltage		V_{EB}	2 Volts
Total Power Dissipation	at 25° C ambient		200 mw
	at 150° C ambient		60 mw

Storage and Operating Ambient Temperature Range -65 to $+200°$ C

SPECIFICATIONS AND TYPICAL CHARACTERISTICS AT 25° C

Common Emitter Parameters:		Min.	Typical	Max.	
Current Gain at 1 Kc	h_{fe}	20	30	50	
Current Gain at 1 Mc	h_{fe}	8	10		
Power Gain *	P.G.		39		db
Noise Figure *	N.F.		20		db
Common Base Parameters:					
Collector Cutoff Current, I_{CO}, at Rated Max. V_{CB}	at 25° C		0.02	0.5	μa
	at 150° C		10	50	μa
Collector Cutoff Current, I_{CO}, at V_{CB} = 6 volts	at 25° C		0.005		μa
	at 150° C		6		μa
Emitter Cutoff Current at $V_{EB} = 2$ volts	I_{EO}		0.01	0.5	μa
Input Impedance	h_{ib}	30	60	90	ohms
Output Admittance	h_{ob}	0.1	0.5	1.5	$\mu mhos$
Voltage Feedback Ratio	h_{rb}		4.0		$\times 10^{-4}$
Output Capacitance at 1 Mc	C_{ob}		7	20	$\mu\mu f$
D.C. Collector Saturation Resistance	R_{cs}		150	300	ohms

* R_s = 1000 ohms, R_L = 30 K, f = 1 Kc. Note: Small signal parameters measured at $V_c = 6$ V, $I_e = -1$ ma.

TYPICAL COMMON EMITTER CHARACTERISTICS

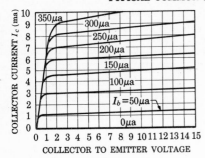

COLLECTOR TO EMITTER VOLTAGE

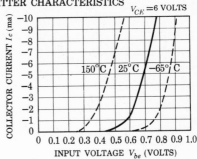

$V_{CE} = 6$ VOLTS

INPUT VOLTAGE V_{be} (VOLTS)

SMALL SIGNAL CHARACTERISTICS vs.
EMITTER CURRENT $V_c = 6$ volts, $T_j = 25°C$

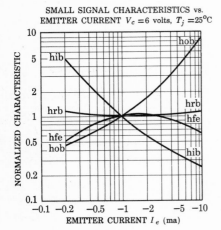

EMITTER CURRENT I_e (ma)

SMALL SIGNAL CHARACTERISTICS vs.
COLLECTOR VOLTAGE $I_e = -1$ma, $T_j = 25°C$

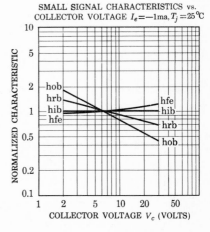

COLLECTOR VOLTAGE V_c (VOLTS)

TYPICAL COMMON EMITTER CHARACTERISTICS

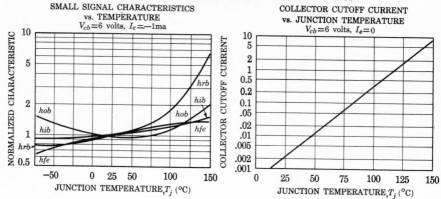

SMALL SIGNAL CHARACTERISTICS
vs. TEMPERATURE
$V_{cb}=6$ volts, $I_e=-1$ma

COLLECTOR CUTOFF CURRENT
vs. JUNCTION TEMPERATURE
$V_{cb}=6$ volts, $I_e=0$

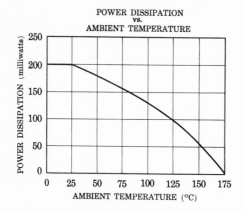

POWER DISSIPATION
vs.
AMBIENT TEMPERATURE

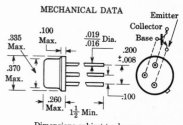

MECHANICAL DATA

Dimensions subject to change
in accordance with industry
standards established by JETEC

ENCAPSULATION: Welded hermetic seal.
MOUNTING POSITION: Any.
NOTE: Case isolated from all leads.

HONEYWELL TYPE 2N539 *P-N-P* GERMANIUM JUNCTION TRANSISTOR

The Honeywell 2N539 is a rugged, hermetically sealed germanium PNP transistor designed for a variety of uses including servo amplifiers, power conversion, voltage regulation, switching, etc. It is capable of carrying 3 amperes, has 80-volt collector diode and punch-through ratings and has a thermal design permitting 10 watts of dissipation at a 70° C case temperature. Limits of current gain and transconductance are the same as those for the former Honeywell type H6. The exact replacement for the H6, however, is the 2N539A which is unilaterally interchangeable with the 2N539 but, in addition, is characterized by power conductance and input resistance limits.

DESIGN LIMITS

Junction Temperature, T_J .... 95° C Max.
Thermal Resistance, Junctions to Mounting Base, Θ .... 2.2° C/Watt Max.
Collector-to-Base Voltage, V_{CB} .... −80 Volts Max.
Emitter-to-Base Voltage, V_{EB} .... −28 Volts Max.
Emitter Current, RMS, I_E .... −3.5 Amps Max.
Base Current, RMS, I_B .... −0.5 Amps Max.

PERFORMANCE SPECIFICATIONS

$T_{MB} = 25° \pm 3°$ C ($\pm 3\%$ tolerance applies to all electrical measurements)

Characteristic	Conditions	Symbol	Min.	Typ.	Max.	Unit
Current Gain, Common Emitter	$I_C = -2a$, $V_{CE} = -2$ v	H_{FE}	30	43	75	
Base-to-Emitter Voltage	$I_C = -2a$, $V_{CE} = -2$ v	V_{BE}	-1.0	-1.7	-2.5	Volt
*Power Conductance, Common Emitter	$I_C = -2a$, $V_{CE} = -2$ v	G_P	35	51	105	Mho
*Input Resistance, Common Emitter	$I_C = -2a$, $V_{CE} = -2$ v	H_{IE}	27	37	54	Ohm
Thermal Resistance, Junctions to Mounting Base		Θ		1.7	2.2	°C/W
Time Response of Junction Temperature		τ	10	30		Ms
Collector Junction Leakage Current	$I_E = 0$, $V_{CB} = -2$ v	I_{CBO}		-0.04	-0.1	Ma
	-28 v			-0.1	-1.0	
	-60 v			-0.3	-2.0	
	-80 v			-0.6	-10	
Emitter Floating Potential	$R_{EB} = 10$ K, $V_{CB} = -60$ v	V_{EBF}		-0.1	-0.3	Volt
	-80 v			-0.4	-1.5	
Emitter Junction Leakage Current	$I_C = 0$, $V_{EB} = -2$ v	I_{EBO}		-0.03	-0.15	Ma
	-28 v			-0.15	-2.0	
Collector Saturation Voltage	$I_C = -2$ a, $I_B = -200$ ma	V_S		-0.15	-0.6	Volt
Cut-off Frequency, Common Emitter	$V_{CC} = -28$ v, $R_L = 14$ Ω	$F_{\alpha E}$		7		Kc
Rise Time, Active Region, Common Emitter	$V_{CC} = -28$ v, $R_L = 14$ Ω $I_C = -1.8a$	t_r		40		μsec
Fall Time, Active Region, Common Emitter	$V_{CC} = -28$ v, $R_L = 14$ Ω $I_B = 0$	t_f		70		μsec

* Applies to 2N539A only.

TYPICAL CHARACTERISTICS, $T_{MB}=25°C$

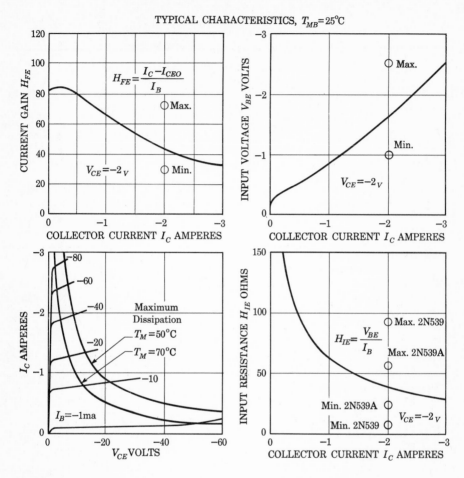

$$H_{FE}=\frac{I_C-I_{CEO}}{I_B}$$

○ Max.

$V_{CE}=-2_V$ ○ Min.

CURRENT GAIN H_{FE}

COLLECTOR CURRENT I_C AMPERES

○ Max.

Min.

$V_{CE}=-2_V$

INPUT VOLTAGE V_{BE} VOLTS

COLLECTOR CURRENT I_C AMPERES

Maximum
Dissipation
$T_M=50°C$
$T_M=70°C$

$I_B=-1ma$

I_C AMPERES

V_{CE} VOLTS

$$H_{IE}=\frac{V_{BE}}{I_B}$$

○ Max. 2N539

Max. 2N539A
○

Min. 2N539A ○

Min. 2N539 ○ $V_{CE}=-2_V$

INPUT RESISTANCE H_{IE} OHMS

COLLECTOR CURRENT I_C AMPERES

MOUNTING

It is very important that a power transistor be provided with a good heat dissipating facility. The surface to which the transistor is attached must be flat and free from burrs. The nut must be tightened securely (150 inch-ounce torque limit when used against a metal chassis or the bushing supplied, provided that all parts are clean and dry).

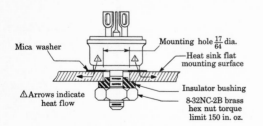

Mica washer

Mounting hole $\frac{17}{64}$ dia.

Heat sink flat
mounting surface

Insulator bushing

△Arrows indicate
heat flow

8-32NC-2B brass
hex nut torque
limit 150 in. oz.

DIMENSIONS AND CONNECTIONS

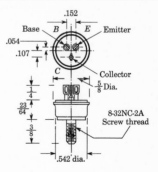

.152

Base B | E Emitter

.054

.107

C

Collector
$\frac{5}{8}$ Dia.

$\frac{1}{4}$

$\frac{23}{64}$

$\frac{3}{8}$

8-32NC-2A
Screw thread

.542 dia.

Appendix II

PARAMETER CONVERSIONS

To Find	Given					
	z	y	h	g	a	b
Z_i	$\dfrac{\Delta^z + z_{11}Z_l}{z_{22} + Z_l}$	$\dfrac{1 + y_{22}Z_l}{y_{11} + \Delta^y Z_l}$	$\dfrac{h_{11} + \Delta^h Z_l}{1 + h_{22}Z_l}$	$\dfrac{g_{22} + Z_l}{\Delta^g + g_{11}Z_l}$	$\dfrac{a_{12} + a_{11}Z_l}{a_{22} + a_{21}Z_l}$	$\dfrac{b_{12} + b_{22}Z_l}{b_{11} + b_{21}Z_l}$
Z_o	$\dfrac{\Delta^z + z_{22}Z_g}{z_{11} + Z_g}$	$\dfrac{1 + y_{11}Z_g}{y_{22} + \Delta^y Z_g}$	$\dfrac{h_{11} + Z_g}{\Delta^h + h_{22}Z_g}$	$\dfrac{g_{22} + \Delta^g Z_g}{1 + g_{11}Z_g}$	$\dfrac{a_{12} + a_{22}Z_g}{a_{11} + a_{21}Z_g}$	$\dfrac{b_{12} + b_{11}Z_g}{b_{22} + b_{21}Z_g}$
A_v	$\dfrac{z_{21}Z_l}{\Delta^z + z_{11}Z_l}$	$\dfrac{-y_{21}Z_l}{1 + y_{22}Z_l}$	$\dfrac{-h_{21}Z_l}{h_{11} + \Delta^h Z_l}$	$\dfrac{g_{21}Z_l}{g_{22} + Z_l}$	$\dfrac{Z_l}{a_{12} + a_{11}Z_l}$	$\dfrac{\Delta^b Z_l}{b_{12} + b_{22}Z_l}$
A_i	$\dfrac{-z_{21}}{z_{22} + Z_l}$	$\dfrac{y_{21}}{y_{11} + \Delta^y Z_l}$	$\dfrac{h_{21}}{1 + h_{22}Z_l}$	$\dfrac{-g_{21}}{\Delta^g + g_{11}Z_l}$	$\dfrac{-1}{a_{22} + a_{21}Z_l}$	$\dfrac{-\Delta^b}{b_{11} + b_{12}Z_l}$

Δ is the parameter determinant. For example, if x parameters were to be defined, $\Delta^x = x_{11}x_{22} - x_{12}x_{21}$.

MATRIX CONVERSIONS

To Find	Given					
	z	y	h	g	a	b
$[z]$	—	$\begin{matrix} \dfrac{y_{22}}{\Delta^y} & \dfrac{-y_{12}}{\Delta^y} \\[2mm] \dfrac{-y_{21}}{\Delta^y} & \dfrac{y_{11}}{\Delta^y} \end{matrix}$	$\begin{matrix} \dfrac{\Delta^h}{h_{22}} & \dfrac{h_{12}}{h_{22}} \\[2mm] \dfrac{-h_{21}}{h_{22}} & \dfrac{1}{h_{22}} \end{matrix}$	$\begin{matrix} \dfrac{1}{g_{11}} & \dfrac{-g_{12}}{g_{11}} \\[2mm] \dfrac{g_{21}}{g_{11}} & \dfrac{\Delta^g}{g_{11}} \end{matrix}$	$\begin{matrix} \dfrac{a_{11}}{a_{21}} & \dfrac{\Delta^a}{a_{21}} \\[2mm] \dfrac{1}{a_{21}} & \dfrac{a_{22}}{a_{21}} \end{matrix}$	$\begin{matrix} \dfrac{b_{22}}{b_{21}} & \dfrac{1}{b_{21}} \\[2mm] \dfrac{\Delta^b}{b_{21}} & \dfrac{b_{11}}{b_{21}} \end{matrix}$
$[y]$	$\begin{matrix} \dfrac{z_{22}}{\Delta^z} & \dfrac{-z_{12}}{\Delta^z} \\[2mm] \dfrac{-z_{21}}{\Delta^z} & \dfrac{z_{11}}{\Delta^z} \end{matrix}$	—	$\begin{matrix} \dfrac{1}{h_{11}} & \dfrac{-h_{12}}{h_{11}} \\[2mm] \dfrac{h_{21}}{h_{11}} & \dfrac{\Delta^h}{h_{11}} \end{matrix}$	$\begin{matrix} \dfrac{\Delta^g}{g_{22}} & \dfrac{g_{12}}{g_{22}} \\[2mm] \dfrac{-g_{21}}{g_{22}} & \dfrac{1}{g_{22}} \end{matrix}$	$\begin{matrix} \dfrac{a_{22}}{a_{12}} & \dfrac{-\Delta^a}{a_{12}} \\[2mm] \dfrac{-1}{a_{12}} & \dfrac{a_{11}}{a_{12}} \end{matrix}$	$\begin{matrix} \dfrac{b_{11}}{b_{12}} & \dfrac{-1}{b_{12}} \\[2mm] \dfrac{-\Delta^b}{b_{12}} & \dfrac{b_{22}}{b_{12}} \end{matrix}$
$[h]$	$\begin{matrix} \dfrac{\Delta^z}{z_{22}} & \dfrac{z_{12}}{z_{22}} \\[2mm] \dfrac{-z_{21}}{z_{22}} & \dfrac{1}{z_{22}} \end{matrix}$	$\begin{matrix} \dfrac{1}{y_{11}} & \dfrac{-y_{12}}{y_{11}} \\[2mm] \dfrac{y_{21}}{y_{11}} & \dfrac{\Delta^y}{y_{11}} \end{matrix}$	—	$\begin{matrix} \dfrac{g_{22}}{\Delta^g} & \dfrac{-g_{12}}{\Delta^g} \\[2mm] \dfrac{-g_{21}}{\Delta^g} & \dfrac{g_{11}}{\Delta^g} \end{matrix}$	$\begin{matrix} \dfrac{a_{12}}{a_{22}} & \dfrac{\Delta^a}{a_{22}} \\[2mm] \dfrac{-1}{a_{22}} & \dfrac{a_{21}}{a_{22}} \end{matrix}$	$\begin{matrix} \dfrac{b_{12}}{b_{11}} & \dfrac{1}{b_{11}} \\[2mm] \dfrac{-\Delta^b}{b_{11}} & \dfrac{b_{21}}{b_{11}} \end{matrix}$
$[g]$	$\begin{matrix} \dfrac{1}{z_{11}} & \dfrac{-z_{12}}{z_{11}} \\[2mm] \dfrac{z_{21}}{z_{11}} & \dfrac{\Delta^z}{z_{11}} \end{matrix}$	$\begin{matrix} \dfrac{\Delta^y}{y_{22}} & \dfrac{y_{12}}{y_{22}} \\[2mm] \dfrac{-y_{21}}{y_{22}} & \dfrac{1}{y_{22}} \end{matrix}$	$\begin{matrix} \dfrac{h_{22}}{\Delta^h} & \dfrac{-h_{12}}{\Delta^h} \\[2mm] \dfrac{-h_{21}}{\Delta^h} & \dfrac{h_{11}}{\Delta^h} \end{matrix}$	—	$\begin{matrix} \dfrac{a_{21}}{a_{11}} & \dfrac{-\Delta^a}{a_{11}} \\[2mm] \dfrac{1}{a_{11}} & \dfrac{a_{12}}{a_{11}} \end{matrix}$	$\begin{matrix} \dfrac{b_{21}}{b_{22}} & \dfrac{-1}{b_{22}} \\[2mm] \dfrac{\Delta^b}{b_{22}} & \dfrac{b_{12}}{b_{22}} \end{matrix}$
$[a]$	$\begin{matrix} \dfrac{z_{11}}{z_{21}} & \dfrac{\Delta^z}{z_{21}} \\[2mm] \dfrac{1}{z_{21}} & \dfrac{z_{22}}{z_{21}} \end{matrix}$	$\begin{matrix} \dfrac{-y_{22}}{y_{21}} & \dfrac{-1}{y_{21}} \\[2mm] \dfrac{-\Delta^y}{y_{21}} & \dfrac{-y_{11}}{y_{21}} \end{matrix}$	$\begin{matrix} \dfrac{-\Delta^h}{h_{21}} & \dfrac{-h_{11}}{h_{21}} \\[2mm] \dfrac{-h_{22}}{h_{21}} & \dfrac{-1}{h_{21}} \end{matrix}$	$\begin{matrix} \dfrac{1}{g_{21}} & \dfrac{g_{22}}{g_{21}} \\[2mm] \dfrac{g_{11}}{g_{21}} & \dfrac{\Delta^g}{g_{21}} \end{matrix}$	—	$\begin{matrix} \dfrac{b_{22}}{\Delta^b} & \dfrac{b_{12}}{\Delta^b} \\[2mm] \dfrac{b_{21}}{\Delta^b} & \dfrac{b_{11}}{\Delta^b} \end{matrix}$
$[b]$	$\begin{matrix} \dfrac{z_{22}}{z_{12}} & \dfrac{\Delta^z}{z_{12}} \\[2mm] \dfrac{1}{z_{12}} & \dfrac{z_{11}}{z_{12}} \end{matrix}$	$\begin{matrix} \dfrac{-y_{11}}{y_{12}} & \dfrac{-1}{y_{12}} \\[2mm] \dfrac{-\Delta^y}{y_{12}} & \dfrac{-y_{22}}{y_{12}} \end{matrix}$	$\begin{matrix} \dfrac{1}{h_{12}} & \dfrac{h_{11}}{h_{12}} \\[2mm] \dfrac{h_{22}}{h_{12}} & \dfrac{\Delta^h}{h_{12}} \end{matrix}$	$\begin{matrix} \dfrac{-\Delta^g}{g_{12}} & \dfrac{-g_{22}}{g_{12}} \\[2mm] \dfrac{-g_{11}}{g_{12}} & \dfrac{-1}{g_{12}} \end{matrix}$	$\begin{matrix} \dfrac{a_{22}}{\Delta^a} & \dfrac{a_{12}}{\Delta^a} \\[2mm] \dfrac{a_{21}}{\Delta^a} & \dfrac{a_{11}}{\Delta^a} \end{matrix}$	—

Appendix III

NBS PREFERRED CIRCUIT NO. 201
SILICON TRANSISTOR VIDEO AMPLIFIER

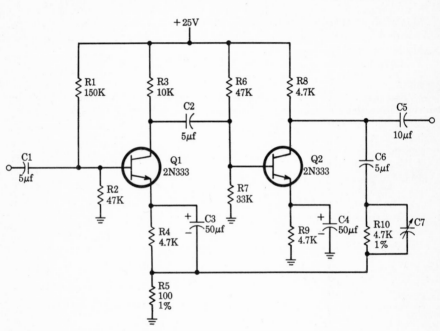

Components:

R5: Select for desired voltage amplification.

C7: Between 4 and 30 $\mu\mu$f, to be selected after total output capacitance is determined.

R5, R10: $\pm1\%$ limits; all other R: $\pm10\%$ limits.   All C: $\pm20\%$ limits.   (Note 1)

Operating characteristics:	100 Ω	R5: 220 Ω	470 Ω
Voltage amplification.............	45	20	10
Rise time [2] (+150° C)...........	1.0 μsec	0.9 μsec	0.7 μsec
Rise time [2] (+25° C)............	0.5 μsec	0.4 μsec	0.35 μsec
Droop for 500 μsec pulse (−50° C)..	3.0%	1.5%	1.0%
Maximum output amplitude [3].....	2 v peak	2 v peak	2 v peak
Maximum input amplitude [3]	45 mv peak	100 mv peak	200 mv peak
Input impedance................	22 KΩ	27 KΩ	32 KΩ
Output impedance..............	250 Ω	210 Ω	180 Ω
Maximum amplification variation with transistor replacement.[4]....	±5%	±3%	±2%
Maximum amplification variation with temperature.[4].............	+5, −10%	+4, −7%	+2, −7%

Minimum load resistance: 10 KΩ.
Temperature range: −50° C to +150° C.

NOTES:
1. The performance specifications are based on component values which do not deviate from the nominal by more than the limits specified above. Thus the term "limits" includes the initial tolerance plus drifts caused by environmental changes or aging.
2. Total output capacitance = 30 μμf.
3. Plus and minus from ac zero level.
4. Load resistance = 10 KΩ.

PC 201 SILICON TRANSISTOR VIDEO AMPLIFIER

1. Application

PC 201 is a high-gain intermediate-level (± 2.0 volts maximum output) transistor video amplifier for use in applications where stability of gain and a wide temperature range are important. It is non-inverting, has an input impedance of 20 KΩ, and will operate into loads of 10 KΩ or larger. Impedance levels are such that it may be cascaded for additional voltage gain.

2. Design Considerations

Silicon transistors are used to obtain a wide temperature range. Negative feedback of 20 db extends the frequency range and stabilizes the voltage amplification against temperature changes and transistor replacement. Selection of R5 provides for a choice of voltage gain.

Either raising the value of R5 or lowering the value of R10 will decrease the voltage amplification with only slight accompanying change in bandwidth. This situation results from the fact that changing either R5 or R10 in a direction to decrease voltage amplification decreases the open loop voltage gain, A_o, while increasing the feedback factor, B. Thus the change in magnitude of negative feedback, BA_o, is slight, resulting in only a slight increase in bandwidth at the lower gain. Changing R5 is preferred since it will not derate the maximum output voltage that may be obtained.

The major limitation on circuit bandwidth and temperature range is imposed by the transistor itself. The input impedance, current amplification and, to a lesser extent, the output impedance of the transistor all have an effect on the voltage amplification. The limitation is imposed because the variation of these parameters with frequency or with temperature is much more severe than the variation in component values. Since all three parameters are interdependent in determining voltage gain, there is no one parameter measurement which will gauge operation of the transistor at extreme temperatures or at high frequency. For this reason the alpha cutoff frequency, $f_{a_{co}}$, though a good indication of high frequency performance, is not directly related to the rise time that may be achieved with any particular transistor.

Resistors R4 and R9, in conjunction with the biasing resistors, serve to minimize the change in quiescent operating point accompanying temperature variation and transistor replacement. A ratio indicating the relative amount of stabilization may be computed for each stage with the value of unity indicating perfect operating point stabilization. The stabilization ratio for Q1 is

$$\frac{h_{fe}}{h_{fe} + 1 + \dfrac{1}{R4/R1 + R4/R2}}$$

where h_{fe} is the common emitter forward current transfer ratio. A similar expression applies to Q2 with R9, R6, and R7 substituted for R4, R1, and R2. The stabilization ratios are 0.8 and 0.87 for Q1 and Q2 respectively.

The value of R8 is low enough so that the total capacitance of the output terminals is driven without a significant increase in rise time and yet high enough to provide sufficient open-loop gain for the circuit.

Capacitor C7 compensates for overshoot produced by the total capacitance at the output terminals and is to be selected after that capacitance is determined. Its value will be between 4 and 30 $\mu\mu$f for output capacitance values up to 100 $\mu\mu$f.

An important aspect of the circuit design is the ability to cascade feedback pairs for additional voltage amplification. This is possible due to the high input impedance and low output impedance resulting from negative voltage feedback.

3. Performance

Voltage amplifications of 45, 20 or 10 are obtained for R5 = 100, 220 or 470 Ω respectively. For each, an output extending plus and minus 2 volts from the average voltage of the waveform may be obtained.

For any 2N333 transistors within the specified limits of beta (18 to 40), the maximum variation of voltage amplification with transistor replacement is given in Figure 201–1 for the three alternate values of voltage gain. Im-

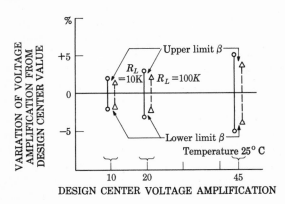

Fig. 201–1. Variation of voltage amplification from design center value with transistor replacement.

proved stabilization is obtained with higher values of load resistance. Replacement of transistor Q2 has considerably more effect on the voltage amplification than replacement of Q1. At 10 KΩ load and R5 = 100 Ω, maximum amplification variation with replacement of Q1 is only ±0.5%.

The maximum variation of voltage amplification with temperature is given in Figure 201–2 for the three alternate values of voltage amplification. Here again, improved stabilization is obtained with higher values of load resistance.

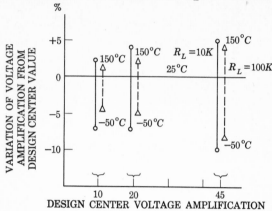

Fig. 201–2. Variation of voltage amplification from design center value with temperature.

Voltage amplification variation with temperature is primarily due to transistor parameter variations. Relatively few 2N333 transistors have the poor temperature characteristics shown in Figure 201–2. For the highest gain circuit, percentage variations of $+2$ and -6% would cover the great majority of cases with proportionately smaller changes for the lower gain circuits.

Though the circuit will operate into loads less than 10 KΩ, the voltage amplification stabilization is poor due to reduced open-loop gain. As the load resistance is increased above 10 KΩ, the open-loop gain becomes larger and the stabilization of voltage amplification is improved. Values of load equal to 100 KΩ or larger appear as no load, beyond which the open-loop gain cannot be increased.

For R5 = 100 Ω (voltage amplification of 45) the maximum droop, occurring at low temperature, is 3% for a 500 μsec pulse. At reduced gain the droop decreases to 1.5% for R5 = 220 Ω and 1.0% for R5 = 470 Ω.

The rise time of PC 201 will vary depending on the transistor in the output stage and the ambient temperature. Rise times given on the circuit sheet and in Figure 201–3 are the worst that may be expected.

Output waveforms at 25° C, 150° C, and −50° C for two sample pairs of transistors are shown in Figures 201–4 and 201–5. The input is a 250 kc square wave having a rise time of .02 μsec. The waveforms of Figure 201–4 have been compensated by C7 for overshoot, while those of Figure 201–5 are the same waveforms not compensated. The two sample pairs chosen are not intended to represent the best or worst waveforms that may be obtained.

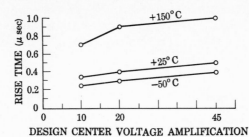

Fig. 201–3. Maximum pulse rise time as a function of temperature and design center voltage amplification.

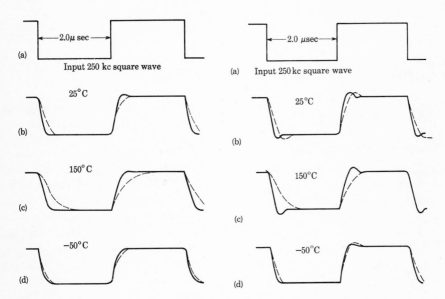

Fig. 201–4. Waveforms of PC 201 for two sample pairs of transistors. R5 = 100 Ω. Output = 4 volts. Total output capacitance = 30 μμf. Compensation for overshoot by C7.

Fig. 201–5. Waveforms of PC 201 for two sample pairs of transistors. R5 = 100 Ω. Output = 4 volts. Total output capacitance = 30 μμf. No compensation for overshoot.

Supply voltage variations of ±10% will affect the voltage amplification by ±1%. Maximum current drain from the supply is 3.5 ma.

INDEX